PROBLEMS OF
PHYSIOLOGICAL PSYCHOLOGY

PROBLEMS

OF

PHYSIOLOGICAL

PSYCHOLOGY

J. R. KANTOR

Professor of Psychology, Indiana University

1947
PRINCIPIA PRESS INC.
GRANVILLE, OHIO

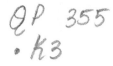

PHOTOLITHOPRINTED BY CUSHING - MALLOY, INC.
ANN ARBOR, MICHIGAN, UNITED STATES OF AMERICA
1965

By their enthusiastic study
of behavioral event-fields
a number of my students
have helped to develop
Interbehavioral Psychology
To them I dedicate
this volume

PREFACE

IN his *Introduction to Mathematics* Whitehead remarks: "It is a well-founded historical generalization that the last thing to be discovered in any science is what the science is really about" (630, p. 223). In the sense that psychologists are now discovering that they are not concerned with mental states or brain processes, but with specific interbehavioral events, this dictum is decidedly applicable to psychology.

What the science of psychology is really about is an especially crucial question when we concern ourselves with the area called *Physiological Psychology* (P.P.). A critical reader of P.P. literature can not escape the conclusion that this area is grievously encumbered by a series of paradoxes and perplexities. Most impressive, for example, is the lack of correspondence between data and doctrines. Because P.P. is still dominated by traditional philosophical ideas the events studied are prejudged to the detriment of investigation, whereas the resulting constructions consist of insalutary admixtures of valid description and historical interpretation.

In the present volume I have critically surveyed the P.P. field in an attempt to clarify its most important issues. In Section I an inquiry is made into its historical development; in Section II current P.P. investigations are scrutinized. In both instances this survey has frankly been guided by the interbehavioral hypothesis which I have developed in a number of previous works (289, 291, 292, 297). The interest throughout is centered on scientific results, on knowledge and theory.

The historical perspective indicates that current P.P. is still thoroughly infiltrated with spiritistic philosophy, and further that the undesirable psychological postulates derived from that philosophy can be substituted for by postulates more in line with observed events. Psychology, far from being subject to any *a priori* and cosmic doctrine, can itself contribute to the formulation of factually-based philosophic conceptions.

As to the investigative phase of P.P.—I have attempted to separate what is factual from what is purely traditional when the relationship between psychological and physiological events is described. P.P.—as that branch of psychology which more than others is concerned with this relationship between the biological and psychological—has been retarded by two erroneous views: (a) that organic actions are accompaniments of or explanatory mechanisms for psychic states, and (b) that psychological events are sufficiently described as simply neural, muscular, and glandular types of physiological actions. The latter view, designed to eliminate psychic factors, has really maintained them as "functions," since obviously psychological events are more comprehensive than is implied by such biological reactions.

Despite the fact that a survey of P.P. frequently calls for unfavorable criticism, my constant emphasis has been upon positive and constructive results. The basic thesis of this work is that when we clear away undesirable materials we make room for an authentic P.P.—a branch of psychological science which is at the same time important and adequate. Suggestions for the emendation of P.P. are formulated in Section III. Nothing now stands in the way of P.P. attaining a completely-objective and independent status, such that its data can be observed and experimented upon without hindrance from traditional theory.

Basic to authentic P.P. is the proposition that physiological or biological actions constitute *participating* factors in larger interactional systems. In *all* behavior—whether discriminative, ideational, affective or motive—the operations of muscles, end organs or visceral structures, comprise nuclear components of the response phases of more comprehensive interbehavioral fields. On this basis neither genuine nor invented physiological processes are required to provide explanatory principles for psychological happenings.

The participative principle is equally applicable when (1)

isolated responses or (2) comprehensive adjustments are considered.

(1) Although psychological events consist of nothing less than the interbehavior of organisms and stimulus objects in a specific field, most of P.P. theory has been formulated on the basis of isolated responses or acts. Physiological processes consequently have traditionally been envisaged as counterparts of explanatory mechanisms for psychological responses. This correlating and explaining role of physiological processes has been fostered by both dualistic and nondualistic psychologists. The latter, who disregard or reject psychic factors, correlate physiological processes with names such as discrimination, learning, etc.

(2) When the total psychological event consists of comprehensive adjustments to complex situations, participative roles are again played by physiological actions. In this case the biological factors constitute *components* of complicated psychological fields. Thus an organism's hygienic or fatigue conditions, its malformation or partial destruction play a part in learning, discrimination, speech, and other complex behavior. *Only* when physiological processes and biological conditions are viewed as participants and components can we achieve a factual cooperative relationship between psychology and physiology.

Throughout every stage of writing this book I have been keenly aware of the debts owed to all who have contributed to its inception and completion. It is a pleasure, therefore, to express my appreciation to those who have shared in producing this volume.

I wish first to mention the entire company of Physiological Psychologists, both past and present. Such is the corrigibility of science that advances in particular domains can only be made by taking account of the labors of all its workers, including their errors, false steps, and failures, as well as their successes. Accordingly I wish to acknowledge what I owe to all those writers from whose work I have profited, even though I have had to criticize some of them stringently. To the majority of authors I have referred directly, either by quotation or bibliographical reference.

In every detail of making this book, as well as my previous ones, I have enjoyed the constant collaboration of H. R. Kantor. To record this fact is to do more than express gratitude; it is disavowing credit for another's labor.

Several of my student assistants have rendered valuable service in connection with the large amount of library work, checking, and collating. For their efforts I can only inadequately thank them.

My sincere appreciation is extended to Dean Payne and the Graduate School of Indiana University for providing the stenographic aid required in preparing the manuscript for the press.

Dr. A. E. Kanter has placed me under deep obligation by generously contributing to the fund which made possible the publication of this volume.

To Mr. C. A. Peerenboom and the Staff of the George Banta Publishing Company I am extremely grateful for their careful and prompt efforts during a trying period for the book-producing industry.

September, 1946   J. R. K.

PUBLISHERS' ACKNOWLEDGEMENTS

THE Principia Press herewith acknowledges with thanks the formal permission received from the following individuals and firms to quote from works of which they are copyright owners. The listing indicates the names of authors with titles of their works, and the pages in the present book on which the quotations appear.

D. Appleton-Century Company.
>   S. R. Hathaway. *Physiological Psychology*. 1942, p. 293.
>   E. R. Hilgard and D. G. Marquis. *Conditioning and Learning*. 1940, pp. 52, 104, 133, 227.

Dr. Richard Brickner.
>   R. M. Brickner. *The Intellectual Functions of the Frontal Lobes*. 1936, p. 261.

McGraw-Hill Book Company.
>   C. T. Morgan. *Physiological Psychology*. 1943, pp. 234, 238, 248.
>   N. R. F. Maier and T. C. Schneirla, *Principles of Animal Psychology*. 1934, pp. 228, 234.

The Macmillan Company.
>   F. Wertham and F. Wertham. *The Brain as an Organ*. 1934, p. 222.
>   W. K. Livingston. *Pain Mechanisms*. 1943, p. 183.

D. Van Nostrand Company.
>   S. H. Bartley. *Vision: A Study of Its Basis*. 1941, pp. 146, 170, 181.

Prentice-Hall Company.
>   F. A. Moss (Ed.). *Comparative Psychology*. (rev.) 1942, p. 103.

The Ronald Press Company.
>   J. McV. Hunt. *Personality and the Behavior Disorders*. 1944, pp. 282, 285.

Charles C Thomas and Drs. W. Freeman and J. W. Watts.
>   W. Freeman and J. W. Watts. *Psychosurgery*. 1942, pp. 269-70.
>   W. Penfield and T. C. Erickson. *Epilepsy and Cerebral Localization*. 1941, p. 221.

CONTENTS

SECTION I

THE HISTORICAL BACKGROUND
OF
PHYSIOLOGICAL PSYCHOLOGY

Chapter 1

PROBLEMS AND PARADOXES OF PHYSIOLOGICAL PSYCHOLOGY

1. What Is Physiological Psychology?

PHYSIOLOGICAL psychology (P.P.) is still the domain of equivocation and paradox. Though both the term and the concept have a fairly long history, the reflective student who begins to study the subject finds himself searching for a subject to study. What is physiological psychology? In an attempt to answer this question, the student can, of course, consult the writings of physiological psychologists. Disagreeing with each other, they offer no clearcut reply. To be sure, the student discovers in P.P. treatises many common data, both physiological and psychological, but so compounded are these data with traditional interpretations as to allow a series of divergent views concerning the events treated.

Among such views are the following: (1) P.P. is a type of system or theory, one that stresses the dependency of mental states or experience upon bodily substrates, especially the nervous system. According to this belief P.P. contrasts with general psychology which deals only with purely mental constructs. (2) P.P. constitutes a specific method or methods for studying and explaining mental processes—for example, the impression and expression methods of investigating "emotions." (3) A third view is that P.P. is concerned with the basic mechanisms of behavior. Of those who share this last attitude some favor the notion that the behavior the mechanisms subserve comprises either (a) mental states, (b) bodily adjustments, or (c) both. Also, some believe that these mechanisms consist exclusively of neural tissues and their functions, whereas others insist upon including additional tissues and organs as well.

Obviously these divergent views are rooted both in philo-

3

sophical tradition as well as in current investigation. It is no less certain that the entire subject, both in origin and current modification, is influenced by dualistic thinking. In consequence, psychologists interested in psychophysical relations lean more toward P.P. than others, though they differ in their evaluations of it. In general, those concerned with human sensory activities emphasize the explanatory role of organic events. Others, working with infrahuman organisms, are prone to stress physiological facts as action mechanisms, without regard to dualistic theory. The latter may go so far as to deny the importance of historical P.P. altogether, in favor of neurophysiological facts or general behavior.

Probably the most outstanding paradox is that although P.P. was originated and cultivated to provide a scientific foundation for psychology, it has served on the whole to fetter it in doctrinal chains. Certainly the traditional notion that P.P. is a factual discipline rings true only because beliefs are transformed into facts. No better example can be found than the Wundtian incident. P.P. for Wundt is the name for experimental psychology, but his experiments constitute investigations into the nature of the soul. Physiology he regards as sharply sundered from psychology, and as a devout parallelist he could not regard the former as an explanatory discipline for psychology. At most he thought physiological facts exist as concomitants of psychic processes.

How deep-seated is the Wundtian paradox appears plain when writers on psychological history adopt Wundt's opinion that he succeeded in his ambition to emancipate psychology from metaphysics (43, p. 326). Those who accept Wundt's assertion that his voluntaristic psychology has developed into an empirical discipline with methods of its own and that it has become an independent science free from all metaphysical theories (650, pp. 1-2) simply meander in his ideological footsteps. What Wundt's declaration amounts to is merely that the scientific doxy of Herbart and others is a metaphysical heterodoxy, whereas his own metaphysical doxy is scientific orthodoxy.

Despite Wundt's empirical or experimental methods, his

doctrine of consciousness and experience constitutes the grossest metaphysics. More, such metaphysics has stood in the way of developing a satisfactory P.P. Not only has Wundt failed to integrate physiology and psychology, because of his particular consciousness doctrine, and thereby dismissed the body from psychology (43, p. 328), but further, the psychologists who have continued his metaphysics have demonstrated that the more emphasis one places on physiological processes in psychology the less scientific psychology becomes. The more stress the psychologist puts upon the brain, the nervous system as a whole or even the functions of the entire anatomy, the more established is the metaphysics of the psychic, and the less chance have actual psychological events to influence the psychologist's work and theories.

2. Physiological Psychology Calls for Clarification

Surely the confused condition of P.P. calls for a new orientation concerning its investigation and theory. For one thing, investigation must be completely separated from the Wundtian theories with which it is still enshrouded. P.P. studies need to be analyzed in order that the original events and the problems they present can be examined with respect to hypotheses advanced, techniques employed, and interpretations made. Such an analysis is a necessary prelude to freeing P.P. from objectionable adhesions.

Unambiguously the history of psychology reveals that P.P. was born as a legitimate child of traditional philosophy. Thus if one is interested in avoiding such metaphysics one must develop a discipline with other antecedents. To do so entails understanding the factors obstructing one's way. Psychologists, however, are apt to imitate those misguided persons who refuse to learn the language of their enemies, and thus forego the information necessary both to defend themselves and to pacify the former. Not only does the psychologist avert his eyes from philosophy, but with such good effect that metaphysics becomes thoroughly infiltrated into his thinking.

To accept metaphysics while denying it, results in extremely unsatisfactory scientific conditions, to say the least. It means practicing the philosophy of the psychic while preaching a scientific psychology. Specifically, legitimate relations of physiological and psychological events are overlooked, with the paradoxical result that a proper P.P. or biopsychology remains unachieved. To refer, however, to the paradoxes of P.P. is not to remain content with discontent, no matter how divine, but to point out a field of work, to open the way to a clarification of issues, to suggest a means of incorporating important investigative results into a system of constructions promising the advancement of psychology as a whole.

3. Two Methods of Clarifying Physiological Psychology

Two modes of procedure are available to carry out this clarifying task. The first is historical—namely, tracing out the origin and background of P.P. to secure information concerning its basic character. The second is analytic, examining the work done on the basis of the blueprints used and an estimate of the cost and results—in sum, a procedure of scientific job analysis.

A. *The Historical Background of Physiological Psychology*

Those who are not oriented in the history of psychology may well be surprised that P.P. should be so confused and contradictory a discipline. Those who are so oriented, however, understand that a scientist is not only obliged to seek facts but also to achieve clear ideas concerning the data with which he works. Unless indeed one is cognizant of the postulates governing one's work one is not likely to attain proper final constructions. There is hardly any question that a knowledge of history is essential for the proper evaluation of the P.P. field.

To be conversant with the history of psychology signifies three things. First, to be acquainted with the continuity of psychological development—in short to know the origin and evolution of the ideas and work within particular domains—in this instance, P.P. Secondly, it implies an appreciation of the cultural background of ideas and experiments in P.P. and in consequence a competency to criticize both. Thirdly, and above all, it means to be alert to the reference frame affording a scale for calculating the effect of old traditions upon current thinking and assaying the value of particular techniques for future developments.

B. *Analysis of Physiological Psychology*

The analysis of P.P. as a clarifying procedure demands a consideration of what actual events are isolated for study and the way the events are scientifically treated. In addition to the problems the worker sets himself, and the hypotheses and the techniques he employs, we must inquire into the assumptions basic to his investigations. Scientific methodology makes clear that basic postulates constitute the bed governing the velocity and direction of the investigative stream.

Thanks to the recent rebirth of interest in the science of science we are now equipped better than ever before to analyze scientific enterprises. Nothing surpasses in importance the ability this science gives us to distinguish between data and constructions. By taking into account the postulates which dominate an investigation we can proceed to estimate how closely the findings follow from the original events. In general, we can determine whether the field of work is cultivated on the basis of: (a) events or (b) a set of doctrines stemming from a broad cultural or philosophical background or from a more restricted source, for example, some particular scientific school of thought.

CHAPTER 2

THE PHILOSOPHICAL AND SCIENTIFIC BACKGROUNDS OF PHYSIOLOGICAL PSYCHOLOGY

1. PHILOSOPHICAL BACKGROUND

The Growing Place of the Body in Psychological Thinking

LIKE all scientific enterprises, P.P. sustains a continuous development. Glancing at its origins we see in full view its essentially metaphysical background. For our purposes we can not go beyond the 17th century, a period we may designate as the starting point of our present-day segment of the subject. Standing out prominently in this development is the growing emphasis of the body as a basis for naturalizing the soul or psyche.

Among the children of science the following folktale has long been current:

Once upon a time the intellectual ménage consisted of an indolent but wisdom-loving Mother and a large brood of Children. From her arm-chair position she directed her thoughts far afield in speculative meditation upon all things at once. Each child, as he grew up, looked askance at the sentimentality of his Mother's universal curiosity and instead looked forward to a nimble-fingered exploration of some particular domain of things.

The first of the offspring to carry out such a scientific plan became interested in the stars. But since star gazing at best allowed only a distant contact with things he could only improve upon his Mother's behavior by specializing upon the things he observed and by making numerous calculations. Still he succeeded in establishing an independent household, *astronomy*.

Not long afterward, another member of the family, learning to use the square and compass, built a house of his own which he furnished with steelyards, levers, and inclined planes. With this apparatus he achieved considerable manipulatory power and gained control over objects, the size, weight, and motion of which

8

he studied and recorded. In this manner was set up the autonomous domicile of *physics*.

As a third child grew to youth's estate he odiously compared the maternal prating about the combination and separation of air, fire, water, and soil, by the forces of love and hate, with the transmutative effects which he himself could induce by means of alkalis and acids. So he left the scene of his childhood to acquire skill with crucible and alembic. Around his hearth and forge grew up the house of *chemistry*.

The discontent becoming contagious, and the advantage of manual industry demonstrated, there followed a serial loosening of the maternal ties, with the resulting erection of *biological*, *geological*, and finally *psychological* households.

Since no tale can be created out of nothing, this one too contains a germ of truth. There was a time when the distinctions between the sciences were less prominent than they now are. Those who rightly consider science as an item in the development of civilization understand that this fact is a matter of the evolution of man and his culture. As work proceeded and formulations multiplied, men specialized, but this in no sense denies the continuity existing in their thought and work. Though the sciences radiated from a philosophical center, they unwittingly carried with them the inevitable marks of their early cultural setting, and upon frequent occasion even returned for guidance and ideational nutriment. So it happens that the sciences are not completely severed from philosophy, nor even from the folklore conventionally believed to have preceded metaphysics. For this reason the broader the scientist's horizon, the more versatile he is, the less is he interested in denying his intellectual ancestry. Thus as we shall notice, it is not at all true that the early workers in P.P. (Helmholtz, Spencer, Lotze, Fechner, Wundt, Avenarius, Mach, and others) failed to acknowledge their intellectual heritage.

Furthermore, the expansion of science in the 20th century, bringing to a high degree of development the interrelationships between sciences, as indicated by the hyphenated disciplines such as physical-chemistry, biophysics, biochemistry, astrophysics, mathematical-physics, etc., indeed suggests a renewed recognition of the interrelatedness of events which scientists have sometimes been prone to forget. Nor can we safely ignore that in the guise of logic, philosophy of a sort has come to play a part in the various specialized scientific domains.

For some decades now, probability logic has been incorporated in the work of astronomers and physicists. For that matter, in some statistical form logic is not unwelcome in every investigative domain. Also as operational and relativistic principles, logical and other philosophical ideas have been brought back, or, perhaps better said, discovered, in sciences most solidly established and independent. Today, any scientist who takes seriously the necessity to indicate his postulational background is forced to analyze the basis of his investigation. Of course, there are all sorts of philosophies, and not excluded from the list is that discipline which interrelates the sciences and brings to bear a critical check of one upon the other. Unfortunately the philosophy firmly intrenched in psychology is not of this type. Small wonder, then, that psychologists want to deny their philosophical connections, since it is undeniable that the kind of philosophy they still harbor is none too palatable. Certainly P.P. is dominated by a philosophy which ought to be superseded.

The history of P.P. conclusively shows that it is founded solidly in dualistic metaphysics, which bisects the world into two utterly different kinds of existence. With respect to specific psychological issues, conventional P.P. centers around a mind-body problem. While in no sense founded upon any existing or observed natural event, this kind of issue continues to dominate P.P. and transmutes an essentially theological construction into current scientific formulations.

Among historical writers it is the custom to single out Descartes (1596-1650) as the first of the moderns. Possibly a more discriminatory estimate, one which takes account of cultural continuity, more properly sees in him a Scholastic machinist. It was no mean achievement to become alive to the possibilities afforded by the developing machine technology for improving medieval philosophy and transforming science. Yet it would be a serious error to ignore the fact that Descartes symbolizes the work of many men in correlating the developing use of machinery with persisting medieval doctrines. Though Descartes marched in the vanguard of Renaissance science he was still essentially a Scholastic Rationalist. Like so many thinkers of his time he weaves his way between the lines laid out by his cultural forerunners and the new paths formed by the technological evolution of the time in which he lived.[1]

As a background for our consideration of the expanding place which Descartes accorded the body in psychological science we must consider his development of analytic geometry as a powerful tool for mechanical calculation, and his attempt to explain planetary motion by the principle of vortex mechanics. The same sort of adaptation of mechanical or machine principles to psychological events gave him a prominent position among those who attempted to bring psychology into the domain of the sciences. This fact can be no better realized than by considering Huxley's extravagant praise of him as a great and original physiologist who did for the physiology of motion and sensation what Harvey did for the circulation of the blood (248).

It is an excellent example of the continuity of thinking in P.P. that Huxley so highly exalted the automaton theory of Descartes. For, Huxley in the 19th century still continued the emphasis on body which Descartes had taken over from the medievalists. The latter taught that man's soul is closely related to the body, while the infrahuman animals possessing no soul were sheer automata. This view was especially emphasized by Descartes, who in his time found a technological advance which not only favored the machine operation of animals but also of humans.

The soul, then, as the unextended and really unknowable

[1] Cf. the argument concerning the competition and coordination of method and metaphysics (589).

feature of the cosmic scheme could be grasped only by observation of the body through which it exerted its influence
on other mechanical things. It is no mistake to regard this
doctrine as a cultural trend which continues to our day.
The soul which Descartes connected with the body was
interpreted by Huxley first as psychoses or consciousness,
and later reinterpreted as sensations, sensory processes, and
other mental functions of present-day P.P. And so it is of
interest to observe Huxley's attempt to show that the following five propositions, which he regards as "the foundation and
essence of the modern physiology of the nervous system," are
fully expressed and illustrated in such works of Descartes
as the *Principles of Philosophy* (118) *and the Passions of
the Soul* (117).

I. The brain is the organ of sensation, thought, and emotion;
that is to say, some change in the condition of the matter of
this organ is the invariable antecedent of the state of consciousness to which each of these terms is applied.

II. The movements of animals are due to the change of form
of muscles, which shorten and become thicker; and this
change of form in a muscle arises from a motion of the substance contained within the nerves which go to the muscle.

III. The sensations of animals are due to a motion of the substance
of the nerves which connect the sensory organs with the brain.

IV. The motion of the matter of a sensory nerve may be transmitted through the brain to motor nerves, and thereby give
rise to contraction of the muscles to which these motor nerves
are distributed; and this reflection of motion from a sensory
into a motor nerve may take place without volition, or even
contrary to it.

V. The motion of any given portion of the matter of the brain
excited by the motion of a sensory nerve, leaves behind a
readiness to be moved in the same way, in that part. Anything which resuscitates the motion gives rise to the appropriate feeling. This is the physical mechanism of memory
(248, pp. 194-197).

As historians of philosophy well know, the asserted connection of mind and body so satisfying to Huxley was not

altogether pleasing to Descartes himself. In his time mind was soul, an absolutely unextended substance which in no wise could be encompassed by spatial coordinates. A physiologist of the 19th century, however, with his increasing knowledge of the organism might not be bothered by the idea that mind is simply an epiphenomenon hovering over the activities of the brain. But in the 17th century the problem was still acute and later challenged Descartes' successors. Thus Leibniz (1646-1716) invented his doctrine of parallelism which he supported by the analogy of the two clocks (362, p. 96 f.). Spinoza (1632-1677) followed with his double-aspect view that there really were not two substances but only one which appeared under two guises (575). In some form or other, psychologists have maintained these constructions, though they have refused to acknowledge both their origin or significance. Here it is interesting to note that Bain, one of the earliest physiological psychologists, declares that Aristotle's idea of the inseparability of form and matter was not logically required (20, p. 152 f.). Bain asserts that though in reality there is a close alliance between soul and body there would not be any self-contradiction in supposing them separate.

. . . for anything we can see, the body might have its bodily functions without the soul, and the soul might have its psychical functions in some other connection than our present bodies (20, p. 53).

2. SCIENTIFIC BACKGROUND

The Nervous System as a Basis for Establishing Psychology as a Science

Following upon the general interrelation of the psychic with the body there arose in the history of psychology a series of specialized formulations of the connection between psychic phenomena and physiological processes. Naturally these formulations appear *pari passu* with an expansion of knowledge concerning physiological processes and especially the operation of the nervous system. After biologists learned about the anatomical differentiation of the brain they veered from the general correlation of mind with brain to the special localization of functions in the several parts. Then came the attempt to describe special mechanisms (drainage paths, traces, etc.) to account for particular acts such as learning, remembering, and willing.

In brief, to be oriented in the history of P.P. is to understand that just as the early physiological psychologists deliberately performed experiments to support their metaphysics, so now new generations of psychologists continue their labors in the identical philosophical framework, albeit with the probable disadvantage of being unaware of the psychophysical dualism involved.

Not to be overlooked, of course, are the specific variations in P.P. doctrine reflecting detailed differences in metaphysical speculation. For example, writers who incline toward a unified mind bring forth a different construction from those who lean toward an atomic view. The important point is that whatever particular kind of metaphysics influenced the early writers they did not fail to understand and acknowledge this influence, and so should we. Since the British and Continental writers varied their P.P. formulations somewhat, it is convenient to treat them separately. We shall not, however, ignore the crossing over of ideas from the one center of thought to the other.

Chapter 3

THE BRITISH TRADITIONS OF PHYSICAL INVESTIGATION AND BIOLOGICAL EVOLUTION OF MIND

MODERN psychological historiography involves an expository choice. On one side writers may delineate the changes of opinion concerning the nature of the soul or mind without stressing its connection with the body. This procedure constitutes a recount of the changing preoccupation of post-Greek writers with spiritual substances or processes. On the other side, there is the succession of descriptions of man as a psychic being; so that while the same subject is dealt with, it is always regarded as an aspect or correlate of organisms. Usually the psychic aspect of man is regarded as simple wraith-like epiphenomena associated with his organic operations.

Which procedure the writer follows depends upon his sensitivity to the practical aspects of culture. For example, the historian may or may not be influenced by a technological development in the milieu of the psychologists whom he is discussing. If, however, he is influenced by the fact that psychologists are inevitably concerned with individuals actually immersed in a complex economic, political, and social world he undoubtedly will not limit himself to abstracted psychic entities.

Psychological historians of necessity must follow the psychologists of whom they treat. For instance, when writing of British psychologists, they can not overlook the former's stress of the mechanical and observable. It is inescapable that many British writers were interested in the practical aspects of psychology, they were concerned with man and his nature as a political or ethical creature. As early as Hobbes (1588-1679), then, man was regarded as a body; motion not only constituted the basis of its behavior but also of the bodies affecting it. In keeping with his time, however, Hobbes adopted the medieval inversion of Aristotle and simply employed bodies and motions as the base and occasion for the apparitions and fantasies of which psychological processes are made to consist.

Hobbes' position is excellently set forth in the following four propositions (237, ch. II).

That the subject wherein colour and image are inherent is *not* the *object* or thing seen.

That there is nothing *without us* (really) which we call an *image* or colour.

That the said image or colour is but an *apparition* unto us of the *motion*, agitation, or alteration, which the *object* worketh in the *brain*, or spirits, or some internal substance of the head.

That as in *vision*, so also in conceptions that arise from the other *senses*, the subject of their *inherence* is not the object but the *sentient*.

When Hartley (1705-1757) published his *Observations* (201) in 1749 he appeared to be offering a rather elaborate exposition of the physiological counterpart of the psychic processes. Actually he was simply applying to the brain the doctrine of vibrations, which had been established with the authority of Newton, as the basis for all authentic natural phenomena. So far as psychological descriptions are concerned, the vibrations were localized in the nervous system. This did not imply, on the one hand, that Hartley knew anything significant about the brain or nervous system, or that, on the other, he was building his psychological propositions on anything more solid than the metaphysics and theology of his century.

For Hartley, the immediate instrument of sensation and motion was the white medullary substance of the brain, spinal marrow, and the nerves proceeding from them. This medullary substance, also the instrument by which ideas were presented to the mind, operated by forward and backward motions or tremblings of the medullary particles. Hartley made plain that the psychic changes only corresponded to changes in the medullary substance and were not identical with them.

Physiologically to distinguish the cruder sensations and the more subtle ideas, Hartley postulated a difference in magnitude of vibrations. Sensations corresponded to small vibrations in all the variously located particles of medullary substance, though chiefly those of the brain. Ideas by contrast correlated exclusively with the even smaller vibrations called miniatures or vibratiuncles in the brain substance.

Whether or not Hartley is regarded as the originator of P.P. (53, II, p. 279) depends upon the value one places upon the parallelistic as over against the interactionistic construction. Certainly the vibrational principle is merely an historical stage in the development of an acceptable statement of the correspondences between the two ultimately different features of traditional psychophysical dualism. Mentalistic psychologists may properly celebrate Hartley as a pioneer in bringing mental states into contiguity with the nervous system. Nevertheless it is essential to recognize his proper position in the metaphysical and theological continuity of psychological thought. The Hartleian parallelism of associations and vibrations is simply a point on the continuum which differentiates between organism and mind, body and soul. The first part of his book concludes with the remark: "I would not be in any way interpreted so as to oppose the immateriality of the soul."

Bain (1818-1903). Writers who regard the linking of the organic with the mental as an important step in making psychology scientific accord Bain a prominent place in the history of P.P. Though in the early fifties of the 19th century[1] he was only one of several writers to show the concomitance between the psychic and the physiological he is regarded as a prominent British founder of this branch of psychology.

Indeed, the whole history of P.P. is anomalous. For one

[1] Lotze is considered the earliest Continental physiological psychologist because he produced his *Medicinische Psychologie* in 1852.

thing, there are so many founders. In each instance, of course, we find the encomium bestowed by an admirer of a new statement of an ancient doctrine. In the case of Bain, it was an attempt to assimilate the developing knowledge of his period. This fact is explicit in his statement of intention and achievement, which we quote from his Preface to the first edition of *The Senses and the Intellect.*

Conceiving that the time has now come when many of the striking discoveries of Physiologists relative to the nervous system should find a recognized place in the Science of Mind, I have devoted a separate chapter to the Physiology of the Brain and Nerves.

In this sentence we notice two points. First, Bain presents material not directly of his own study, in a chapter somewhat isolated from the remainder of the exposition. In the second place, this chapter out of the way, he says: "We now commence the subject of MIND proper" (19, p. 57). Obviously the neural and other organic materials can be made to play only a very minor part in the body of the work. Their explanatory function is admittedly close to nil, though as Bain continued to expand his views he increasingly loaded the nervous system with psychic functions.

Bain's attempt to connect organic factors with the psychic is certainly no new enterprise. It must be kept in view that the psychic itself was invented for the purpose of accounting for the theological nature of man and his destiny. Even medieval writers were actually concerned with human individuals despite their extreme interest in the soul.

What is new in Bain, therefore, is bringing into his psychological scheme some echo of the evolution of the physiological branch of organic studies. The significant references to Ludwig, Müller, duBois-Reymond, and others in his psychological writings attest his sensitivity to the great physiological development taking place in the German laboratories. Recall that the early decades of the 19th century stand out as a blossoming period of biological work. It was in 1828 that Wöhler discovered how from inorganic ammonium cyanate

NH_4OCN, urea $OC \begin{smallmatrix} NH_2 \\ NH_2 \end{smallmatrix}$ an organic compound, could be derived. This was the time, too, when Liebig did so much at Giessen to establish biochemistry and the chemistry of agriculture.

It has been asserted (427, II, 511n.) that Bain carried out what Thomas Brown (1778-1820) called the "physical investigation of the mind," and Johannes Müller's (1801-1858) idea "*Psychologus nemo nisi physiologus.*" At any rate, he certainly did as much as Wundt to bring mind and body together. The point here is that the linking of the two in close connection is simply the development of the cultural trend. Certainly no more than Bain could Wundt or any of his successors establish anything about the psychic. Interesting also is the use each made of evolution ideas to bring the organism into psychology.

At the basis of Bain's P.P. is the claim that the brain is the principal (19, p. 10) and chief (p. 12) organ of the mind. For this proposition he offers the following five "proofs."

(1) In time of great mental agitation or unusual exertion of thought the aching or oppression in the head tells where the seat of action is.

(2) Injury or disease of the brain impairs in some way or other the powers of the mind.

(3) Unusual exertion of the mind results in an increase of nervous waste products. This is true especially of phosphates (ammonium and magnesium phosphates) since phosphate abounds more in the brain than in any other tissue.

(4) There is an indisputable connection between size of the brain and the mental energy displayed by the individual man or animal.

(5) Experiments such as cutting a main trunk nerve or removal of hemispheres prove the immediate dependence of sensation, intelligence or volition on those parts.

That such proofs were not conclusive, even in Bain's own day of limited biological information, is indicated by his reference to the fact that "Cases have been recorded of disease of large portions of the brain in both hemispheres

at once, without apparent loss of function. . ." (19, p. 42),
and also that a blow on the head could remedy derangement.
"There are cases on record, where a blow on the head has
cured Idiocy" (20, p. 13). Though, unlike some present-day
writers, Bain seems unsurprised at the slight interference of
extensive brain injuries, he uses similar arguments to explain
the fact. All that is required is . . . "to extend still farther
the supposition of a plurality of nervous tracks for a single
mental aptitude" (19, p. 46). In many ways this is a better
dodge than the more recent doctrine of vicarious function.

Clearly, Bain's contribution to P.P. amounts to no more
but to as much as juxtaposing the developing interest in
biological science with his own interest in mind. As to the
latter, in the first edition of his treatises mind is simply the
traditional Associationism of the British School. Later, under
the influence of Spencer and Darwin, he slants his work in
an evolutionary direction. As a result, associational processes
are not confined to ideas or psychic processes exclusively, but
also include the interrelation of unit movements to make up
various complex actions.

Nevertheless, for Bain P.P. is above all a matter of establishing a mind-body relationship. Not only is this relationship
for him essentially a philosophical and not a scientific problem, but also the solution was metaphysical. This holds
despite Bain's apparent factual emphasis that psychological
phenomena are not only connected with the nervous system
but with the body as a whole (19, p. 53). Though the brain
is the chief organ of mind, the organs of sense and the
muscular system are also brought into the scheme. But how
the mind and the body are conjoined is a profound mystery
for Bain, since once and for all the two belong to different
orders of existence. Body as matter is extended, whereas
mind has no extension and can not be joined in local union
(20, p. 136).

Bringing together mind and body is thus not only a
metaphysical problem but one requiring a spiritistic solution.
At this point Bain's philosophy came to the fore.

The arguments for the two substances have, we believe, now entirely lost their validity; they are no longer compatible with ascertained science and clear thinking. The one substance, with two sets of properties, two sides, the physical and the mental— *a double faced unity*—would appear to comply with all the exigencies of the case. We are to deal with this, as in the language of the Athanasian Creed, not confounding the persons nor dividing the substance (20, p. 196).

Here is revealed Bain's basic philosophy in which his psychology is irremovably imbedded. Despite the assertions to the contrary (43, p. 223; 455, p. 112), Bain was in no sense a psychologist starting with actual events called sensing, perceiving, emoting, remembering, etc., but a metaphysician with an apparent determination to assimilate such events with the Berkeleyan form of spiritual philosophy. This point is corroborated in his declaration:

There is no possible knowledge of a world except in reference to our minds. Knowledge means a state of mind: the notion of material things is a mental fact. We are incapable even of discussing the existence of an independent material world; the very act is a contradiction. We can speak only of a world presented to our own minds (19, p. 375).

Darwin (1809-1882). Darwin's connection with psychology illustrates two fundamental scientific items. First, the continuity of the events with which scientists are concerned, and secondly, the illumination of one science by another which this fact affords. We have already pointed out that since psychology is concerned with organisms it inevitably must take them into account. This was the case even with the theological and metaphysical psychology of the Patristic and Scholastic period. It was just as inevitable then that advances in biological knowledge should not only make organisms significant in psychological studies but in a genuine way basic to them. Thus the importance of Darwin in P.P. must be gauged by the transformations which evolutionary doctrine has effected in the conception of mind, even though its nonspatial and therefore nonnatural character is continued.

Without distinguishing between Darwin and the other evolutionists who established and fostered Darwinism we may list a number of developments that have contributed to the enhancement of P.P.

To begin with, we indicate the important achievement of Darwin's reversal of the Cartesian doctrine of the organism as a machine. In that doctrine the psyche constitutes not only the source of all motive power but also the locus of end or purpose. By Darwin's time the organism becomes a natural object organized and operating in interaction with a set of environing conditions. Not to be overlooked is the emphasis Darwin and other evolutionists placed upon the factors of growth and development as conditioned by selective components of the environment. Thus both extraneous vital and psychic powers are weakened.

Next and closely related to the former is clearing the way to a biological conception of psychological events. Instead of following through the physical and chemical analogies of mind as developed by the Mills and others, the Darwinian view allows for a more intimate connection of the mental and the organic. Still more, stress is placed upon the organism in action, even so far in fact as to make the mental serve in the adjustment of the organism.

Within the biological domain the adjustmental view fosters the development of ecological along with morphological and physiological studies. It is the machine idea which stresses form and organization with a secondary consideration of operation, whereas the biological conception impels the observation of life conditions, of the birth, development, and changes of organisms. Anatomical and physiological events are now considered as operating within the larger and more comprehensive sphere of organismic behavior.

The emphasis of organisms in interaction with environment brings in its train the actional side of mentality. States and elements, in short, atomic and substantive constructions, give way to processes and functions. While not one iota of the characteristics of the psyche is relinquished, there is an enlargement of view which allows for affective and volitional actions in addition to the cognitive. It is interesting to note here the great influence of Darwinian ideas upon Wundtian psychology. Whereas on the side of sensitivity and intellectual activities Wundt does not go beyond the assertion that his chemical elements are processes, his treatment of such topics as affection and volition as well as the complex developments of language and social mentality leaves no doubt that psychology is concerned with the actions of organisms. That Wundt regards these activities as definitely evolved demonstrates Darwin's influence upon his thought and work.

By focussing upon the continuity of human and infrahuman organisms Darwinism integrates the psychic and the organic in a way not possible before. Not only did this result in the development of animal psychology, but the lines were effaced that formerly separated the instinctive and the rational. Immediately, innumerable problems of contrast and similarity between reflexes and instincts, on the one side, and habits and learning, on the other, were brought to the surface.[1] Still more, the assumption that the psychic is function or guide for the organic lowered the high barrier between the two. So much did the organic come to fill the house of psychology that primacy could pass to the organic, especially to the brain. Forthwith the psychic could be reduced to the shadowiness of epiphenomena, and such psychological activities as learning and habit could at least be discussed with a tremendous emphasis of the nervous system.

How little the psychic was actually dissipated may be gathered from the fact that the stress of the organic led to a reintroduction of the psychic-unity doctrine into the English scene of Association Psychology. As Darwin attempted to show in his *Expression of the Emotions in Man and Animals* (109), emotional acts were continuous and transmitted from the lower to the higher forms, even as the lower species of animals were transformed into the higher.

[1] As in the works of Romanes (1848-1894) (523, 524, 525) and Morgan (1852-1936) (440, 441, 442, 443).

In the wake of Darwinian theory came a flood of ideas concerning the innateness and heredity of individual differences and likenesses, and thus the mental became an inherent possession of organisms descended from particular progenitors. Native intelligence as well as ingrained instincts and reflexes symbolized the viability of the mental, despite the growing importance and effectiveness of organic factors in psychological situations.

Through the influence of Galton (1822-1911) and others the mind with its innate powers became a locus of psychic possessions, So far as P.P. is concerned the floodgates were loosed for speculations concerning neural structures and organizations, which gave rise to innate and transmissible psychological differences. And so general metaphysical trends influenced the maintenance of a fine balace between the increasing emergence into psychology of organic and behavioral factors and the continuation of psychic conceptions. A tremendously important by-product was the contamination of genuine biological knowledge concerning neural action with the invention of all sorts of neuro-psychic "functions."

Spencer (1820-1903). Though Herbert Spencer was neither a psychologist nor a physiologist he must be accorded a prominent position among the early progenitors of P.P. This position he merits because he promoted evolutionary principles in psychology and moreover influenced such writers as James, the precursor of Functionalism, and Hughlings Jackson (1835-1911), who contributed much to the development of P.P. doctrine.[1] For still other reasons Spencer is important in the history of P.P. In the first place, as a syntheticist he has helped to bring together biological and psychological thinking, and secondly, he was among the first to initiate the basic ideological techniques of P.P.

Symbolizing Spencer's synthetic viewpoint which lies at the core of P.P. development is his famous pronouncement:

---

[1] For example, the conception of a hierarchical evolution of functional levels in the nervous system. This conception Jackson credits to Spencer (252, II, p. 45, p. 50n., p. 80 et passim).

"The life of every organism is a continuous adaptation of its inner actions to outer actions" (574, p. 134). This formula is intended to stress two fundamental principles. On the one hand, it sets forth the inseverable interrelationship of bodily or organic and mental phenomena, and constitutes the basis for the presumed naturalistic view concerning psychic processes, since the formula localizes such processes in the organism's activities. On the other hand, Spencer intends to stress the interaction of the organism with the environment. As he says, "A complete interpretation of the inner actions involves recognition of the outer actions" (574, p. 134). James (1842-1910) (267, I, p. 6) commended this feature of the formula as contributing to the naturalization of mind. Spencer specifically contrasts the purely biological study of organisms in terms of structures and functions with the psychological which is essentially concerned with the environment as well.

As to Spencer's pioneering in P.P. ideology, there is his further emphasis of the difference between psychology and biology. On its objective side, that is, as connected nervous coordination, psychology is really a part of biology, but insofar as it is subjective, the science of consciousness, it is absolutely independent. Though he believes ". . . that mind and nervous action are the subjective and objective faces of the same thing" (574, I, p. 140), such that a nervous shock is the ultimate unit of consciousness (574, I, p. 151), "we remain utterly incapable of seeing, and even of imagining, how the two are related" (574, I, p. 140).

Thus Spencer foreshadows today's prevailing situation in P.P. Despite the persistency with which current writers ignore the difficulties in the parallelistic and identity methods of making compatible the mental and neural, it is clear that they are in the same position as Spencer.

As an early physiological psychologist and as a non-professional writer Spencer clearly presented his view.

Suppose it to have become quite clear that a shock in consciousness and a molecular motion are the subjective and objective faces of the same thing we continue utterly incapable of uniting the two, so as to conceive that reality of which they are the opposite faces (574, I, p. 625).

The poignancy of this passage is emphasized when we consider Spencer's basic idea of the complete unknowability of psychic phenomena. Precisely here is revealed one of the basic techniques of P.P.—namely, since the mental is outside the range of observation one can proceed to achieve a semblance of knowledge by stressing the palpable facts of organic life. As Spencer demonstrates, however, the multiplication and piling up of statements about nervous action—which is presumably basic to and isomorphic with processes of consciousness—really tell nothing concerning the impalpable mental (574, I, p. 48).

Huxley (1825-1895). Though Huxley is best known as a physiologist and as he described himself, the general agent for Darwinism, he occupies a large place in the history of P.P. Quite as much as Spencer and Darwin he put the organism into the forefront of psychological thinking. His conception of the psychic as an epiphenomenon was helpful in pointing the way to the basic inclusion of nervous action and general organic functioning in psychological description. Certainly he formulated effectively and transparently the views encountered in the field even today. Some no doubt would say that his expository career outweighs his originality, and that even his famous aphorism of no psychosis without a neurosis is anticipated by Bain's "no (nerve) currents no mind" (19, p. 53). Still, who can deny that he helped to bring psychology and physiology together, and placed psychophysiological doctrine in its proper metaphysical setting.

Contrary to the desire of current psychophysiologists to tone down the metaphysical foundation of P.P., it is to Huxley's great credit that he has stated with extreme clarity that P.P. doctrine is simply a focalization of dualistic metaphysics. In his usual forceful style he inveighs against those who would make metaphysics contraband of intellect. Following this line he asserts how curious:

. . . that those who most loudly profess to abstain from such commodities, are, all the while, unconscious consumers, on a great scale, of one or other of their multitudinous disguises or adulterations. With mouths full of the particular kind of heavily buttered toast which they affect, they inveigh against the eating of plain bread (249, p. 291).

The importance of Huxley for P.P. is that he shows as convincingly as possible the infiltration of Berkeley's (1685-1753) philosophy of sensationism into the sensory physiology department of P.P.

Since Huxley's arguments are no different from those still current in P.P., they are worth quoting at some length.

Suppose that I accidentally prick my finger with a pin. I immediately become aware of a condition of my consciousness—a feeling which I term pain. I have no doubt whatever that the feeling is in myself alone; and if any one were to say that the pain I feel is something which inheres in the needle, as one of the qualities of the substance of the needle, we should all laugh at the absurdity of the phraseology. In fact, it is utterly impossible to conceive pain except as a state of consciousness (249, p. 253 f.).

So much for pain. Now let us consider an ordinary sensation. Let the point of the pin be gently rested upon the skin, and I become aware of a feeling, or condition of consciousness, quite different from the former—the sensation of what I call "touch." Nevertheless this touch is plainly just as much in myself as the pain was. I cannot for a moment conceive this something which I call touch as existing apart from myself, or a being capable of the same feelings as myself. And the same reasoning applies to all the other simple sensations. A moment's reflection is sufficient to convince one that the smell, and the taste, and the yellowness, of which we become aware when an orange is smelt, tasted, and seen, are as completely states of our consciousness as is the pain which arises if the orange happens to be too sour. Nor is it less clear that every sound is a state of consciousness of him who hears it. If the universe contained only blind and deaf beings, it is impossible for us to imagine but that darkness and silence should reign everywhere (249, p. 254 f.).

In a similar manner localization, extension, figure, form, motion, rest, solidity, and whatever else philosophers call primary qualities are equated by Huxley with conscious states mediated by the nerves and brain. Referring back to the pain which is presumed to be in the finger he says:

> And yet nothing is more certain than that it is not, and cannot be, in the spot in which I feel it, nor within a couple of feet of that spot. For the skin of the finger is connected by a bundle of fine nervous fibres, which run up the whole length of the arm to the spinal marrow, which sets them in communication with the brain, and we know that the feeling of pain caused by the prick of a pin is dependent on the integrity of those fibres. After they have been cut through close to the spinal cord, no pain will be felt, whatever injury is done to the finger; and if the ends which remain in connection with the cord be pricked, the pain which arises will appear to have its seat in the finger just as distinctly as before. Nay, if the whole arm be cut off, the pain which arises from pricking the nerve stump will appear to be seated in the fingers, just as if they were still connected with the body.
>
> It is perfectly obvious, therefore, that the localization of the pain at the surface of the body is an act of mind. It is an *extradition* of that consciousness, which has its seat in the brain, to a definite point of the body (249, pp. 258-259).

In this manner Huxley demonstrates that the nerves and brain support such metaphysical doctrines as Berkeley has so fantastically designed. Knowing the power exerted by dualistic ideas upon the physiological psychologists of Huxley's time as well as our own, we are not surprised by his overlooking that the nerves and brain must be reduced to states of consciousness. Of course, no individual is presumed to see or know his own brain; so A's brain becomes dissipated in B's mind by means of his brain, which likewise becomes C's consciousness through the working of his brain which exists only in D's consciousness *ad infinitum*. Huxley's master, Berkeley, had God's mind, which didn't need a brain, as the final locus of everything (67, pp. 313 ff.).

Since it is our purpose to show the origin and basis for modern P.P. doctrine we might pause to consider some of the basic confusions Huxley piles up to rationalize his acceptance of the cultural dualistic views. First, he confuses objects known with objects. Next he confounds acts of knowing with objects known. Then he identifies objects with acts of knowing. It is a sheer gratuity to make knowing or acts of discrimination into psychic processes requiring the intermediation of the brain. Berkeley did all this without prating about the brain. Perhaps in his time it could not be expected that he would differentiate between behavior or reaction to things, or discrimination, on the one hand, and knowing, on the other. To go further and expect Huxley to see that knowledge itself is a type of interaction with things is to upset the order of history. With Huxley as an example it should not today, however, be difficult to see that the fact that organisms comprise brains and nerves provides no support for the fundamental dualism of historical P.P.

Chapter 4

THE CONTINENTAL TRADITION OF LABORATORY PHYSIOLOGY

O N the European continent Physiological Psychology may be traced back to the problem whether psychology can be a science. That this should be a problem at all, of course, is a fact of cultural history. From our present point of vantage we may find it anachronistic to question whether we can observe the events in which organisms interact with stimulus objects, and construct laws concerning such actions. Considering that the engendering period of P.P. was so heavily dominated by Renaissance dualism the question was naturally a poignant one. That an affirmative answer was finally given demonstrates that upon occasion scientific thinking gets detached from the intellectual traditions to which it is powerfully geared.

As is well known, Kant (1724-1804) declared that it was impossible for psychology to be a science for two reasons. First, as a link in the chain of modern thinkers who followed Descartes he placed psychological happenings in the domain of the inextensible. Accordingly he believed that mathematics was inapplicable to psychology, which had only a temporal dimension. In the second place, Kant argued that psychology could not be experimental because psychic states could not be controlled and altered at will or even remain constant under observation.

Such basic beliefs did not radically change during the evolution of P.P. If Herbart (1776-1841) rejected Kant's anti-mathematical idea it was only by asserting that psychological states were intensive as well as durative. For the same metaphysical reasons he accepted Kant's pronouncement concerning psychic experimentation. Coming to Fechner and his experiments we know that his driving force was not merely metaphysical but religious, as Wundt informs us. "Das ganze

Interesse Fechners gehört eben nicht der Psychologie als solcher an, sondern diese ist für ihn nur ein Bestandtheil der Natur- und Religionsphilosophie" (648, p. 84; 654a, p. 303 f.).

Nor do these metaphysical ideas lose ground when Lotze and Wundt bring to fruition the conception of P.P. Fechner's (1801-1887) inner psychophysics, the establishment of a definite relationship between the psychological and the organophysical, continues unabated to this very moment. What are changed are merely the details of the psychophysical relationship both as ontological and methodological (really epistemological) doctrine. The body or the organic remains the seat of the soul or consciousness, whatever terms are used. The formulae that the nervous system constitutes the mechanism of psychology, that it mediates psychological processes or that organic functions simply parallel psychological actions are completely equivalent.

To remind us of the specific variations within this continuity of ideas we examine briefly some of the early Continental progenitors of P.P.

Lotze (1817-1881). Probably the most constructive contribution of Lotze to the development of P.P. was his attempt to interrelate the soul and the body or to provide a physiology of the soul. No one in the history of psychology believed more intensively in the immutability and inextensibility of mind. Actually, Lotze was an archmetaphysician who insisted upon autonomous theological and value principles as equally basic and real as natural events. But in consonance with the cultural trends of his time he moved in the circle of the psychophysical conception of nature. After all, he was a physician and a student of E. H. Weber (1795-1878). And so he evolved the formula that though an immaterial being can have no extension it may have place and be localized (380, p. 82). This he regarded as a valid basis for physiologizing the soul.

The student of psychological history alive to cultural development observes that the accumulating facts of human activity modify but do not basically change cultural trends. Physiology of soul in the 19th century is simply an elaboration of the place of the pineal gland in the soul's affairs, as developed by Descartes in the 17th century. Thus the pyramiding of facts simply forces those who move in the soul's orbit to impose deeply-ingrained beliefs upon their operational findings. As a consequence the investigations of organisms result not in constructions derived from the findings but in constructions which harmonize such findings with established theory. Lotze no more than any medieval thinker has observed anything answering to a psychic principle. No one in the history of science has been in contact with inextensible objects, but the availability of words makes assertion possible.

Helmholtz (1821-1894). Though Helmholtz as primarily a physicist and physiologist did not write a systematic treatise on psychology there is no question about his participation in the development of P.P. Perhaps because he did such thorough acoustic and optic work he really offers more detailed analyses of psychophysical doctrine than other more professional writers on the subject.

So frank and clear an exposition leaves no doubt as to the antecedents of his theories. Proximally, Helmholtz, builds on Müller, especially his doctrine of specific nerve energies which Helmholtz admires excessively[1] and elaborates inordinately. The nerves and brain really produce or create sensations which only exist as subjective phenomena (213, p. 258).

Distally this idea is none other than the prevalent metaphysical notion concerning the dichotomies between subjective and objective, and the thing-in-itself as over against phenomena which Locke and Kant crystallized. As Müller and Helmholtz adopted the idea, the mediator between the thing-in-itself, which has no qualities corresponding to the internal sensations, is the nervous system. That there is no coincidence, for example, between sensation of color and

[1] Going so far as to compare it with the discovery of the law of gravitation (215, I, p. 378; II, p. 181).

qualities of light Helmholtz specifically declares is in line with the thought of Locke (1632-1704) and Herbart and completely in accord with Kant's philosophy (213, p. 261).

The question here is: Has not sensorial physiology in its origin and present-day continuation simply translated and adapted physiological facts to fit established metaphysical theories? As Lange (336, III, p. 202) states:

The physiology of the Sense-organs is developed or corrected Kantianism, and Kant's system may, as it were, be regarded as a programme for modern discoveries in this field.

This is the view that Helmholtz himself clearly presents in the *Optics*.

Müller's law of specific energies was a step forward of the greatest importance for the whole theory of sense perceptions, and it has since become the scientific basis of this theory. In a certain sense, it is the empirical fulfilment of Kant's theoretical concept of the nature of human reason (214, II, pp. 19-20).

Is it necessary, however, in view of the events (interactions of organisms with things) to follow the philosophical traditions rather than construct new terms and new propositions to describe the events?

That Helmholtz is thoroughly suffused with the spiritistic traditions of his time is apparent in (1) his general doctrine of the phenomenal or nonspatial character of qualities of things and (2) his special theory of unconscious inference. The former he expounds in the form of the sign or symbol character of sense qualities. He says, "The quality of the sensation is, so to speak, a symbol for our imagination, a sort of earmark of objective quality" (214, II, p. 4). There is no identity between the quality of sensation and the quality of the object by which it is aroused. The former, of course, is created through the mediation of the nerves and brain. This is simply the age-old doctrine that sensory qualities are not real qualities of things but only signs of them in the mind (635, p. 403).

Helmholtz's doctrine of unconscious inference similarly

imports into physiological optics the metaphysical doctrine of the ego or transcendental unity of apperception. Following the Kantian philosophy it is not only necessary to have sensations in the mind created through the operation of physical stimulation on the physiological organs, but also to organize these sensations into objects and to account for their simultaneous variabilities in different individuals and in the successive perceivings of the same individual. It is, of course, gratuitous for Helmholtz to regard unconscious inferences as the basis for such events as illusory reactions, color-contrast effects, and the constancy of reaction.

The student of psychological history can scarcely miss the point that Helmholtz's physiological and psychological contributions constitute primarily the translation of Kantian philosophy into physiological terms. Since obviously the assiduous investigation of anatomy and physiology can not transform philosophy into science, what is actually happening is that anatomy and physiology are being assimilated to metaphysics.

How can such a situation prevail? How can physiological and experimental psychology be metaphysical? The answer is, of course, that a great gap exists between the dominant cultural views of scientists and what they actually do in the laboratory and field. Scientists as well as politicians construct documents which do not fit or parallel their performances. Psychology is not unique in building a scientific edifice in the pattern of metaphysics. Nordenskiold (467, p. 383) offers a vivid picture of Johannes Müller who regarded himself as rejecting the experimental method for physiology and studying the subject from the standpoint of the Schellingian idea of life, and yet he became the father of experimental physiology.

The lack of coordination between the cultural framework and what actually is done within it forces the implication that whatever may be the power of tradition to distort our knowledge of events, the possibility always remains of separating the events from the cultural background. Whatever may have been the circumstances of Helmholtz's time it is plain today that different constructions are now available.

Wundt (1832-1920). The career and works of Wundt illuminate perfectly the origin and background of P.P. In the first place, Wundt is justly accorded full credit for really establishing the subject. His training as a physician, his entering scientific work as a physiologist, his instituting and directing a psychological laboratory, as well as his production of standard treatises, not only comprehensive in exposition but also of tremendous influence in psychological development, certainly place him in the forefront of P.P. In addition, as an energetic and versatile writer Wundt produced many philosophical treatises; thus unlike those who draw their fill of doctrine from the unseen depths of philosophic culture he clearly faced the metaphysical issues which bear upon P.P. problems. For this reason Wundt and his works constitute excellent materials for the effective study of the interrelationship between psychological doctrines and their philosophical background.

It is of no small significance, of course, that Wundt regarded his philosophy as different from that of the prevailing mode. His, he insisted, was scientific philosophy, a system established on the basis of the special sciences. He defines philosophy:

. . . als die allgemeine Wissenschaft, welche die durch die Einzelwissenschaften vermittelten allgemeinen Erkenntnisse zu einem wider-spruchslosen System zu vereinigen hat (649, I, p. 9).

It is this kind of philosophy which, even when metaphysics loses caste, is inevitably pursued by scientists as an expression of the ineradicable impulse of human understanding toward speculation and unification (655, pp. 110, 119). It is this kind of philosophy which is inescapable even for such professed antimetaphysicians as Haeckel, Ostwald, and Mach (655, pp. 119-128).

Wundt believes that whether one advances toward or retreats from philosophy, depends not only upon the espousal of a proper metaphysics but also upon how the moves are made. Philosophy must be attained as he himself attained it, through the avenue of the special sciences (649, I, p. xi). He scores those who begin with some prevailing form of metaphysics and then make excursions into some domain of natural science, or even start with some special science and then seek intellectual support in a ready-to-hand philosophical system (649, pp. xi-xii). Though he always took care that psychology assume and maintain its independent position as an empirical science outside philosophy, he was no less concerned that it should make its contribution to philosophy.

We can not underestimate the value of studying Wundt when we are interested in the origin and development of P.P. Not only has he given us elaborate documentation concerning his own encyclopedic learning, but also he was sun-clear in his thinking and writing about the basic roots of the subject and its concomitant development with the other sciences. One of the fundamental lessons he teaches is that P.P. is securely set in a cultural matrix, which is at the same time philosophical and scientific. As he himself tells us, his philosophical system was formulated in 1866 and the results partially laid down in his *Grundzüge der physiologischen Psychologie* and in his various works on logic and ethics (649, p. viii). As indicated above, Wundt claims to have reached philosophy through the special sciences, since in 1866 he had been for ten years Dozent in physiology, though turning more and more toward psychology. But it is not to be gainsaid that in his time these special sciences were certainly related to general philosophy.

Here we must be reminded that Wundt's *Beiträge* (647), published sectionally beginning in 1858 and in complete form in 1862, articulate basically with the work of Weber, Müller, Lotze, and others—work that is definitely grounded in the *Naturphilosophie* and its background of general German idealism. Note too that the occupation with science, laboratories, and experimentation is a definite part of the German intellectual culture of the time. It was only in 1863 that the private physics laboratory of Magnus (1802-1870) evolved into the physical laboratory of the University of Berlin (72, p. 393). This is likewise the period of Müller's experimental laboratory and the development of Liebig's work. The psychologist will also take note of the great upsurge of scientific claims in psychology, so many treatises of which carried in their titles the name *Natural Science*.[1]

The focal point here, of course, is the idea of experience. The empirical movement in philosophy emphasized experience as the basis for science, and as a precipitation of the scientific solute from the general philosophical solvent. For psychology the salient issue is whether experience is to be regarded as a series of actual events uncontaminated with spiritual constructions or whether it is of a piece with them. As we shall see, Wundt's emphasis of science, objective fact, and experimentation did not save him from the deeply-rooted cultural tradition which transforms into spiritual constructions the actual events with which scientists begin.

As far as Wundt's P.P. was concerned it is true that as a child of his time he attempted, like so many other writers, to bring psychology down to a natural basis. This meant an emphasis of the organic, the stress of physiology, especially the nervous system. Thus, as mental elements or processes, sensations directly and feelings indirectly have to be stimulated by or correlated with brain processes whether or not other stimulations are involved.

Nevertheless, in all the chapters of his *Grundzüge* (651) and other writings which deal with the nervous system Wundt simply inserts in the text unrelated materials borrowed from anatomists and physiologists. Did he, however, give us any essential and verifiable propositions concerning the physiology of mind? It is a matter of record that once he

[1] For example, Herbart, *Psychologie als Wissenschaft;* (1824-25); Benecke, *Lehrbuch der Psychologie als Naturwissenschaft* (1833); Drobisch, *Empirische Psychologie nach .Naturwissenschaftliche Methode* (1842).

delivered himself of his assertions of the scientific character of psychology and the connection of the mental processes with the nervous system, he then went on to discuss the mental processes in complete independence of any physiological foundation. His actual psychology was much more closely connected with the physical and chemical analogies of British thought[1] than even the developing biological especially evolutional, ideas permitted. In his *Grundzüge* (651) as well as in his *Grundriss* (652) he compounded and recompounded mental states, or processes as he preferred to call them, from simpler atomic and molecular elements.

Physiological elements Wundt repeatedly declared are supplementary aids to psychology. Physiological facts being of a different order belong to physiology alone and not to psychology. Experimental psychology is called physiological psychology simply because experimentation in psychology was introduced on the pattern of experimentation in the physiology of the sense organs and the nervous system (650, p. 27). Although the brain appears as the immediate organ of consciousness (650, p. 229), the physiological processes are only correlates and parallels of psychic processes. The principle of parallelism of changes in sensation and in physiological stimulation, as well as the general principle of psychophysical parallelism, allows for no explanation of psychical processes by physiological ones.

There is only one kind of causal explanation in psychology, and that is the derivation of more complex psychical processes from simpler ones (650, p. 27).

Despite Wundt's protestations that he began with natural science and then turned to metaphysics, and his expressed objections to the criticisms of those who accused him of drawing his psychology out of metaphysics (649, I, p. 11) he was thoroughly and consistently a spiritualistic monist. He reiterated that everything begins in experience and that there

[1] For example, that of James Mill's *Analysis of the Human Mind,* and John Stuart Mill's revision of that work (433).

is only one homogeneous experience. The motive here is to avoid all school traditions. His view is uncompromising empiricism; his intention is to avoid idealisms and materialisms and in general all poetic metaphysics as practiced by theologians who constructed a cosmic scheme founded upon aesthetic or ethic predilections. Equally opposed he was to dialectic metaphysics which categorically creates a cosmos, and to critical metaphysics which fits ultimate categories to contents of experience. For Wundt experience was all in all. It was in this sense that he regarded psychology as the special science basic to metaphysics.

But the critical student of Wundt asks: What is this experience? No doubt he intended to regard experience as the materials of observation, the raw data with which the sciences begin. For this reason he made knowledge and knowledge processes basic to his philosophy. Yet he rose no higher than the level of his culture. In offering the governing principles of his psychological position he gives a very clear and decisive statement of what must be denominated spiritual monism. Psychological experience, he declares, is immediate experience in its totality. Out of this immediate experience the natural sciences construct conceptions; thus the natural sciences are concerned with mediate experience. The psychologist, on the other hand, does not deal with objective mediate concepts but with immediate experience in itself, as the materials of direct perception. What can be meant by immediate experience in its totality? Certainly this is nothing more than a metaphysical reduction of the universe to psychic or spiritual substance. That subjective and objective can be differentiated from this immediate total experience is a view thoroughly metaphysical in a sense that Wundt condemned upon many occasions.

Indeed, such immediate experience, which comprises not only sensations (colors, sounds, etc.), but also feelings and volitions, is very remote from the actual materials with which the psychologist works. Certainly Wundt was not observing experience directly when he regarded his studies of color and sound differentiation as introspective. It is clear then why he did not make the brain and nervous system, to say nothing of the entire organism, the materials he worked upon. Paradoxically the founder of P.P. had little use for the nervous system, since obviously it could throw no light on his sensations, feelings, and other psychic states. Doubtless it was Wundt's knowledge of physiology that made him unwilling to connect it more closely with psychology. It is interesting to compare his view with that of duBois-Reymond (1818-1896), (125). Wundt's emphasis of the independence of psychology simply carried him over to the realm of pure psychics and could not serve to differentiate two lines of work, one the study of the organism and its functions, and the other the study of the reaction of the organism to color and sound objects.

CHAPTER 5

THE HISTORICAL SUM AND DIVISION OF
PHYSIOLOGICAL PSYCHOLOGY

THE history of P.P. naturally follows the general development of psychology. We find, therefore, all sorts of detailed interpretative ramifications stemming from the three basic P.P. views mentioned at the beginning of Chapter 1. Because of the unrewarding effort of tracing out these variations upon their original themes we choose the more worthwhile task of observing how these interpretations have been transferred from one type of data to another. On this basis the history of P.P. may be divided into two periods, using the date 1890 as a convenient point of departure for the second period. This date symbolizes the advance of experimental psychology from its primary preoccupation with sensory processes to include animal studies, learning, and the investigation of individual differences.

The more inclusive concern of psychologists with human and animal behavior coincides with an emergence of the objective views of behavior mechanisms, the views previously numbered 3b or 3c (p. 1). Those physiological psychologists who espouse view 3b turn away in large part from mentalistic toward behavioristic interpretations of the activities they investigate. Proponents of view 3b regard psychological behavior as altogether the physiological actions of organic structures. As we shall see, however, even the most extreme physiological psychologists do not break completely with the dualistic tradition. What they do is to reject one of the two phases of the psychophysiological way of thinking, and retain the other. Undoubtedly this shift of attitude signifies a slight deviation from the long tradition that psychology is concerned with psychic phenomena. Nevertheless, we may still ask whether P.P. has enlarged its scope sufficiently to approach psychological data as they actually occur and uninfluenced by traditional theory.

1. The Sum of Physiological Psychology

Our first period may be summarized by a consideration of Titchener's writings. Not only did Titchener (1867-1927) assiduously pursue the "new" physiological and experimental psychology, but by his able and learned evaluation he also helped to bring it to its logical conclusion. As a student of Wundt, Titchener, of course, accepted his master's main ideas. Like Wundt and others he sought to renovate and transform psychology by resorting to the concept of experience. On the ground that all sciences have experience as their basis he claimed that they all begin with the same subject matter and differ only in point of view. Matter and mind, he asserted, must be fundamentally the same thing (597, p. 6). As to the relationship between the nervous system and the subject matter of psychology—namely, consciousness—there is a very intimate parallelism. Psychology studies the world of experience as it depends upon man, and man is reducible primarily to the brain and the nervous system (597, p. 16).

Psychology is the science of existential experience regarded as functionally or logically dependent upon the nervous system (or its biological equivalent) (600, p. 142, *et passim*).

Certainly this statement makes some reference to fact. Psychological events are activities of individuals, and since the nervous system is an important component of behavior, such behavior is intimately involved with the operation of the brain and nerves. But unfortunately this formulation is not really a statement of concrete behavior events, but of spiritistic metaphysics, as are all constructions based upon problems of mind and matter. As long as consciousness or psychic qualities are implied, the nervous system is not treated as an actual biological structure with operations characteristic of that cellular system.

As is well known, the formulation that the world of experience is dependent upon the nervous system Titchener derived from Avenarius (1843-1896). This philosopher, wishing to establish his subjective idealism on an empirical basis, attempted to connect experience with biological events. In consonance with venerable tradition, he associated this spiritual experience with the nervous system (16), and in this manner achieved his *"biologische eingesenkte Psychologie"* as Petzoldt (16, p. ix f.) puts it.

That reference to the nervous system, or "the system C" as Avenarius calls it, does not really involve concrete biological facts Titchener makes plain when he mentions the copious debate on the question whether the system C is physiological (600, p. 117). He concludes that for psychological purposes it is. But we must take into account that Titchener himself follows Avenarius in regarding psychological processes or sensations as only logically or in a mathematical sense functionally connected with the nervous system. Certainly if any other connection of psychic processes with the brain is postulated, the nervous system must surely be counted as an autistic construction. The important point is that all P.P. which implies a dependence of psychological events on the brain has its roots in the kind of metaphysical theory which Avenarius expounds.

The basis of that metaphysical theory, of course, is pure experience; that is, an immediately intuitive essence which constitutes the basic qualities of all things. The various kinds of things—physical, biological, or psychological—simply consist of different aspects or points of view. Avenarius was strictly a philosopher who followed Spinoza in his general *Weltanschauung* and who consequently sought for a universal principle to condition all philosophical thought, and a single simple presupposition from which to draw all theoretical and practical consequences. Thus, pure experience is a cosmic construction, which under the pressure of specific and scientific considerations is connected with the general psychological basis of everything as limited only by dependence upon an organism (16, p. xix).

Titchener's adaptation of Avenarius' philosophy is contingent upon the ultimate purification of experience. While Titchener is tremendously impressed with the possibilities pure experience provides for not separating psychology from the other sciences on the basis of subject matter, he does not find the pure and universal experience of Avenarius pure enough. Specifically, Avenarius did not exclude values from scientific experience (600, p. 138), whereas Titchener considers it to be purely established only when freed from all involvement with values. As one of Titchener's students explains, Titchener went further than all psychologists in purifying psychology, in making it deal only with existential qualities, to the exclusion of all meaning and significance (625, pp. 61-70).

Titchener's justification for so immersing himself in spiritual cosmology is that he was attempting to make psychology a science as existential and as autonomous as physics. He was opposed to the view that psychology is a science of a special class of "psychical" phenomena or phenomena of "consciousness" (600, p. 133). Right here is the importance of P.P. for Titchener. Psychology in its pure-experience foundation is no different from any other science, but it is selective in that it cleaves to that phase of pure experience which is dependent upon the existence of nervous systems.

How far P.P. as an experimental science has pushed cosmic mentalism is attested by Titchener's struggle with the problem of meaning. Since for Titchener consciousness or psychic processes must be purely existential, the elements and qualities of experience simply *are*, and are without meaning. The subject matter of psychology is formally systemic; it correlates with a total environmental complex (600, p. 264) and possesses no human value or reference beyond itself (600, pp. 32, 69 f.). It is thus autonomously ontological and without epistemological involvement. Materially, consciousness or experience is sensing, and meaning is nothing but context and grouping. "One mental process is the meaning of another mental process if it is that other's context" (597, p. 367). Titchener's doctrine is, of course, at the same time insufficient and contradictory, though completely and consistently psychic and cosmic.

What, then, have the brain and nerves to do with psychology? At the outset, Titchener follows Wundt in asserting a strict parallelism between the brain and consciousness, but goes further in declaring that the brain can explain mind. This explanation is not causal, but still the nervous system constitutes the condition for the formation of ideas. Nervous processes, Titchener writes, direct and guide consciousness (597, p. 274). Yet he declares:

Reference to the body does not add one iota to the data of psychology, to the sum of introspections. It does furnish us with an explanatory principle for psychology (597, p. 40).

The significance of this explanatory principle is evident from Titchener's discussion of meaning. Because meaning is apparently not always conscious, Titchener declares: "Meaning may be carried in purely physiological terms" (597, p. 369). Elsewhere, however, he speaks of the physiological domain as a millstone about the neck of the psychologist (600, p. 137).

Into what a peculiar predicament P.P. has fallen? Physiological or nervous-system facts which were to make psychology into a science and to help assimilate psychology with the natural sciences have become only logical concepts allowing but a mathematically functional dependence of mind and matter. This formal outcome of historical P.P. was, of course, an inevitable consequence of its contact with psychological events. No findings of physiological science can help in elucidating anything about mental introspections, about conscious or psychic qualities. Titchener could surely go no further than Wundt, who, when he tried to bring the brain and facts of consciousness into relationship, could only hint at indefinite localizations. To Wundt's credit, he saw clearly that only certain pathological and anatomical observations can be employed. For example, "The cortex of the occipital lobe is connected with the retina . . ." (650, p. 230), and on the pathological side, injuries to certain parts of the brain are correlated with certain deficiencies of action.

Can anyone doubt, then, that traditional P.P. was and remains a philosophical discipline despite its connection with physiology and experimental procedures? But what is frequently overlooked is the traduction which traditional P.P. effects in physiology in general and the nervous system in particular. Scientifically it is most reprehensible to impose psychic functions and powers upon biological events. The answer to those who say: "Let physiology take care of itself" is that, after all, physiologists and psychologists mutually influence each other, and when scientists establish improper intellectual precedents they operate to retard hypothesis-making and the investigations dependent upon it.

For the first period of our history, then, the fundamental outcome of transforming psychology into a science by means of the organic was that the nervous system became a medium or means whereby psychic factors could be brought into juxtaposition with natural processes. Through the nervous system, nonspatial psychic qualities, processes, or existences were projected into the spatiotemporal domain. The point to be emphasized is that P.P. as experimental psychology, did not constitute a break in the perennial commerce with mental states or qualities, but simply was employed to legitimize them.

This outcome illustrates the viability of cultural trends. The psychophysiological dualism of Hellenistic origin continues unabated as a conceptual scientific doctrine, though of course it has periodically changed its character from the original theological formulation through its ontological and epistemological shapes. As has been frequently pointed out, even the materialisms of the 18th and 19th centuries simply constituted a scheme of connecting the psychic with the organic. The authors of such formulations in no sense appreciated the possibility of eliminating altogether such psychic factors from their thinking. They simply made them palatable.

Probably the most ineffective and intellectually sterile formulation concerning the psychic and the organic is to assume an identity between them. This formulation merely leads to such undesirable constructions as "the physical dimensions of consciousness" (44).

Proponents of "physical dimensions" constructions apparently are so dominated by traditional metaphysics that they fail to recognize the paradox of using such metaphysics to make a science of psychology. Transparent as such doctrines are, we can not resist delineating their main features. To begin with, the constructors shift temporarily from pure or immediate experience or psychic essence to an actual event of awareness. Next they translate the descriptive properties of natural things, colors, sounds, shapes, sizes, etc., into sensations or compounds of psychic states which are mediated by neural and other tissues and organs or are identified with their action. Then they discuss such facts as the frequency, duration, intensity, and number of neural-fibre actions. And finally when it becomes obvious that, for example, intensity or duration of neural action really has nothing to do with psychical quality they resort to the dodge that all scientific data consist of inductive inferences. In this way they allow themselves to "infer" an identity of neural and mental "phenomena."

Those who believe that such verbal gymnastics absolve P.P. from the taint of metaphysics overlook that the verbal dodge of abstractionistic theory is also a form of metaphysics. To occupy oneself with sensations or psychic qualities in any form is to diverge from the investigation of discriminative interbehavior with actual things. There is no question that physiological psychologists have rung all sorts of changes on traditional metaphysics, with the result that whatever events they treated became patterned as foci of the great dualistic tradition which for twenty centuries has dominated the thinking concerning psychological happenings. To a great extent, writings on P.P. constitute arguments. Like all theorists the mental-neural identifiers begin with events, but the descriptions of these events and their interpretations are wrought metaphysically, not scientifically.

As we have seen, it was the early physiologists, especially Johannes Müller, the founder of modern sense physiology, who simply translated Kantian epistemology into the science of sensation. This whole development is much clearer in the case of Helmholtz who worked at a time when physiological materials became more copiously available. It is impossible to miss the very close parallels between the essential philosophy of Kant and the psychophysiology of Müller, Helmholtz, Wundt, and all their followers.

Essential to this translation is the production of sensations through the operation of the sense organs and brain. These physiological operations are performed upon unknown "things in themselves" which become transmuted into physical energies or stimulus conditions. The organization of the basic sensation and image elements into objects is effected in part by principles of mental association and in part by a lingering transcendental unity of soul through various modes of apperception as invented by Leibniz, Herbart, and Wundt. A unique form of this principle is unconscious inference. Today this scheme of construction lies at the core of sensory physiology and psychology.

2. THE DIVISION OF PHYSIOLOGICAL PSYCHOLOGY

Although our second period of P.P. marks a sharp turning point in the history of psychology, it is advisable to note the basic continuity of the two periods. Despite the change in investigative interest dualistic doctrine persists. Psychological events continue to be regarded as at the same time mental and bodily, psychic and organic. Again, while psychologists turned away from a predominant preoccupation with sensory problems, the newer learning investigations had some of their roots in Ebbinghaus' (1850-1909) work on memory, (131a) as well as in the animal studies of Romanes and Morgan.

Doctrinal continuity is best symbolized by the perennial

concern with the physiology of the nervous system. Lashley says:

Studies of the nervous system and of physiological psychology have as a common aim the understanding of mental processes in terms of the activities of the brain (353, p. 461).

It is, of course, interest in the nervous system that makes traditional P.P. a special area in psychology despite all the variations in presupposition and investigation. Moreover, this concern with the organic also marks the change in the two periods, since prominent early physiological psychologists really did very little with the nervous system. In this newer period, psychologists profited by the increased knowledge of the nervous system and proposed sophistically to relate it to psychological events. They did not, as was true of Wundt and others, simply offer neurological information without more relevant connection as a correlate and anchor of psychic processes. Rather, they attempted to make the nervous system into a basic mechanism and determiner of psychological behavior.

It is questionable, however, whether physiological psychologists have actually freed themselves completely from the original conception of the mind-body relation. To determine the extent of their emancipation we point out the transition steps in the evaluation of the nervous system. In historical order these steps may be arranged as follows:

(1) The N.S. is the seat or medium of the soul or consciousness.
(2) The N.S. is the surrogate of the mind, that is, performs psychic functions.
(3) The N.S. governs and determines behavior.
(4) The N.S. is one (the most important) of the behavior mechanisms, that is, factors of a response.

Both the continuity and variations in the development of P.P. are excellently illuminated by Titchener's resistance to the fettering of psychology by physiology. He made his objections in the name of pure science. According to Boring, Titchener organized and fostered a group of psychologists in order to retain for the term *experimental psychology* the connotation that Wundt and his contemporaries gave it.

Animal, child, abnormal, and applied psychology, no matter how much they experimented, were not called "experimental psychology" nor are they today (43, p. 407).

The basic point is that pure and impliedly-correct psychology is concerned with introspective studies of mentality and not so much with organic acts. As might be expected, however, it was the psychologists interested in animal studies who pursued P.P. in such a way as to make possible the cooperation of physiologists and psychologists and eventually the attainment of a proper attitude toward the place of physiological events in psychological situations. Titchener, on the contrary, insisted that experiments should yield information about psychic states, for that was his idea of proper psychological work. He could not accept the view of the learning investigator who turned to behavior and changes in behavior. Titchener happened to be right about psychology being independent of physiology, but utterly wrong in his conviction that psychology is concerned with psychic processes, which can never be other than logically—that is verbally—connected with neural and other organic action.

The various stages in P.P. development constitute only points on the general psychophysiological continuum. Whether the nervous system is considered the seat or surrogate of psychic processes or the determiner of action is actually a small difference from the standpoint of a nonmetaphysical interpretation of physiological and psychological data. True, the departure from psychic processes brings us closer to events, but there is still a gap between the events and the physiologically-dominated descriptions.

Nevertheless, we must not minimize the importance of the transition from the psychic-seat and surrogate conception to one of antimentalistic attachment to physiology and the nervous system. As suggested, the transition was occasioned by interest in animal and child-psychology studies and the impetus provided by the theory of biological evolution. The lack of a break between human and other organisms brought into relief the organic factors which by their gradual structural and functional transitions encompassed human and nonhuman animals in a single series. Similar emphases of organic structures and functions were stimulated by the growth of organisms in their transition to maturity. Following the line of neural tradition, psychologists at first stressed the brain and nerves, but regarded these structures as the seats and surrogates of psychic powers.

By gradations various behavioristic constructions arose. Mental factors were either neglected (methodological behaviorism) or their existence denied altogether (radical behaviorism).[1] In every case, however, they operated under the aegis of the perennial dualism. At most they retained its organic aspect and attempted to translate psychic powers and characteristics of organs into neural terms. A classic illustration is Lashley's (342) effort to show that all the categories of traditional psychology can be evaluated in physiological terms.

Both the sum and division of P.P. expose the wide gulf between P.P. theory and the data of observation and experimentation. As knowledge of neurological and general physiological events increases, scientists should progress toward a treatment of organic things and actions as biological events (anatomical, physiological, ecological, pathological) and not tranform them into psychological happenings. The original events plainly indicate that the organic factors, as structural and functional components of interacting organisms, simply participate in total psychological events. Under the influence of mind-body tradition, however, psychologists persist in stressing a neural basis or explanation of psychological events. It is to the credit of psychologists nevertheless that though they continue to discuss the biological basis of learn-

---

[1] Whatever the case may be with respect to movement and manipulation learning studies, in the field of sensory discrimination the denial is essentially only verbal.

ing or other psychological activities, they do acknowledge the tremendous amount of negative findings. And so we find, on the one hand, the search for neural facts and theories, as exemplified in the following quotation:

It is to be hoped, nevertheless, that the physiological correlate of the consciousness of blue and the rest of the secondary qualities may be discovered (337, p. 107).

And, on the other, a resumé of neurophysiological theories of conditioning, with the comment that "evidence is lacking for any of the proposed explanations" (232, p. 335).

The obvious insufficiency and viability of neural explanations as atavistic remnants of the mind-body dichotomy lead to the inevitable conclusion that physiological psychologists operate on two levels. On the theoretical or interpretative level they are dominated by psychophysical tradition, whereas on the data level they follow the lead of investigative results. It can not be denied therefore that psychologists are contributing to the advancement of neurological knowledge, though they may be doing less than necessary to further the independent science of psychology. It is not a negligible criticism that an inordinate amount of time is being devoted to disproving traditional psychoneurological theories.

Doubtless the most objectionable consequence of the behavioristic emphasis of the nervous system is the exclusive identification of psychological events with the acts of the organism. This manner of thinking has been reinforced by the development of reflex doctrines following the popularization of conditioning facts and theories by Pavlov (1849-1936) and Bekhterev (1857-1927). Underlying such doctrine is the presupposition that it is the nervous system which governs and regulates the organism's muscles, glands, and other tissues. This belief not only does violence to the fact of the unitary organization and operation of the organism, but also clashes with the concept of the field character of all psychological events (296). Still more, insofar as this reflexological presupposition influences preoccupation only with events falling within its scope, it serves to divert psychologists from the study of most types of complex and distinctly human behavior. Thus arises the anomalous situation in which many academic psychologists adopt the view of psychoanalysts that all characteristic human behavior can only be treated on the basis of mystic urges, drives, and the complexes of conscious and unconscious psyches.[1]

Whether one does or does not seriously criticize the materials and development of P.P. certainly depends upon how compliantly one accepts its underlying philosophy. In the next chapter, accordingly, we examine some of the implications philosophy has for psychology as a science.

[1] See, for example, the historical sketch of psychology in the first chapter of Masserman (405).

Chapter 6

PHILOSOPHY AND PSYCHOLOGICAL SCIENCE

PSYCHOLOGISTS more than most scientists are uniquely involved with the contentious problem concerning the relation of philosophy and science. This is evident from the perennial attempts to base all knowledge and existence on psychological and even psychical foundations. For instance, when physicists and astronomers trace events back to the basic qualities of mental experience (271-274) they build upon traditional psychology, which in turn is an outgrowth of spiritualistic philosophy.

We face here a vicious circle, the points of which symbolize psychology and other intellectual disciplines including philosophy (290, pp. 197-214). First, philosophy established a dualism of which one member transcends the spatio-temporal domain. This superspatial realm was subsequently adopted not only by traditional psychology but by other disciplines as well. Finally, each discipline fortified its acceptance of that nonspatial domain by means of the support received from the other sciences. The entire system may be eliminated, of course, by merely rejecting the original dualistic postulates.

In examining the nature of philosophy and science and their relation we hope to obviate some of the misconceptions engendered by this historical circle. In any case such an inquiry marks a preliminary step toward the clarification of some P.P. problems. Naturally, we are chiefly interested only in the effect that improper philosophy has had upon P.P.

It is a well-known historical item that physiological psychologists, like other specialized scientists, have vigorously opposed philosophy, with the paradoxical result that they have surreptitiously intermixed their investigations with a metaphysics really detrimental to their work and findings. On the other hand, there are many scientists who realize that actively to be aware of their basic presuppositions is of great help in avoiding all undesirable philosophy and in making the most of whatever useful postulates appear available.

VARIETIES OF PHILOSOPHY

The term *philosophy*, we must note, has different referents which should be kept distinct, especially if some type of philosophy may be a helpful tool in scientific work. We suggest, therefore, that the various forms of philosophy be fitted to a scale. At one end are grouped those purely autistic constructions consisting of an integration of traditional beliefs rooted in faith. At the other end we place the development of propositions which serve to orient scientists with respect to the entire domain of scientific data and operations. Such propositions, referred to as the logic or methodology of science, are concerned with the analysis and ordering of experimental and other scientific data.

As early as the first inception of modern inductive science, observers became aware that data without hypotheses or leading principles do not make up a science. No less an experimental scientist than Helmholtz was moved to assert:

Isolated facts and experiments have in themselves no value, however great their number may be. They only become valuable in a theoretical or practical point of view when they make us acquainted with the *law* of a series of uniformly recurring phenomena, or, it may be, only give a negative result showing an incompleteness in our knowledge of such a law, till then held to be perfect (213, p. 369).

Poincaré writes in a similar vein:

Science is built with facts, as a house is with stones, but a collection of facts is no more a science than a heap of stones is a house (497, p. 127).

Johnston, writing currently on the development of chemistry, refers to Lavoisier as having had a much better philosophical attitude toward chemical composition than chemists since his time. He adds:

. . . Until recently chemists were so much occupied in accumulating observations that they were prone to neglect the philosophy by means of which these multitudinous observations can be correlated (281, p. 82).

Philosophy as indicated in these quotations amounts to a series of propositions not confined to a particular science or even to all sciences, but including knowledge and wisdom gathered from observations of every sort.

Envisaged as scientific organization or the study of basic postulates philosophy contrasts markedly with traditional metaphysics, which simply integrates beliefs developed from various items of folklore, and for the purpose chiefly of escaping from or going beyond occurring events. Between these two types of philosophy there are many others partaking of the characteristics of both. In all of them various cultural attitudes are intermixed with results of observations. In other words, the events observed are interpreted to conform to basic cultural beliefs.

It goes without saying that the philosophy of autistic construction is altogether dissociated from any scientific pursuit, though, as we have indicated, it may influence a particular worker. Science may perhaps best be described as the study of some specific event or type of event, stimulated by some problem of nature or operation. On this basis science is very closely related to technological pursuits, although the aims and activities of scientific workers are broader. Scientists aim at general principles or laws, and not immediate practical achievements as do technologists. Of course, even the most practical technologist may assume a general attitude toward his work. The routine analytical chemist in an industrial plant may regard himself as an agent of some transcendent power, commissioned to manipulate materials in order to understand or carry out some divine purpose.

Such a chemist merely aligns himself with the theologically-tainted classic scientists, Kepler, Galileo, Newton, and others, who have so brilliantly inscribed the credit pages of scientific history, while on the opposite sides they have recorded their indebtedness to the ancient Fathers of the Church. In our day, Jeans especially has distinguished himself by his assertion that the mechanical or mathematical theories of astronomy reveal a God who geometrizes. The antidote to such double dealing is, of course, the superb Newtonian *"Hypotheses non fingo."* When engaged in investigations of nature the rule is to be directed only by observations of and operations upon things. There is to be no mingling of conjecture and certainty, howsoever much one may indulge in purely verbal construction in the superior domain of grace. That the belief in the existence of two worlds results in an inevitable though unwitting admixture of the two is the warning of history.

EXPERIENTIAL PHILOSOPHY AND PHYSIOLOGICAL PSYCHOLOGY

Crucial for the relationship between philosophy and science is the problem of knowledge and experience. Historically, science was presumed to be characterized by its adherence to experience; philosophy, by its assumed ability to transcend it. It is hardly necessary to consider those transcendental philosophies completely centered in the pure *a priori*. The philosophy from which psychology has attempted to free itself has always been regarded as admitting a minimum of *a priori* factors. In its attempt to achieve a scientific position psychology has strained to make certain that both its materials and methods were deeply rooted in experience. The supposition here is that as a science psychology could not be concerned with transcendental states or processes.

But what is experience? Unfortunately, cultural tradition is more potent than present aims, wherefore experience has been misconstrued to admit nonscientific formulations into what psychologists have been most ambitious to make scientific. Whenever psychologists have faced the problem of dealing with subjective qualities as opposed to the indubitable objective facts of physics they have attempted to save the situation by resorting to experience. They have even said experience is immediate and the basis for objects and reals, which are derived from it by inference and construction.

Since our survey has indicated that P.P. was developed under the aegis of Kantian philosophy, it may be instructive to inquire how that philosophy paved the way for a misconstruction of experience, and how all its later modifications have weighed heavily against the psychologist's striving to make his discipline scientific. The experience problem has traditionally been tied up with the problem of knowledge. As is well known, the philosophy of the 18th century centered around the extent to which knowledge is derived from experience. As Kant puts the matter:

> That all our knowledge begins with experience there can be no doubt. For how should the faculty of knowledge be called into activity, if not by objects which affect our senses, and which either produce representations by themselves, or rouse the activity of our understanding to compare, to connect, or to separate them; and thus to convert the raw material of our sensuous impressions into a knowledge of objects, which we call experience? In respect of time, therefore, no knowledge within us is antecedent to experience, but all knowledge begins with it (285, p. 715).

Note that Kant speaks of objects which affect the senses, and of knowledge of objects, but what does he understand by objects? Certainly not what in his gross naïveté the ordinary man thinks they are. In the next paragraph he makes this clear.

> But although our knowledge begins with experience, it does not follow that it arises from experience. For it is quite possible that even our empirical experience is a compound of that which we receive through impressions, and of that which our own faculty of knowledge (incited only by sensuous impressions), supplies from itself, a supplement which we do not distinguish from that raw material, until long practice has roused our attention and rendered us capable of separating one from the other (285, p. 715).

Objects are constructions; the raw materials are sense qualities which remain unformed and chaotic until reworked, on the one hand, by the intuitions of space and time and, on the other, by the categories of quantity, quality, relation, and modality. These intuitions and categories are, of course, the contribution of the soul or the transcendental unity of apperception, as he called it. It is this soul which is the source of all order and necessity and which makes firm knowledge possible, that is, laws basic to certain and predictive science.

Corresponding to the organizing and ordering *a priori* intuitions and categories of knowledge, Kant constructs a thing in itself always unknown and unknowable, which is the source of the raw materials received through impressions. *It is this philosophy which has been deftly translated by the early physiological psychologists into the physiological language still current.* All this spiritual material has become embodied in their work. The thing in itself has become the physical stimulation which, through the operation of the brain, is transformed into sense qualities. As duBois-Reymond puts the matter:

Die Sinnesempfindung als solche entsteht also erst in den Sinnsubstanzen, wie Johannes Müller die zu den Sinnesnerven gehörigen Hirnprovinzen nannte, von welchen jetzt Hr. Hermann Munk einen Theil in der Grosshirnrinde als Sehsphäre, Hörsphäre u.s.w. unterschied. Die Sinnsubstanzen sind es, welche die in allen Nerven gleichartige Erregung überhaupt erst in Sinnesempfindung übersetzen, und als die wahren Träger der "specifischen Energien" Johannes Müller's je nach ihrer Natur die verschiedenen Qualitäten erzeugen. Das mosaische: "Es war Licht," ist physiologisch falsch. Licht ward erst, als der erste rothe Augenpunkt eines Infusoriums zum ersten Mal Hell und Dunkel unterschied. Ohne Seh- und ohne Gehörsinnsubstanz wäre diese farbenglühende, tönende Welt um uns her finster und stumm. (125, p. 15 f.)

Here is the continuity running through scientific thought since the Renaissance. Kant is a direct successor of Kepler, Galileo, and Newton. It is interesting to compare the above quotation with one from Newton's *Opticks.*

If at any time I speak of light and rays as coloured or endued with Colours, I would be understood to speak not philosophically and properly, but grossly, and according to such conceptions as vulgar people in seeing all these Experiments would be apt to frame. For the rays to speak properly are not coloured. In them there is nothing else than a certain power and disposition to stir up a sensation of this or that Colour. For as sound in a Bell or musical String, or other sounding Body, is nothing but a trembling Motion, propogated by the Object, and in the Sensorium 'tis a sense of that Motion under the form of sound; so Colours in the Object are nothing but a disposition to reflect this or that sort of rays more copiously than the rest; in rays they are nothing but their dispositions to propogate this or that Motion into a Sensorium, and in the Sensorium they are sensations of those Motions under the forms of Colours (464, p. 80).

What the physiological psychologists added is simply the alleged work of the brain in transforming primary radiations into sense qualities.

Renaissance scientists were vigorously haunted by a transcendent reality lurking behind the appearances of everyday things. Moreover, immersed as they were in a spiritualistic culture they believed reality was spiritual. But, on the other hand, they were inevitably pushed on by the irresistible force of technological evolution to aim at the laudable elimination of occult qualities and forms. Even though for them reality was spiritual, they became convinced that the only safe and dependable scientific formulation could be made in terms of spatial changes, mechanical motions.

Thus, colors, sounds, and other specific qualities of things were removed from objects and localized in the individual's interactions with them. In this manner they sought a solution of their predicament. For them there was no question that man was only partially natural and partially supernatural. Colors, sounds, and other spiritual qualities were thus "experienced" and mediated by organs.

The experienced characteristics of things became signs for external realities, a doctrine effectively fortified by the neo-Platonic Pythagoreanism of the time. Just as numbers symbolized the ultimate realities of motion, shape, and size, so sensations or other psychic states or processes were signs of the sensory qualities of bodies. Renaissance scientists never considered that always and inevitably they were concerned with qualitative things and quantitative relations which could be properly treated in a growing series of abstracting formulations.

Today, of course, it is anomalous to occupy oneself with psychic qualities in the name of experience, so that objects, —say a rat (501, p. 13)—are denied independent existence on the ground that objects (in part) are dealt with in science by means of recorded descriptions. Such a view confuses the object with which one interacts with the interaction itself and with the descriptions resulting from the interaction. This is the ubiquitous fallacy of confounding things with knowledge of them. To distill things from experience and consciousness results in two sorts of confusions. Firstly, mental qualities are confounded with the fact of knowing or being aware of the qualities of things. Secondly, the variations and instability of things and their qualities under variously environing circumstances are confounded with the problems of the contingency and incompleteness of human knowledge.

The final result is that experience is easily made into the opposite of actual interbehavior with events. Mach (1838-1916), the enemy of mysticism and metaphysics, provides an excellent example. For him, science must begin and end in experience. Yet he descends to the depths where "nature is composed of sensations as its elements" (388, p. 482). In his opinion "a thing is a thought-symbol for a compound sensation of relation-fixedness" (388, p. 483). This is a familiar doctrine in P.P.

Whether psychologists minimize mental qualities as experienced epiphenomena or magnify them as the essence of experience they are presupposing some kind of absolute and universal existence or knowledge. They depart from actual things, their operational qualities and the events of organisms interbehaving with them. The machinery for doing this in P.P. is, of course, the nervous system. Obviously the assertions concerning the part the nervous system plays do not go beyond analogical and autistic statements.

Since it was Helmholtz who helped so much to establish

the traditional philosophical way of thinking in P.P., we might glance at his elaboration of the experience doctrine. While he rejected in some form the nativistic conception of space, his doctrine of unconscious inferences, which makes objects depend upon judgment or some internal process, fits in with this tradition. Oddly enough, the emphasis of experience, which in philosophy has been regarded as bringing that discipline down from the clouds, in science has resulted in continuing the oldest spiritualistic traditions of Hellenistic thought. In P.P., experience is treated as interior states, as inner sense or as a diffused general chaos from which everything in the way of objects and knowledge of them are derived.

Typical of the recent use of experience to implement supernatural qualities is the assertion that the reality and extension of sensory qualities are guaranteed by experience, although the technical constructions make such qualities into nonexistential, nonspatial entities. And so Titchener (597, p. 6) asserts: "All human knowledge is derived from human experience; there is no other source of knowledge." He then goes on to exploit the notion that experience may be considered from two different points of view. For the physical he considers space, time, and mass as independent of the individual; thus they are constant, always and everywhere the same. But the mental, which is dependent on the person, does not answer to these descriptions. By means of the Müller-Lyer illusion he indicates that the physical lines differ from the mental ones. Similarly, waiting time is different from clock time; lifted weights are different from weighed weights. He asserts, however, that mental experience takes on spatial form as readily as physical experience (597, p. 12).

Titchener, like so many others before and after him, makes a typical philosophical use of naïve common sense to bolster up his science of consciousness. To begin with, he properly points out that without instrumental means persons vary in their discriminations and reports concerning the lengths of lines, time intervals, and the weights of things. But by verbal legerdemain he transforms simple noninstrumental reactions to things into *experience* and experience into sensations or sensory processes, which only become realities by the operation of the brain.[1] The verbal legerdemain is deft. First, he treats experience as dependent upon the experiencing person. There is no objection to this use of the term in its common-sense fashion, but he does not point out that this experience is different from the technical philosophical entity which makes it identical with sensation. Neither does he notice that when the person uses instruments to get physical time, space, and mass they are still dependent upon his experience.

Nor, following Wundt and others, does he observe that when the same world of experience is divided into the mental and the bodily or physical he is no longer concerned with common-sense experience. As with Wundt, experience becomes a metaphysical psychic with two aspects. Though criticizing common sense, with its basic division of the physical and the mental, as high Cartesian philosophy (597, p. 12), Titchener himself certainly transforms events into traditional spirituality.

Titchener, however, stands on solid ground when he endeavors to distinguish science from common sense. Science must deal with elaborate and abstractionistic constructions. But he adopts ancient metaphysical constructions instead of deriving them from the common-sense contacts of organisms with objects. As the writer has shown (286), modern physiological psychologists have departed radically from everyday or common-sense things by imposing upon the interactions of organisms with things constructions which other scientists have properly derived from such common-sense contacts. Such nonpsychological contacts are not substitutable for constructions which the psychologist must make for himself on the basis of his own investigations.

[1] Later Titchener (598) came to believe that sensations are logical constructs whereas attributes are the immediate introspective data.

EXPERIENCE AS INTERBEHAVIOR

By contrast with traditional usage the term *experience* may be used to describe actual interbehavior of organisms with stimulus objects. The evolution of science can therefore be treated as a natural history of the development of constructions concerning such interbehavior. The physical scientist builds his constructions in terms of space, time, and mass, in such a way as to free them from the inexactitude of common-sense discriminations. For that reason, he intersperses instruments between himself and the length, duration, and weight of things. Because the physical scientist is primarily interested in things and their interbehavior he certainly can not proceed far with an observer's unaided contacts with things. For the most part, too, he is untroubled with problems of observational method as long as he is interested in the macroscopic behavior of atoms in a compound, compounds with one another, dynamos wired to engines or cathode tubes wired to other electrical apparatus. When working with microscopic events such as atomic constituents he does face problems of investigative techniques.

The psychologist, on the other hand, is interested in the immediate responses of organisms to things. When he uses instruments he is simply attempting to refine his observations of the organism's interbehavior with other organisms or things. Unlike the physical scientist, he finds it necessary to get away from both the objective introspection which limits scientific study to self study, and the psychic interpretation which converts contacts with organisms into psychic processes. The psychologist, however, does not limit his studies to such immediate responses. He is equally concerned with remote interbehavior (thinking, speaking, remembering) requiring substitute stimulation, such as signs and symbols of various sorts. The basic importance of the interbehavioral view of experience lies in the fact that it can obviate the confusion of (1) things and events, (2) events and constructions, or (3) constructions of different sorts. The philosophy based upon such a view can never be harmful to science and frequently may be exceedingly beneficial.

OPERATIONAL PHILOSOPHY AND PHYSIOLOGICAL PSYCHOLOGY

At the beginning of this chapter we mentioned the great variety of philosophies from the standpoint of definition and attitude. So far we have been concerned with traditional philosophies characterized by a professed interest in absolute and universal sources of knowledge. In whatever form they appear, whether as idealisms or realisms, as epistemologies or ontologies, they are of a piece with historical metaphysics and theology. As such they are, of course, bounded by the ideal of certainty and the dogma of transcendence. Philosophers harboring the certainty ideal have historically presumed to have reached it by interrelating contingent and temporary events with some form of: (1) God-nature, (2) the ultimate and final principle of knowledge, and (3) laws of the universe.

In contrast stand those recently-formulated systematic constructions designed to articulate exclusively with the work and findings of science. Presumably the operational philosophies are limited to the logic or methodology of science. The boundary, therefore, of an operational philosophy, like the science it organizes, is set by the actual operations of particular individuals with events. But since it is such interbehavior with events that in the final analysis is the starting point of all traditional metaphysics, the operational philosophers employ various techniques to block the path to objectionable conclusions from the original premises. Essentially these techniques are designed to prevent any interpolation of autistic constructions into a set of propositions which must be derived from authentic operations. No matter how abstruse the propositions of such philosophers become they are presumed to be inevitably derived, howsoever indirectly owing to the selective and analytic character of investigation, from actual contacts with things.

Obviously it is outside the scope of this work to review the numerous versions of operational philosophy. It will suffice merely to sketch briefly some of the main contentions of the operational philosophers and to indicate the broad background of this type of philosophical thinking. What is of greatest interest is to show how the prevailing ideas of P.P. and the dualism which it presupposes have influenced the assimilation of operational philosophy, without P.P. becoming modified by it in a more factual direction. Another instance of the incoordination of good principles and bad practice! Just as physiological psychologists adopted the experimental and investigative techniques of science to implement mentalism, so now they employ operational philosophy to achieve the same end.

Aside from the momentum of cultural traditions this assimilation of operational philosophy by dualistic physiological psychologists has been facilitated by a change in attitude—namely, an inhibition of the fear of philosophy. But with what result? Driven by the need to alter their basic views without really dispensing with them, physiological psychologists transformed a laudable principle into a tool for maintaining ancient errors.

Contributing to this misfortune is the double aspect of operational philosophy. On one side is logical positivism, which originated as a restrictive technique for controlling autistic construction. This restriction was intended to regulate both the definition of terms and the descriptions of investigative protocols. On the other side, is the admonition to confine oneself to interoperation with events, indeed a useful regulatory function which operational philosophy can exert in the field of P.P. But what is done in fact is to incline toward the logical aspect and to propose that physiological states can be equated with mental states, or that by a process of equating terms the identification of the mental and the physiological is validated.

Operationism. Not long after Bridgman (56, 57) published his ideas concerning the process of deriving concepts in physics, psychologists became interested in the use they could make of the operational theory. Stevens (577, 578) wrote as though the laboratory manipulation of carboloid cylinders under enormous pressures could be equated with the acts of discriminating objects. It is true that aside from the essential use of apparatus in the high-pressure situation we have here two different types of comparable operations. But since according to P.P. tradition, qualities and properties of things exist only through the operation of neural and other anatomical structures, the perceiving action is regarded as the basic type of operation, and in consequence operations are made to consume the operands (294).

Critical Linguism. Both of these two phases of operational philosophy stress the development of propositions. Since propositions are regarded as primarily linguistic, the logical-positivism phase, which has taken the form of critical linguism, has emphasized the interdiction of language systems or propositions that are only formally analogous to sentences or statements based on contact with things.

Unfortunately, operational philosophers who incline toward logical or sentence-analysis maneuver exclusively within the framework of the old dualistic postulates. Thus they have not really transported themselves to the domain of actual operations. They attempt to set aside metaphysical dualism by asserting that all sentences or statements referring to psychical states may be translated into sentences referring to physical things (82-85, 137, 462, 490). This doctrine of logical syntax and semantics has been named physicalism. The upshot of physicalism is that one may justify one's concern with psychic matters if only one uses physical terms. This translation of sentences about psychic things into sentences about physical things is proposed in disregard of the fact that contacts with things leave no place either for psychic sentences or any significant procedure for translating them into physical sentences.

Carnap who has figured prominently in the circle of analytical linguists has focalized the translation and conversion technique by inventing his reduction sentence (84, 85), formulated as follows:

> If . . . a certain term x is such that the conditions for its application (as used in the language of science) can be formulated with the help of the terms y, z, etc., we call such a formulation a *reduction statement* for x in terms of y, z, etc., and we call x reducible to y, z, etc., (85, p. 49 f.).

Let us see what use the physiological psychologist has made of analytic linguism. In attempting verbally to dispose of the objectionable mental, Boring employs a magical process of transmuting it into its physical allotropic modification.

We now know that operational definitions can always transform a psychological description, expressed in terms of consciousness, into a description in behavioral or physiological terms (46).[1]

True enough, one can terminologically transform anything into anything else. But a rose . . . When such verbal performances are presumed to justify a dualistic P.P., we not only object to the perpetuation of the psychic but the traduction of the valuable operational principle as well.

Such an operational philosophy as the above really does not stem from actual scientific interoperations of laboratory and field. Instead, it harks back to the abstractionistic or formalistic phenomenology of Bolzano (39), Brentano (52), Frege (155, 156), Husserl (246, 247), Külpe (329-331), Meinong (422-425), and others. The operations involved in traditional, linguistic, and phenomenological philosophy consist of manipulating verbal abstractions instead of original events.[2] It is this commerce with words that provides the omnipotence for equating and identifying anything with anything else and even with nothing at all—for example, neural processes with sensations.

With verbal tools it also becomes possible to reduce all

---

[1] See also (45).

[2] The basic thinking here ties in with the familiar notion that science as well as mathematics consists basically of language. Cf. (299).

the factors in an event to defining operations and to make psychology into a propaedeutic science (578, 579). With such tools all science is reduced to differential reactions: Query: Performed by? Answer: Doubtless some brain-mediated, ultimate unity of apperception.

Evolution of Linguistic Operationism

How operational philosophy could be so easily assimilated to the perennial dualistic thinking in P.P. is made clear by a brief examination of its development as a synthesis of formalism and sensationism. Despite the claims of the proponents of linguistic operationism that it is a derivation from the postulational control of scientific work, it really stems from the attempt to reconcile the certainty of the *a priori*, in the form of deductive demonstration, with the relativity or contingency of observation and experience.

All science is characterized by the obvious search for laws to provide stability in changing and recurring events required for organization and prediction. Throughout the history of science this need for law constituted a rallying point for the perennial urges to transcend natural events. Hence speculative scientists have always evinced a greater or lesser dissatisfaction with the mere description of observed events, yielding only inductive laws. Even the most extreme empiricists can not conceal their deductive and rationalistic ambitions. Certainly Hume (1711-1776), the archempiricist, who sought to banish unity from mind and causality from nature, clung to abstract reasoning (mathematics) throughout his emphasis of experimental reasoning (observational science) (241).

Deductive principles with their characteristic certainty and assumed independence of the reasoner were always sought and presumably found in mathematics. For in that domain, formulae as products of operations have perennially been taken for *Forms*, that is, fixed and abiding aspects of things as well as of thoughts. The history of modern philosophy centers around the alternate emphasis of things, or the mathematical laws of their qualitative contents or their quantitative relations.

Now since philosophers have never been able to avoid the dichotomy between thought and things, between the contribution of mind and nature to knowledge, they have always been concerned with the psychological aspects of mathematics. However strange it may seem to a psychologist interested only in the immediate facts of behavior, the problems of linguistic analysis have had their origin in the connections of psychology and mathematical thinking.

Current linguistic operationism may be traced back to the objections made by Bolzano (39), Frege (155, 156), Husserl (246, 247), Meinong (422-425), and other scholastically-inclined writers to the *Psychologism* fostered by Kant in mathematics. It will be recalled that Kant was the champion of intuitionism—namely, that mathematics is based on the fundamental psychic intuitions of space and time.

Kant was fundamentally wrong, these modern Scholastics argued, in regarding the mathematical or formal aspects of things as imposed by reason on their sensationistic materials or contents. Reincarnating Platonic realism, they argued that mathematics is objective, that number and form exist independently of mind. Thus arose a crusade against *Psychologism* in mathematics and logic. The result was an emphasis on process, on act, and a slighting of content.[1]

The psychological phase of this movement revealed a stress of a unified mind as over against the sensationistic organization of elements, an emphasis of process as exemplified by the psychology of Brentano and all those influenced by him, including the Gestalt psychologists.

As history would have it, the modern attempt to scholasticize and platonize mathematics could not prevail. For one thing, the utter formalization and overemphasis of the structure of things could not suppress the claims of qualities for due and proper recognition. Moreover, while the intuitionis-

---

[1] We say emphasis, because Kant and his physiological-psychology followers all made a place for process and act in some manner.

tic idea of mathematics is ungrounded, there arose the postulational and conventional theories of mathematics and deduction in general. The stage was set, then, for the appearance of the view that the formal side of things consisted of propositions or sentences. These sentences or propositions became described as the "language of constructs." As to content, that was treated by sets of propositions constituting the "language of data." In this philosophy the age-old dichotomy of the sensory and ideational, of the perceptual and conceptual, of content and process has been neatly translated into linguistic terms.

To a considerable extent those who think in terms of sentences for data and for constructions appear to acknowledge the work of persons in scientific description and mathematical creation. But they overlook the fact that mathematical work is also interbehavioral. It is an error to draw an absolute line between relations and things as stimulus objects. That relations may frequently be products of interbehavior, as in the case of contrived systems, offers no warrant for assuming a realm of platonic essences for relations or for stressing a persisting unitary and rational mind which deals with them. Doubtless the end result of such phenomenology is Husserl's transcendental consciousness or ego dwelling in phenomenological community among a corpus of eternal truths (246, 247).

Linguistic and Interbehavioral Operationism

By dispensing with the dualistic postulates of linguistic operationism and its ideal of comprehensiveness and absolute certainty, it is possible to construct an operational philosophy which is not only in line with scientific investigation but also redounds to the advantage of P.P.

Such a philosophy irrevocably rejects all nonpragmatic *a prioris* and omnipotent deductive systems, in favor of sets of propositions which serve to order actual events. An operational philosophy conceived in interbehavioral terms demands that all elements of the system constitute precipitates from direct contact with events. Interbehavioral operationism never transforms everyday events or the contrived events of the laboratory into any absolutistic substances, processes, or symbols. Much less does such a philosophy stop to reify authentic scientific formulae and equations into ultimate realities.

Psychology as concrete interbehavioral operations is concerned only with practical deductive and inductive methods. Interbehavioral deduction is simply a process of anticipating or predicting a specific event ascertained to be of a type or class already investigated and thereby made amenable to future handling. Similarly induction constitutes operations upon events that result in ordering them on the basis of similarities of properties and hence providing dependable systematization.

Applied to P.P., such a philosophy does not look for physiological correlates or explanations of sensations or mental processes of any sort, and instead studies visual, auditory, or any other type of discrimination as the activity of the organism in interoperation with stimulus objects.

Stimulus objects are necessarily treated in complete independence of any historical metaphysical postulates. They are dealt with as definite materials for chemical and electrical description. To rely upon concrete scientific investigations makes unnecessary the building of comprehensive theories by arbitrarily selecting light colors as over against pigment colors as absolute prototypes. Why should refraction events be made basic to all perceptual theory instead of letting all ranges of specific interbehavior have their rightful place as materials for theoretical construction?

Because we can correlate some hues with radiation frequencies we do not substitute the radiation for the hues as the stimuli interacted with. We have traced out the basis of this type of thinking in traditional metaphysics, and we can not traduce operational principles to justify that metaphysics. On the other hand, while the psychologist may report what are proper findings for the physiologist concerning the operation of receptors and conduction tissues, those partial events of the total discriminative interbehavior can not be substituted for the total interaction nor create the presumption that the psychologist is not studying that total event but only the sensations or conscious correlates of the physiological events.

ONE EXPERIMENT, THREE PHILOSOPHIES

We conclude this discussion with a summarizing illustration showing how a single experiment is made use of by the proponents of three different types of philosophy.

The Experiment. An experimenter presents his subjects by means of a tachistoscope with sets of four nonsense syllables, each syllable containing three letters, twelve in all. The syllables are printed in four different hues and are irregularly spaced to form different patterns. The subjects are differently instructed to report what they see as follows: (1) total number of letters, (2) syllable colors, (3) patterns of the letters, and (4) their identity.

The results the experimenter obtains depend upon the instructions. If the task is to report on the colors the subjects may not give satisfactory answers concerning the patterns and vice versa. Similarly with the other aspects of the nonsense syllables.

Experiential Philosophy. The experimenter who works on the basis of experiential presuppositions regards himself as investigating the subject's mind, and is either interested primarily in (1) the content of the mind or (2) what the mind does. In either case the reacting organism or the act performed is presumed to constitute two types of properties, mental and organic. On the whole, the content psychologists assume that by means of electromagnetic effects on the eye, changes are produced in the brain which somehow make up the percept or mental object. One of their typical problems is to determine whether the color, pattern, syllable qualities, and other attributes constitute the mental object or percept or whether there is some more basic thing or process in which the attributes inhere. The act or process psychologists, on the other hand, assume that the mind is an organized and unitary something which acts on physical objects exclusively or primarily. In the latter case there is a total mental object as content. Their primary problem therefore is: How does the mind of the subject act in judging what is placed before him as the stimulus? The typical P.P. solution is to propose hypothetical principles of organization and dynamic relations of brain elements.

Philosophy of Linguistic Operationism. While historically, as we have seen, the linguistic operationist has been aligned with the act or process rather than with the content type of psychology, now his main task is to solve such a general problem as how to reconcile a psychologist's simultaneous preoccupation with mind and nervous system. He begins by differentiating between protocols—that is, the records of what subjects report—and the interpretation made by the psychologist. The former he regards as the language of fact or data. If there are any improbabilities in the interpretations, as, for example, how two such utterly different things as the mental and the organic can be related, he assumes that the difficulty is all in the language of constructs. This he overcomes by performing various feats of translation and transformation, and in this way satisfies himself that the difficulties have all been dissipated. He does not, however, eliminate the traditional presuppositions which make necessary his linguistic reductions and transformations. On his own ground he fails to reconcile the divergences between the level of construction language and that of data reports.

Philosophy of Interbehavioral Operations. By contrast with the two former types of philosophy, interbehavioral operationism concerns itself with the original experimental set-up and results. The basic problems concern the actual contact of the subject with nonsense-syllable stimulus objects. The influence of the instructions on types of results is important. For example, could the subjects learn to report on all four characteristics of the nonsense-syllable objects?

In the interbehavioral operationist's handling of the situation the stimulus objects and responses are taken at their face value. No constructions are made concerning minds or bodies. The factors to be worked out are: (1) the understanding of the instructions, (2) normality and acuity of vision, (3) the willingness to cooperate, and so on.

The interbehavioral operationist is prepared for such comments as: "Where is the philosophy of this?" "There is nothing deep or sophisticated about such a treatment of the experiment." The answer is that it is philosophical enough to bring critical acumen to bear on the actual situation. Among the questions considered are: (1) Whether or not this is an experiment, (2) What kind of experiment, in the sense of what sort of hypothesis is chosen, (3) The relation between the actual event observed and its description and interpretation, (4) How far descriptions in the form of records and protocols depend upon postulates and presuppositions, and (5) What is the basis for mentalistic presuppositions and interpretations?

The value of the supervisory or critical work of interbehavioral operationism lies not only in avoiding mentalistic descriptions and interpretations, but also in illuminating the details of various treatments of the experiment. For example, when the content psychologist is puzzled by the diversity between single qualities (sensations) and things (percepts) he simply speaks of the added meaning that accrues to the sensations because of their context. The interbehavioral critic, on the other hand, points to the actual pattern and organization of the things interacted with.

The interbehavioral operationist in turn asks: What need is there for the pseudosophistication of mental qualities and brain processes? Is not the attitude of the psychologist who demands such things similar to the religious fundamentalist who believes that only those who talk about spirits and other mysterious powers comprehend the higher values of life.

CHAPTER 7

THE BRAIN IN THE HISTORY OF SCIENCE

LIKE all history, the history of psychology bears the deep impress of its writers. Those who write on the history of P.P. take the position that they are tracing through ideas of brain function as definite scientific developments. Usually they begin with the Bell-Magendi law which differentiates between sensory and motor functions of nerves, a differentiation presumed to occur also in the brain. This procedure is followed through by repeating the story of Broca's discovery of the locus of the speech function. Then Fritsch and Hitzig receive due credit for their studies on the electrical stimulation of the cortex. Thus an elaborate story is built up, to climax in cortical localization of sense qualities, associatio, memory, and thought. Though the foundations of the story are certainly laid down upon definite observation, the structure erected thereon consists mostly of the gossamer of traditional opinions.

The most serious criticism that can be leveled at such history writing is not that it is devoid of facts, but that by including materials of questionable relevancy and by effectively selecting data the result is a picture with an improper focus and false perspective. What is this picture? Briefly, an organ functioning to mediate or create introspective sense qualities, and subserving memorial and thought "processes" or "functions." From the psychological standpoint this picture includes, in the first place, the psychologically irrelevant facts of organic integration; secondly it displays the selected facts of mutilation and other abnormalities. If we do not arbitrarily set the picture in a traditional mental fráme but instead provide a natural background, an entirely different story can then be told.

One fact and only one underlies the whole history of brain functions and localizations. Organisms are involved. Turning to the earliest point in the continuum of modern localization theories we find the tradition that the organism, especially the human, is not merely a biological entity, but also endowed with a soul. While this soul idea continues throughout the entire development of western European thought it takes on various forms. Even today it is believed that the brain is the locus for processes very different from neural impulses.

In tracing out the details of this historical continuum we note a shifting relationship between the brain and what is located in it. At first, as we know, that which required localization was tremendously more important than the locus. It is probably safe to say that by the time of Descartes a fair balance existed between the two. This estimate is based on Descartes' belief that by means of the brain and its reflex action subhuman organisms could carry on their activities without the cooperation of a soul. With the development of biology in the 18th and 19th centuries the importance of the brain becomes magnified until by the time of Vogt (1817-1895) it is the brain which secretes thought as the liver secretes bile and the kidneys urine (608, 609), a formula traceable back to Cabanis (1757-1808) (71;336, II, pp. 242n., 312n.) and before (125, p. 57).[1]

In the history of mind-body relations we find among the Patristics a glorification of the soul with a corresponding vilification of the flesh. By the period of the Scholastics it becomes important to make the body a suitable correspondent for the soul. With Descartes and others of the 17th century the seat idea indicates a hitherto unrecognized importance of the soul's locus. Among the materialists of the 18th century there is a subordination of the soul—which has become mind or psychic processes—to the body and even special organs. This chain of importance ratios culminates in the current dependence of consciousness upon the brain or general nervous system.

[1] It is possible that the secretion analogy was favored if not foreshadowed by Descartes' election of the little conarium gland to be the seat of the soul (116, letter no. 199; 117, arts. 31, 32).

The Function Conception. Throughout the entire history of brain study a balance is maintained between the conceptions which treat brain action as biological functions of a particular bodily organ and those which attribute psychic or psychological functions to the brain. The difference here involves an abstractional process. In the second type of construction the brain is conceptually lifted out of its place in the anatomy of the body and made to carry powers more or less governing its other parts. In addition to the physiological functions of conduction, coordination, and integration the brain is endowed with various "psychological functions."

When this abstractionistic procedure is carried further, different anatomical parts of the brain are made to subserve specialized functions—certainly a striking contrast to the organismic conception according to which the brain is always left in its proper biological environment and its actions considered as intraorganic. On the latter basis, if abstractionistic differentiation is made, the influences are mutual. The brain is just as much controlled by other organic parts as vice versa.

Biological and psychological brain functions are easily and sharply differentiated. Generally speaking, biological brain functions are based upon investigations of organs and functions which though complex and difficult to study are after all definite details of biological organization. The errors made here, like all scientific mistakes, are intrinsically self-correcting. The belief that the brain is a master organ, and, though dependent upon vascular tissue, is still a unique organ, can be set aside by further investigation.

Psychological brain functions, on the other hand, are clearly and purely constructional. In fact, many of them are imaginatively created. For the most part such psychological functions as seeing, remembering, and thinking are conceptual evolutions of the activities of the soul. Though the brain is presumably being described, in historical order it is made to serve first as the seat of the soul, then as the basis of psychical faculties, and finally as localized mechanisms for actual behavior and localized psychic functions (p. 49).

Following the development of behavioristic psychological views criticism has increased with respect to the constructional use of the brain. The warning against imaginary neurology (287, 288) which first met sharp opposition (614, 615) is now being more sympathetically considered (32, 416, 417, 561, 562) though still unheeded (384, 501).

Ideological Stages of Brain Function. Treatises on the history of psychology, physiology, anatomy, and general biology are replete with statements concerning psychological brain functions. For the most part, the accounts imply a continuity of theory reaching back to the earliest extant literary records. All these treatises have two characteristics in common. First, they are concerned with the localization of generalized functions. Beginning with the brain they raise the questions whether ancient writers recognized its proper functions and at what period this actually happened. A typical statement follows:

From the time of Galen in the second century of the Christian era the cerebrum has been recognized as the organ of intelligence and conscious sensations. Galen established this view not only by anatomical dissections, confirming the older work of the Alexandrian school (third century B.C.) in regard to the origin from the brain of the cranial nerves, but also by numerous vivisection experiments upon lower animals (240, p. 183).

Howell continues to assert his approval of early findings:

All modern work has confirmed this belief and has tended to show that in the cerebral hemispheres, and especially in the cortex of gray matter, lies the seat of consciousness (240, p. 183).

And again:

The cortical gray matter, therefore, is the chief organ of the psychical life, the tissue through whose activity the objective changes in the external world, so far as they affect our sense organs, are converted into the subjective changes of consciousness. The nature of this relation constitutes the most difficult problem of physiology and psychology, a problem which perhaps is beyond the possibility of a satisfactory scientific explanation (240, p. 183).

The views expressed in these quotations are retained by Fulton as editor of the 15th edition (161, p. 255).

Secondly, historians of brain function almost invariably hold Aristotle up to scorn for persisting in maintaining wrong ideas on the subject. It seems intolerable to entertain any other idea than localization of psychological functions in the brain, in spite of the fact that brain-localization doctrines are certainly influenced more by cultural belief than by investigative evidence.

Though Galen lived in a transition era between the objectivity of the Greeks and the growing subjectivity of later time, it is doubtful whether he really held to the same kind of localization doctrine as Howell indicates. This is evident from an historical resumé of localization doctrine.

a. *Objective Greek Localization*

Until the emergence of recent field conceptions of psychological interbehavior, scientists have continuously attempted to localize psychological processes. We should, however, sharply separate the objective facts the Greeks attempted to locate from the very different processes the Hellenistic writers dealt with. Before Aristotle (384-322 B.C.), the interest centered only in different constituents of the organism which were responsible for particular activities. If Anaxagoras (ca. 499-428 B.C.) localized Nous in the brain as Theophrastus (ca. 372-288 B.C.) asserts (de Sensibus, 587, p. 28), he did not regard Nous as anything but a more refined type of material than the constitutents of any other part of the organism.

Were writers not so bound by the brain tradition they would not be so disturbed at Aristotle's reasons for making the heart more prominent than the brain as a locus of psychological processes. Since Aristotle could not be expected to know what modern physiologists have discovered about biological events, his doctrines from that standpoint do not seem so unusual. The following summary derived from Ogle (1827-1905) presents Aristotle's arguments for connecting the heart rather than the brain with psychological activities.

(1) Aristotle thought he discovered connecting links between the sense organs and the heart. The sense-organ of touch and taste directly, while the other organs were connected by ducts with the blood vessels and therefore ultimately with the heart. (2) The heart is the center of the vascular system and of the vital heat. (3) The heart is the first part to enter into activity, and the last to cease. Therefore it is probably the seat of sensibility—the essential characteristic of animal life. (4) The heart's action is augmented or diminished when intense pleasure or pain is felt. (5) Loss of blood causes insensibility. (6) Keenness of sensibility is diminished or annulled in anaemic parts, increased in hyper-anaemic; and bloodless parts are insensitive. (7) The heart has the central position in the body, which seems to fit it to be the organ of central sense. Moreover disease of the heart is most fatal (471).

The reasons against the brain are:

(a) It is insensible to external mechanical stimulation. If the brain of a living animal be laid bare, the hemispheres may be cut without any signs of pain whatever, and without any struggling on the part of the animal—a difficulty which was insuperable to Aristotle. (b) He could find no brain or anything apparently analogous to a brain in any of the invertebrates except in the cephalopods, the cephalic ganglia in the other animals having, owing to their minute size, escaped his unaided vision. Yet sensation was a special characteristic of an animal. The absence of a brain, then, from numerous sentient creatures, was quite incompatible for him with the notion that the brain was the central organ of sensation. (c) The brain he erroneously regarded as bloodless, as also did Hippocrates; and all experience taught him that those parts alone were sensitive that contained blood. (d) He thought it manifest to inspection that there is no anatomical connection between the brain and the sense organs. (e) And finally, he believed himself to have good grounds for supposing another part, viz. the heart, to be the sensory center (471).

What scientists chiefly hold up to scorn is Aristotle's idea of the brain as a refrigerative or temperature-controlling organ. Though we certainly can not overlook the obvious fallacies in Aristotle engendered by ignorance, possibly extenuation is available in the fact that he wrote so many centuries ago. But after all, on the other side of the picture, as Ogle (471) points out, the heart and the brain for him constituted one consolidated organ. Some justification for this is available in Aristotle's discussion of sleep and madness (13, II, s. 7) in which brain lesions are intimately connected with vascular functions.

To Aristotle's credit stands his organismic attitude toward the parts of animals. Aristotle was the first to point out the intimate connection and rapid sympathy between heart and brain. Ogle quotes from an article of Claude Bernard (1813-1878) in which the latter writes: "Le coeur et le cerveau se trouvent des lors dans une solidarité d'actions réciproques dès plus intimes . . ." (34). By no means may we overlook the fact that Aristotle is an objective biological psychologist for whom psychological activities are specific functions of the entire organism.

Though it certainly can not be said that modern physiological research supports Aristotle's crude observations, it is interesting to notice recent findings concerning temperature-controlling mechanisms in the brain. Fulton (160, ch. 23) points out that as far back as 1875 Hughlings Jackson appreciated that visceral functions must be regulated by all neural levels including the cortex. He writes:

> The experiments of Pinkston, et al., thus clearly establish that the cerebral cortex by virtue of its regulatory action on the autonomic system, is an essential part of the bodily mechanism of heat regulation (160, p. 434).

In substantiation of this conclusion he cites a series of ablation experiments on dogs and cats by Pinkston, Bard, and Rioch (494), Pinkston and Rioch (495), and Kennard (304, 305). Though Zollinger and Schnitker (660) controvert Kennard's findings on the human organism (301), there appears no basis for regarding Aristotle's views as bizarre.

In this connection it is interesting to refer to the various experimental researches that were required to establish the heat-regulating function of the brain. When Isenschmid and Schnitzler (250) suggested in 1914 that the hypothalamus was concerned in heat regulation the idea was first overlooked and then questioned (160, p. 235n). Finally, through the work of Keller (300, 301), Ranson (512, 514), and their coworkers as well as others already mentioned, the organismic character of the brain must now be regarded as established.

In consonance with Aristotle's objectivity and his common-sense observations of the activity of organisms is his tremendous general emphasis of vascular processes. Though he separates and localizes various sensory processes he relies upon the vascular system and the blood to account for the organization of reactions to things. It would be a mistake to read into Aristotle's differentiation of the senses the kind of metaphysical elaboration which modern scientists have developed, such that through the eye only visual qualities are sensed and through the ear only auditory. We must not overlook that for Aristotle there exist visual and auditory objects and that each is primarily in contact with the eye or ear. Unlike, then, more modern and less objective views, the organizing function or *sensus communis* does not consist of organizing *qualities* into objects but refers rather to more complicated processes of representing and judging. These common functions are attributed to various phases of the vascular system. Not only is the vascular apparatus the general organizing medium of all activities, but as Beare points out (31) it is the basis for *sensus communis* or *koinè aesthesis* activity. Indeed, aside from vascular processes only one other similarly-objective and natural factor is basic to all sensory processes—namely, the *symphyton pneuma* or connatural spirit. This is the moving air which occupies the sensory-channels with their seat or *arché* in the heart. In line with Aristotle's biological psychology the *symphyton pneuma* is basic to all physiological and psychological activities.

As Beare puts it:

> The *symphyton pneuma* had, for him, a primordial and subtle efficacy operative through the origin and development of animal existence. It was the profoundest cause and the most intimate sustaining agency from beginning to end of life and sensory power (31, p. 336).

Since ancient science is a development from common sense we should expect Greek doctrines of psychological localization to be evolutions from the results of everyday observation. In fact, early scientific doctrines may be traced back to everyday beliefs. The attempt to connect psychological processes with the operation of particular anatomical details, as writers have frequently pointed out, has its counterpart in general literature. For example, Patroclus killed Sarpidon.

> . . . and the midriff followed with the spear, so that he drew forth together the spear point, and the soul . . .

And Homer also says:

> In them is understanding at their hearts . . . Odysseus joyed in heart to hear; . . . though well your own hearts knew . . .

Not only has the diaphragm given rise to such localizations as indicated by the words frenzy and phrenitis, but, as everyone recalls, the Scriptures are replete with such expressions as "bowels of compassion," etc.

All those who are not entirely dominated by the cultural tradition of brain localization must be impressed by the complete objectivity of the Greek way of thinking as well as their first-stage translation of everyday ideas into scientific terms. As scientists and physicians evolved their technical doctrines they refined their concepts of actions and their seats. Historians of medicine point out how the elementary principles of the early scientists, fire, air, earth, and water, with their combining and activating principles such as nous, pneuma, heat, and cold, were developed into the humors. These, of course, could be localized in the bodily parts and made to account for the organism's psychological conditions.[1]

An excellent illustration of the Greek localization picture is drawn by Socrates (469-399 B.C.) in his attempt to learn

---

[1] As Allbutt (9, p. 133) points out, the humors were derived from Egypt, and in Greece connected with the Sicilian elements.

what science had to offer concerning psychological processes. In the form of questions he enumerates the doctrines prevalent among those who know.

Is the growth of animals the result of some decay which the hot and cold principle contract, as some have said? Is the blood the element with which we think, or the air, or the fire? or perhaps nothing of this sort—but the brain may be the originating power of the perceptions of hearing and sight and smell, and memory and opinion may come from them, and science may be based on memory and opinion when no longer in motion, but at rest (496, p. 96).

Again, in his classic complaint against Anaxagoras for disappointing him concerning the explanation of behavior he reveals how matter of fact were the Greeks.

As I proceeded, I find my philosopher altogether forsaking mind (nous) or any other principle of order, but having recourse to air, and ether, and water, and other eccentricities. I might compare him to a person who began by maintaining generally that mind is the cause of the actions of Socrates, but who, when he endeavored to explain the causes of my several actions in detail, went on to show that I sit here because my body is made up of bones and muscles; and the bones, as he would say, are hard and have ligaments which divide them, and the muscles are elastic, and they cover the bones, which have also a covering or environment of flesh and skin which contains them; and as the bones are lifted at their joints by the contraction or relaxation of the muscles, I am able to bend my limbs, and this is why I am sitting here in a curved posture; that is what he would say, and he would have a similar explanation of my talking to you, which he would attribute to sound, and air, and hearing, and he would assign ten thousand other causes of the same sort, forgetting to mention the true cause, which is, that the Athenians have thought fit to condemn me, and accordingly I have thought it better and more right to remain here and undergo my sentence; for I am inclined to think that these muscles and bones of mine would have gone off to Megara or Boeotia,—by the dog of Egypt they would, if they had been guided only by their own idea of what was best (496, pp. 98, 99).

Extremely instructive too is Socrates' common-sense theory

of motivation with which he attempts to correct Anaxagoras.

There is surely a strange confusion of causes and conditions in all this. It may be said, indeed, that without bones and muscles and the other parts of the body I cannot execute my purposes. But to say that I do as I do because of them, and that this is the way in which mind acts, and not from the choice of the best, is a very careless and idle mode of speaking (496, p. 99).

Since it is not at all improbable that our current seeking of internal principles is no different a process from that indulged in by the ancients, there is considerable point in indicating some samples of Greek localization. *Nous*, Anaxagoras located in the lateral ventricles of the brain (9, p. 252). Pythagoras (fl. 532-496 B.C.) placed the affective processes in the heart, the intellectual functions in the brain (9, p. 251). His disciple, Philolaos (ca. 450 B.C.), divided the organic functions into four types; thought and reason were ascribed to the brain, feelings and perception to the heart, growth and seed formation to the region of the navel, while generation was, of course, seated in the reproductive organs (119, Frg. 13). The separation and localization of organic functions are no doubt reflected in the Aristotelian doctrine of Psyche.

Empedocles (ca. 490-430 B.C.) made the heart the primary organ and so the seat of thought.

From the waves of the blood, pushing on, the heart nourishes itself. Here before all sits, what is called by men, the power of thought (119, Frg. 105).

Empedocles also suggests the refrigerative function of the brain. As a final example we indicate the view of Diocles of Carystos (fl. ca. 365 B.C.) who held that though the heart was the principal seat of psychological functions the special senses were localized in the right hemisphere and the understanding in the left (9, p. 138).

b. Alexandrian Transition Period

The Alexandrian period of intellectual development constitutes a definite transition stage between the objective

Greeks and the spiritually-minded medieval and modern thinkers. Alexandria served as the meeting place for Eastern ideas, originating as far away as India, and the thought of Greece. As a consequence a sharp separation developed between the scientific and humanistic branches of study.

Though, at first, Greek science flourished and indeed made advances, the peak was soon reached. After a period of stable collation and consolidation of previous results a decline set in which lasted until the Renaissance. Every medieval historian writes laudatorily of Herophilus (ca. 335-280 B.C.) and Erasistratus (ca. 304-258 B.C.), who in the third century B.C. worked so assiduously to differentiate motor and sensory nerves and to trace them to their cerebral origins. Both of these physicians followed the Pythagorean-Coan-Platonic tradition of the hegemony of the brain, though Erasistratus, influenced by his master, Praxagoras, did not fail to acknowledge the great importance of the heart as a locus of psychological functions.

c. Roman-Hellenistic Stage

So far as the history of P.P. is concerned, the Roman Period is of the greatest interest. Here the foundations were laid for changes in conception concerning psychological processes which have persisted to our own day. Characteristic of this period is the culmination of the translation of Greek objective doctrines through the work of the Patristics. The mixture of Hellenic and Eastern ideas begun in Alexandria reach a point at which all the organic functions of the Greeks become spiritual; their naturalistic conceptions are converted into symbols for supernatural religious entities. Throughout a long list of writers it is argued that despite the soul being spiritual it can also be corporeal (509, p. 117 f.) and vice versa. Thus the conception of an essence is reached, which though attached and belonging to the body of man, still is absolutely different from it.[1]

[1] For an interesting statement of changing conceptions of the psyche by a modern hylopsychist, see Ellis (132).

With the development of soul as spirit Greek localization doctrines are completely transformed. Psychological processes become functions of the soul rather than activities of the organism. As Gregory of Nyssa (331-394) puts it, none of the facts concerning disease or the theories of heart or brain localization proves to him "that the incorporeal nature is confined by certain local barriers" (509, p. 126 f.). The mind for him pervades the entire organism, and as long as it remains in the body is regulated by God.

The keystone of the period is set by Augustine (354-430), a thinker who departs radically from the tradition of natural science, and carries to the extreme the humanistic trend begun by Alexandrian scholars. For him, knowledge originates in the Scriptures, in books, in literature. Among the many threads woven into his thought two are outstanding. The first is the cultural transformation which puts a uniting infinite and creative spirit in the place of the finite, objective cosmos of the Greeks. By the time of Augustine the monotheistic conception has replaced the casual polytheism of the pagan world. The second and related thread is the complete preoccupation with general human issues and essentially the problem of personal salvation. Augustine lived in the days of the dissolution of the eternal Roman Empire, a time when personal salvation was not only a poignant but an immediate necessity. Through personal argument and imaginative construction an eternal and supernatural home for man in the kingdom of God was developed.

The supremely important fact about Augustine is that while he is the complete opposite of a scientist he became one of the founders of modern thought (635, p. 276). What this means essentially is that he gives voice to the developing cultural trends which still continue. His significance, consequently, for science in general as well as for psychology can not be underestimated. As Windelband puts it:

So there begins, as over against the Greek philosophy, a new course of development, which indeed, during the Middle Ages, made but little progress beyond what was achieved by Augustine in his first cast, and the full development of which is not to be found until the modern period (635, p. 277).

In substance Augustine turns to inner consciousness which guarantees existence as well as knowledge. Consider that living, remembering, thinking or judging as the power of the elements, of atoms, of brain, or heart may and has been doubted.

Yet who ever doubts that he himself lives, and remembers, and understands, and wills, and thinks, and knows, and judges? Seeing that even if he doubts, he lives; if he doubts, he remembers why he doubts; if he doubts he understands that he doubts; if he doubts, he wishes to be certain; if he doubts, he thinks; if he doubts, he knows that he does not know; if he doubts, he judges that he ought not to assent rashly. Whosoever therefore, doubts about anything else, ought not to doubt of all these things; which if they were not, he would not be able to doubt of anything (15, Bk. X, sec. 14).

That this line of thought is substantially reproduced by Descartes is fully recognized by all scholars. The Cartesian *Cogito, ergo sum* may well have been derived from Augustine's *Quod si fallor sum*. But what is not perhaps sufficiently considered is that our whole modern psychology, even throughout its experimental sphere is of the same essence. All the notions of immediate experience, the doctrines of sensation and other conscious states are of the spirit spiritual.

d. *Medieval and Scholastic Stages*

Interested as we are in the evolution of localization ideas we need not be long detained in the present period. No new principles evolve. As we have indicated, the spiritistic aspects of psychology are completely developed; no technical or scientific systems are produced. While the common-sense conditions of man are, of course, appreciated, the lack of science affords no opportunity for further construction. It is important to note, however, that in the Scholastic period a psychological development occurs which makes for a definite continuity between the evolution of spiritistic ideas and modern psychology—namely, the rediscovery and exploitation of the Aristotelian treatises.

Brett (53, II, p. 113) says:

> The most obvious feature of the whole movement called Scholasticism is the steady restoration of Aristotle's doctrine.

This is a true statement in the sense that it is possible to trace back the science of psychology step by step to the work of the Scholastics. Though it became a tradition in the Renaissance period to cast aspersions on Aristotle, as far as psychology goes his views have lived on. Confirming evidence may be found in Brentano's claim to be an Aristotelian, and the Brentano influence on present-day gestalt psychologists.

What is not properly indicated by Brett, however, is that the appearance of Aristotle in the Scholastic period is by no means a restoration but a sublimation. Certainly the classic Scholastics, St. Albert (1193-1280) and St. Thomas (ca. 1225-1274), have reinterpreted Aristotle to bring him into line with modern psychology, but have in no sense maintained his doctrines as they were established in naturalistic Greek Athens.

Fundamentally the translation or sublimation consists in the transformation of the Aristotelian psyche or function into psychic states or faculties. This transformation constitutes the basis for the prominence of the mind-body and localization problems in modern psychology.

e. *Modern Period*

Our brief survey of the development of P.P. in the British and Continental tradition (chs. 3, 4) indicated that even when the early physiological psychologists presumably were stirred by scientific ideas to take advantage of the development of physiological knowledge, they simply followed the dualistic tradition. There certainly was not at that time and probably could not have been a vigorous movement to study psychological events which were in part also biological. On the contrary, all the facts of brain organization and brain injury were simply interpreted in line with the tradition of the soul and its seat.

It is not to be denied that there was value as well as progress in the changing conception of the psychic part or aspect of organisms as mind, consciousness, and mental processes. There is no point in decrying the evolutional stages of a science. What *is* important is to recognize that all these variant constructions refer to a single basic interpretation of psychological events. The modern expression "The brain is the organ of the mind" is intrinsically no different from the statement that the brain is the seat of the soul.

The significant point is to recognize the brain dogma for what it is. The value of so doing is the pragmatic one of discovering that various interpretations may severally constitute faulty ways of describing events. To think in terms of psychic powers or processes is to overlook that one is concerned with interbehavior, whereas to think of a brain in which these processes are localized is to disregard the biological nature of the brain as a part of the organism concerned in the interbehavior.

CHAPTER 8

THE BIOLOGY AND PSYCHOLOGY OF THE
NERVOUS SYSTEM

THE DOGMA OF THE NERVOUS SYSTEM

BOTH biologists and psychologists agree that the nervous
system is as important as it is complex. But it is
anomalous to proceed further and maintain that it is the
basis and seat of psychological and even psychic processes.
Still the cult of the brain constitutes one of the most effective
examples of scientific traditionalism. Surely no better illustration can be found of an uncrossable chasm between data
and constructs.

The tenacity with which scientists cling to the doctrine
that the nervous system is the seat of mentality or at least
furnishes explanatory principles for psychology is no more
remarkable, however, than the arguments employed to support it. As we know, the strength of the dogma lies in the
fallacious belief that only by means of its acceptance can
psychology and psychologcial processes be scientific. The
great paradox remains that nervous-system dogma actually
does the opposite. It perpetuates the error that psychology
is concerned with intangible and unapproachable processes,
the existence of which can be justified only by verbally at-
taching them to the brain.

In a scientific context it is always a pertinent question
whether the venerability of a doctrine should not create a
presumption against it. Far from agreeing that the ancients
discovered a truth which it is wise always to cherish, we ask
how could the ancients establish the truth of brain localization when they knew so precious little about the brain, even
relatively to our still incomplete information. An even more
pertinent question: Should we confound the view of Hippocrates (ca. 460-370 B.C.) and other Greeks, whose views may
be properly interpreted as simply stressing the biological

importance of the brain for human action, with the later doctrines of soul localization?

The fact to remember throughout all discussion of the interrelation of the nervous system and psychological events is that the more our knowledge of the nervous system increases the greater the evidence that that system is no more important for psychology than many other features of the absolutely integrated and unitary organism. We emphasize again that if both biologists and psychologists disregard this fact, it is because established doctrine in science is more powerful than factual evidence. So powerful in fact that a mutual ideological contagion affects the members of various scientific branches.

BRAIN ARGUMENTS

Because of the importance of neurological facts for psychology in general and P.P. in particular it is worth while to bring together the primary arguments for the retention of the nervous-system dogma. We require no justification for emphasizing the brain in our discussion, since despite the common knowledge that this organ differs in nothing but complexity from other parts of the nervous system (163, 550), it is nevertheless regarded as the seat of the soul as well as the primary mechanism of psychological processes.

How eloquent the biologist waxes when he approaches the study of the brain:

No organ is so distinctive of man as his brain. Long recognized as the seat of his mental life, it is that portion of his body most concerned with his personality. Here take place those changes that give rise to his sensations, his memories, his volitions; here arise his emotions, the figments of his imagination, his dreams; and here too, in abnormal states, appear those idiosyncrasies and moods that pass over step by step into insanity. In short, the brain is the organ of his mind, his very soul. Not that the brain alone is all this, for this organ is buried in his body, which, as an environment, yields among other things the whole range of internal secretions determining as they do in so many ways the setting for the individual life. But notwithstanding the importance of these surroundings, the brain harbors what is one's truest self and in this respect no other organ in us is its peer (475, p. 91).

Or glance at the arguments of the mentalistic psychologists whose professional stock in trade consists of nebulous and evanescent states of consciousness. They declare that one must cleave tightly to the brain as the only means of bringing mental processes into the domain of science. Next there is the neurologist's claim that unless you regard the brain as a machine that thinks or as the mechanism for psychic processes you have no way of handling mind and consciousness. And finally the behavioristic psychologist insists that only by an exclusive preoccupation with brain functions and their connection with other organic structures and processes can one avoid entirely spiritual mind and consciousness.

More impressive than these general arguments for the brain dogma are the detailed vacillations and contradictions to which they lead. The latter are excellently exhibited in the writings of the eminent neurologist Herrick, because of his great interest in the problem of brain and consciousness. To establish his position relative to brain dogma in general, he declares:

Neurophysiology occupies a unique place in the circle of the sciences as the point of convergence of the physical and the psychical (227, p. 251).

Concerning the uniqueness of the brain as an organ and seat of consciousness, he writes: "The human brain is the organ of civilization" (227, p. 265). Since presumably civilization is a product of mentality, he tells us: "Human mentality is a function of the cortex" (223, p. 355). More positively still:

The cerebral cortex is the specific organ of thinking in quite the same sense as wings of birds are specific organs of flight or the legs of a man are specific organs of locomotion (224, p. 249).

Herrick realizes, however, that the nervous system is one of many systems and that the organism is and acts as a unity.

When we are thinking the whole body thinks. We think all

over just as a bird flies all over and just as we are alive all over (224, p. 249).

Applying this to brain and consciousness he says:

The search for a single seat of consciousness, such as psychologists and philosophers have so long sought, is vain (223, p. 349).

In his struggle to keep the brain as the locus of mind and yet avoid the singleness of seat Herrick espouses the unity of brain action as against the power of the parts.

No cortical area can properly be described as the exclusive center of a particular function. Such "centers" are merely nodal points in an exceedingly complex system of neurons which must act as a whole in order to perform any function whatsoever (223, p. 358).

He goes even further, admitting that some consciousness: ". . . particularly simple emotional experience, is not cortical but visceral and thalamic" (224, p. 194). Still more, when pressed hard, he agrees that the individual's "apparatus of the spiritual life" (224, p. 247) includes things (224, p. 248). Herrick agrees with Patrick (477) that mind is not a function of any organ or set of organs in the body but an activity of the individual as a whole in interaction with his physical and social environments (224, p. 343 f.). It turns out that the cerebral cortex is the organ of thinking in that it is "essential" for complex adjustments (224, p. 345).

Underlying these vacillations and contradictions is, of course, an attachment to the traditional doctrine of consciousness, awareness, the subjective, the introspective, etc. At best it is good scientific intention to call the spiritual, life, mechanism. At worst it interferes with observation and valid interpretations.

Another curious feature of the brain-dogma situation is the reciprocal shift of responsibility. As one of the above quotations indicates, Herrick seems to believe that it is philosophers and psychologists who indulge in brain localization. On the other hand, the psychologist turns the table:

The old dogma that the brain is the organ of mind lives on in many high and "authoritative" places. Its most stubborn and uncritical defender is medicine (32, p. 368).

BIOLOGY OF THE NERVOUS SYSTEM

Writers on the nervous system and its place in psychology are characterized by unique thought patterns. Often the crude neural facts are exhibited as though their very presence argues in favor of the writer's conceptions. As if one believed that when one says, "Here is the brain, it is a complex organ," one has shown that the brain is responsible for all sorts of events and alleged events.

To be sure, it is impossible to overemphasize the place of the nervous system in the biological or psychological economy. For this very reason we must maintain a critically analytic attitude. In other words, not overlook the number and complexity of significant factors other than the nervous system which likewise operate in both biological or psychological events. It is a scientific obligation not only to take account of the number of factors, but also their nature as well as the place of each in total biological and psychological events. Precisely because it is possible to isolate factors it is all the more necessary to avoid misinterpretation.

Since the brain tradition can survive only by neglect or misinterpretation of concrete events it is essential to summarize some of the known facts concerning the brain and the nervous system in general.

Complexity of the Nervous System. Neurologists continually point out the complexity of the nervous system. The numbers of cells or neurons run into the billions. Herrick (223, p. 28) estimates there are 9 billion, 280 million in the human cortex alone. These numbers are frequently offered as evidence that there are enough units to form tremendously complex aggregations for the purpose of organizing the organism's activities. It is impossible therefore to minimize the complexity of the nervous system, and those given to wonder at the coordination and agility of complex organisms may gain great satisfaction from the evolution of such efficient mechanisms. But is there any necessity to go beyond the known biological facts? Complex organisms do perform highly intricate actions and insofar as the nervous system contributes to this intricacy of operation one is free to adopt whatever attitude of awe and admiration one chooses.

However, there is no occasion to disregard a similar complexity in other systems. Donaldson (93, p. 187) calculates that a man weighing 155 pounds possesses 26,500,000,000,000 cells. If one adds blood cells the number must be even larger, for Keen (612, p. 132) estimates that in each of the 12 pints of blood in the body of a 144 pound man there are 10,240,000,000,000 red blood cells. Is it not gratuitous therefore to believe that the large number of neural cells are the basis for mental associations?

As another element of neural complexity, note that the brain itself does not consist exclusively of neural tissue but glandular and vascular also. Morever, even the separate anatomical structures comprise both neural and glandular tissue—for example, the hypophysis. Nor is the brain in any sense an isolated or special organ. It is an integral part of an organism. Secondly, as we have indicated, we can not underestimate its biological aspects. The brain cultists on the whole have lost sight of actual brain functions which are obviously biological.

Certainly the brain is enormously complex, but what is the significance of this fact? Complexity of brain signifies a marvelous organization for effectiveness in coordination and facility of organic adjustment. No anatomical investigation has revealed anything more in the brain than concentration of neural elements.

No microscopical, no physical or chemical means detect there anything radically other than in nerve-nets elsewhere. All is as elsewhere, except greater complexity (550, p. 22).

The Wide Distribution of the Nervous System. Biologists specializing in neurological studies frequently point out how widely distributed the nervous system is throughout the organism. Certainly it is in conformity with the structures and functions of the nervous system as a coordinating mechanism to branch into every part of the organism. On the same plan of evolution the most widely distributed neural tissues must have some centralization. These facts naturally lend themselves to varying interpretations. On the one hand there is the obvious attitude that the nervous system constitutes an intricate mechanism for the interrelationship of relatively widely and peculiarly distributed tissues and organs making up the organism's morphology.

On the other hand, there is the view that the nervous system is a governing mechanism, a unique biological system. Especially, "The brain is conceded to be the master organ of the body, the regulator of life, the source of human progress" (596, p. 3). It is one of the anomalies of modern biology that neurologists refer to neural impulses, which are afferently and efferently conducted over the nervous system, as "*messages.*" This habit may be regarded merely as one of metaphorical description, but on the other hand, in view of dualism's cultural dominance there is more than a suggestion that neurologists unwittingly believe in powers transcending actual biological happenings.

It might serve as a check upon extrapolating biological facts to remember that the nervous system is no more widely distributed than the vascular system. Also, if one keeps alive to the inseverable interrelationship between the functioning of the vascular and neural tissues one may be loath to endow the nervous system with mastership and inordinate regulatory powers.

The Integrative Character of the Nervous System. As a conducting and coordinating system the neural tissues and organs necessarily operate in strict integration. The obvious biological conclusion is therefore that the nervous system is one of many differentiated systems of the unitary organism. Because it is evolutionally specialized as a coordinating mechanism it must itself be highly integrated. From a biological standpoint these facts point strikingly toward the unitary operation of organisms. Only the characteristically human trait to overemphasize what one is working at induces neurologists to interpret the integrative character of the nervous system as making for regulative power and behavioral progress.

Integration, after all, is no more characteristic of the nervous system than of other systems. Is it not true that the vascular system constitutes one of the most efficiently integrating mechanisms (80)? It should be just as easy to adopt the erroneous belief that the vascular system is the primary integrator as it is to accord such primacy to the nervous system. Not only does the vascular system integrate the organism's status and activity, but the general facts concerning the biology of blood circulation suggest the effective integration of the entire organism. Those biologists who draw improper conclusions from the integrative character of the nervous system should not overlook that it is in disaccord with the organism's actual morphology and physiology to think of the musculature or the glandular organs as locally static and unintegrated parts.

The Evolution of the Nervous System. The comparative neurologist has been eminently successful in tracing out in great detail the evolution of the nervous system. Neurological writings delineate with admirable accuracy the evolutional steps in the development of a generalized nerve net through the complexities of ganglia and centralized axial brain and cord. Unfortunately the specialization motive leads to the minimization of a corresponding evolution of all other parts of the biological economy.

The next and misleading step is to assert that the complex evolution of the nervous system alone is coordinate with or responsible for the evolution of behavior. To claim that the nervous system is more definitely and intimately tied up with increased complexity of action is based upon the scientific fallacies of preferred selection and bad sampling. Is it true that the cortex solves quadratic equations and designs modish hats and gowns (224, p. 245)? Those who believe that neural evolution is exclusively responsible for behavior evolution not only fail to take account of the unitary evolution of organisms as wholes but also of the changes and transformations of many other factors both organic and environmental which contribute to the same end result.

To adhere rigidly to the biological facts of the anatomy and physiology of the nervous system means to describe coordinate developments in organic evolution and complexity of behavior as facts imbedded in larger field events. To take into account the entire field of components instead of only one, no matter how important, makes unnecessary such a common multiplication of fallacies as exemplified in the following illustration.

Neurologists build up a tremendous ideological system the outcome of which is to demonstrate that neural evolution is the sole basis for behavior evolution. But since organisms without specialized and highly-evolved nervous systems can also perform complex behavior, such as problem solving, comparative neurologists resort to the intellectual dodge that, after all, organisms without complex nervous systems are not *aware* of what they do when solving problems (224, p. 272 f.). Thus the field is left wide open to drag in awareness as a unique kind of function performed by the nervous system.

True as it may be that an organism evolved only with a simple nervous system does not perform complex awareness acts, such as are performed by human organisms taken as a standard, that fact in no wise allows for the implications that awareness is a psychic "function" or concerned exclusively with the nervous system. As a concrete type of interbehavior, awareness must be taken wherever it is found. It is obvious that in simpler situations it will be simpler, but this in no sense implies some absolute difference.

But whatever organism performs awareness actions, that event in every situation constitutes a complex interorganization of factors, and thus can not be adequately described without regard to the organism's development in interrelation with stimulus objects, as well as the characteristics of such objects. Whether an action is automatistic, intelligent, or deliberate is always a matter of how the entire organism is interoperating with its stimulus objects (289, vol. I). Probably the keenest awareness responses are those in which the reactor is responding to his own reaction, whatever else may at the time also constitute his stimulus situation.

PSYCHOLOGY OF THE NERVOUS SYSTEM

Despite the fact that an increasing number of psychologists are beginning to question the powers of the brain (p. 79), the ancient cerebral dogma still maintains its vigor. How powerfully, appears from the literature devoted both to the mechanisms of (1) perceiving and feeling, and (2) remembering and learning. This literature forcibly testifies to the impotence of contrary fact in the presence of scientific faith.

Consider some items in the psychological literature. As early as 1919 Watson (618) warned against making a fetish of the nervous system despite its great importance. Although he merely intended to plead for the consideration of the organism's other components, his suggestion merited less heedlessness than it received. When in 1922 Kantor (287) called attention to the ageing fictional use which psychologists made of the nervous system, his article met with the rebuke entirely appropriate to the sacrilegious treatment of a holy object (614, 615). Since that time, although a voice is now and then raised to protest the inordinate emphasis placed upon the brain, psychologists, for the most part still assume that it is a dominant and even controlling organ.

First of all, let us separate sharply the several kinds of psychological properties attributed to this system of systems. Doubtless the most seriously culpable endowment of the nervous system with psychological properties is found in the writings on sensation and perception. It is in that field that psychic functions are rampant; where all sorts of potencies for producing mental processes are invented.

The attribution to the brain of the power to associate ideas is equivalent to endowing it with a middle type of psychological property. Not that connecting brain processes with ideas is less magical and mysterious than making the brain produce sensations, but rather, the whole procedure is more palpably verbal. As Herrick puts it:

> Even though we do not know how the brain thinks, we know as surely as we know anything in biology that it does so (224, p. 351).

In fact, psychologists and neurologists have written millions of words about associations and association centers, but all they amount to is translating into neural language the old associationistic type of psychic lore. Actually, not one iota of evidence is or can ever be proposed.

Though the attribution of learning powers to the brain appears less objectionable, it really is not. Psychologists who talk about brain-learning functions seem to hold mentalistic constructions in abeyance. However, to attribute psychological-learning functions to the brain is simply to echo the old mind-location assertions. If the learning is complex it is assumed the mind's cortical seat has the power to perform it. If the cortex is injured or removed, then the powers are shoved down to some subcortical region. The following quotation from Woodworth's *Experimental Psychology* admirably illustrates the indecisive treatment of psychological brain functions.

> In learning, work is done by the organism; this work leaves after-effects which we may include under the noncommittal term, *trace*. What is retained is this trace. The trace is a modification of the organism which is not directly observed but is inferred from the facts of recall and recognition (640, p. 6).
>
> *The explanatory concept* of association implies a *direct* connection within the organism, probably within the brain, between the mechanisms concerned with items A and B (640, p. 25).
>
> It seems almost certain that the locus of any practice effect is the cerebral hemispheres and that practice leaves behind some

change in the neural structure or condition (640, p. 188).

Typical of much psychological writing are the strong indications of belief in the powers of the brain with a coordinate negect of it in later exposition and interpretation. A fine example is Marquis's statement in discussing the neurology of learning:

The ability of an animal to learn—the ability to modify its behavior on the basis of previous experience and to adapt successfully to new situations—depends upon the structure and organization of its central nervous system. The difference between an untrained dog and a dog which has been taught to "beg" when food is held out, is a difference in the brain. The dog's reaction, of course, involves the functioning of receptors, sensory nerves, motor nerves, and muscles, but the modification produced by the training is a modification of brain function. The neural connections from the receptors to the brain, and from the brain to the muscles are fixed and unchangeable. When a man learns through long practice to aim and shoot a gun accurately, he has not trained the eye or the finger. He has altered the brain processes in such a way that the movements of the finger are more precisely related to the visual stimulation (399, p. 153).

The later exposition, of course, makes no pretense to substantiate such a statement.

It has become a cultural tradition that the psychological functions of the brain consist of behavior control by the development of complex synaptic connections. This autistic creation of psychological processes is based on no more adequate foundation than the anatomical fact of neural synaptic junctions. The operation of these junctions has been transformed into functions called engrams or neurograms. Lashley, however, has warned against the procedure of inferring changes in neural operation from behavior and then explaining learning in terms of the inferred engrams or functions.

The fundamental importance of the synapse seems a logical conclusion, yet we must bear in mind when evaluating theories of learning that the properties of the synapse are still entirely hypothetical. If we deduce its properties from the facts of learning we gain nothing by explaining learning in terms of these hypothetical properties (347, p. 473).

The objection to *brain functions* is twofold. They not only are of no value in explaining learning or any other complex event, but they prevent all who place such faith in them from explaining behavior events in terms of all the numerous factors the events themselves make available for the purpose. In this connection it is interesting to note that Marquis, whom we have quoted above as espousing this faith, continues to believe it even though he appreciates its futility. Writing in collaboration with Hilgard, he says:

> In the present status of knowledge, neural theory is not basic to conditioning theory. The known facts of neural function cannot be utilized to predict or to limit the results of behavioral studies. . . . Even the basic law that a response varies in magnitude with intensity of stimulus would be equally true if the nerves were copper wires or pneumatic tubes. The facts of speed of conduction and synaptic delay cannot predict the latency of a conditioned response, for we have no idea what length of nerve or how many synapses are involved. . . . Many of the so-called neural facts, such as reflex inhibition, which seem most relevant to conditioning are in reality behavioral laws stated as relations between afferent and efferent nerve activity without direct observation of any intermediate neural event (Skinner, 1931).[1] This point of view of course does not preclude the possibility that on the basis of future work neurological prediction of behavioral facts may be achieved (232, p. 336).

Whenever one wishes to emphasize the presence of biological activities in psychological situations or to consider biological and psychological actions in relationship, one must always differentiate between the two types of events (ch. 10). Anatomical organization, which provides the connections between sense organs and cortical terminals, also between cortical terminals and motor projection paths, is a biological fact. The actions of the biological structures—conduction, coordination, and other functions—are and remain biological

---

[1] The reference here is to Skinner (561).

and can not be connected with psychological events except as participating factors. Psychological events may be regarded as the larger field situations of which the biological activities, howsoever essential, constitute only components. To localize psychological functions in the brain involves an enormous amount of interpretative and attributive construction deviating widely from an observational contact with events. At the least, the questionable commerce with neural constructions does not enrich psychology and makes physiology poor indeed.

Three Views Concerning Psychological Brain Functions

The question concerning psychological brain functions may be exhaustively answered by the three following views.

A. Psychoneural Functions as Emanations

Plato formulated a sublime conception of the consequences of the man who pursues evil ways. Such a man takes on the shape of evil. The application of this conception to students of P.P. is not inappropriate. Biologists and psychologists who (1) do not limit their ideas of neural functions to the actual operations of neural cells, whether in isolation or in tissue and organ organization, and (2) do not take into consideration that psychological behavior consists of the interoperation of organisms with stimulus objects, inevitably adopt an emanation conception of neural functions. Two interrelated steps lead to this erroneous consequence.

The first is to assume that neural functions are of two sorts, that besides the actual and only observable biological functions of conduction, integration, and coordination there are also others of a more general psychological sort. Such alleged functions are hypothesized with a complete lack of observable data.

Fulton and Sherrington have brilliantly stated the dilemma of psychic functions:

But to pass from a nerve impulse to a psychical event is to step as it were from one world to another. We might expect then that at the places of transition from its non-mental to its mental regions the brain would exhibit some striking change of structures. But no; in the mental parts of the brain still nothing but the same old structural elements, with essentially the same old features, set end-to-end in neurone chains as elsewhere, and evidently just as before serving as lines for travel of nerve impulses, and nodal points for their convergence and irradiation, their further launching by excitation, and their restriction by inhibition. We are here faced in perhaps its sharpest form with the age-old ever unsolved problem of the nexus between matter and life and mind (163, p. 263).

Nevertheless, Fulton writes:

The elucidation of mental phenomena, normal and abnormal remains the most challenging problem of neurophysiology (160, p. 491).

The second step is to reduce behavior to general functions. Such terms as consciousness, awareness, and mental processes are not taken as descriptive of specific actions, but of some nebulous wraith of neural structures. Emanation constructions are obviously purely autistic. They constitute only illicit abstractions from actual fields of action, and are supported only by traditional ideas.

B. PSYCHONEURAL FUNCTIONS AS CAUSES

Throughout the history of P.P. the emanation doctrine has been closely connected with another and equally unfounded conception—namely, that neural functions are causes. The cause conception is especially transparent in the historical enterprise of localizing psychological functions in neural mechanisms.

Historical writers concerned with the origin of science and philosophy among the Greeks point out that their achievement consists of setting aside mythology by introducing the idea of cause. Instead of accounting for events by autistically constructing forces and powers unrelated to the events to be explained, they attempted to account for them by interrelating their elements, making some of them precedent and others consequent.

The earliest objective Greeks stressed the essential being or construction of things; for example, what isolated objects did was accounted for on the basis of what they were made of, fire, water, air, etc., in addition to their structure or morphology. Objects behaved differently if they were either moist and cold or moist and warm. Again, motions could be accounted for by the roundness of the atoms constituting objects. When they were concerned with the interaction of things, they added properties to the things, individually or severally—for instance, affinities, attraction and repulsion, harmony, unity, plurality, fitness, organization, what is reasonable, best or purpose-meeting. But throughout, the emphasis is upon the nature of *things*. Aristotle summarized all this in his formula of four causes. (1) What a thing is made of; (2) Its form or shape; (3) The making of the thing or act; and (4) Its end or purpose, or "for the sake of" which it is (14, p. 194b).

While this procedure of accounting for things and events is certainly an advance over the mythological method which it displaces, from our present point of vantage it is certainly naïve and elementary. On the whole, this explanatory procedure misplaces causes. To account for the behavior of objects on the basis of their construction is to overlook that this being or nature is itself a property or properties of interrelationship with things. But by far the greatest objection is the overemphasis of one object in a complex event on account of its construction, even if in some instance more weight may be given to it than to some other thing.

So far as psychology is concerned the simple causal ideas of the Greeks were in no sense objectionable. Howsoever elementary Aristotle's descriptions, he consistently regarded psychological functions as activities of the organism. In consonance with his essentially biological psychology he even treated psychological events as adjustments of organisms in interrelation with objects.

With the changes in Western European culture, psychological processes were shifted from animal behavior to the operation of psychic entities, and thus the sinister aspects of the cause conception came to the front. Post-Aristotelian writers, adopting the spiritual interpretation of psychological processes, located the causes of action in the interior of the individual. Conspiring in this circumstance obviously is the fact that actions of individuals are in the forefront of interest. It is not improbable that this stage of cause evolution constitutes an interiorization of the animistic processes which the Greeks had extruded from their natural philosophy. Even without the animistic feature there would still be an incorrect, causal principle. Not only are the antecedent factors of causal relations arbitrarily constructed, but the notion of one thing doing something to another is unrepresentative of the events. The upshot is a naïve anthropomorphism. The antecedent and consequent construction is based on the analogy of a person pushing or pulling at something, a conception quite at variance with our modern notion of interrelation of factors in a field.

Modern conceptions of cause are constructed altogether differently. Though the term *cause* is retained, it certainly is supplied with entirely new connotations. Today, cause is interpreted as the co-presence of the factors of an event in a field. As a result, the presence, absence, or any modification of factors is tantamount to a different event. As applied to P.P., the brain has an inevitable place in every psychological event, but neither it nor any functions localized within it *causes* the event of which it is a part.. True, without the co-presence and operation of the brain the perceiving event does not exist, but it is a modern form of animism to regard the brain as causing or producing a color quality, or a new way of acting.

The contrast between (1) the antecedent and consequent and (2) the field conceptions is well illustrated by the way events are treated in current neurological writing. Constantly preoccupied with neural mechanisms and observing a correspondence between brain evolution and the development of increasingly complex and effective actions in phylogenetic series, neurologists forthwith declare that brain changes are causal factors. Such an interpretation exemplifies perfectly how a coordinate event is misplaced into an antecedent position and endowed with causal power. The evidences certainly show nothing more than that there is a corresponding evolution of brain structure and action. A more proper interpretation of the phylogenetic series of events is that the succeeding items in the series indicate differing events with diverse participating factors.

In addition to the specialist's exaggeration of his study materials we note the injection of an anthropocentric element. The neurologist clearly places a high value on human behavior which he correlates with the development of the human brain. When comparing organisms there is, however, no scientific privilege to say more than that certain complexities occur. To believe in a scale of values running downwards from human brain development through a nonsynaptic nervous system to a noncentralized one is to inject anthropocentric values into nature.

A similar misplacement of coordinate factors is illustrated when the principle of brain localization is applied to pathological events. Whenever a brain injury or malformation can be coordinated with ineffectiveness of action it is a common belief that the brain injury is the *cause* of the behavior trouble. Here again we suggest the more scientific-field idea of regarding the corresponding sets of conditions as participating factors in a specified field.[1]

Aside from misplacement of factors and their endowment with imaginary powers, neural-cause theorists flagrantly neglect nonneural factors. Those who make the evolution of the brain responsible for the evolution of behavior completely ignore the corresponding evolution of other morphological traits of the organism, as well as changes in life

---

[1] Interbehavioral field. For a description and comparison of various field constructions, see Kantor (296).

conditions. Similarly, those who make brain injuries the cause of maladaptation overlook injuries or malformations of noncerebral organs and tissues. All this concerns so-called organic-behavior pathology. The difficulties of neural-cause theory is greatly multiplied when the *soi-disant* functional disorders are taken into account.

C. Psychoneural Functions as Participations

What we offer in the place of the emanation and cause constructions is the participating principle already so frequently referred to. To repeat: This principle signifies the isolation of the actual biological activities of the nervous system and the evaluation of their contribution to the response factor of an organism's interoperation with stimulus objects. No one should miss the point that the term *psychological function of the nervous system* is retained merely for comparison of views. As it turns out, the comparison is, of course, equivalent to a denial that there are any such functions in the traditional sense.

What the nervous system does on the participative basis is accorded its full value as a factor in a larger total event. In addition, to deprive nervous action of its accumulation of invented and ascribed powers is a primary step in giving it its full interpretive place in scientific description.

This chapter may fittingly be closed with a remark upon the claim of those who justify their belief in psychological brain functions on the ground that this belief has been productive of much valuable research. It is true that many scientific discoveries have been made on the basis of false beliefs. Furthermore, one may find some practical extenuation for illicit beliefs in the opportunities they provide for scientific work. Considerable psychological research has been made possible because some donor was interested in establishing the existence of supernatural entities. Poincaré comments on how useful the belief in astrology has been to humanity.

If Kepler and Tycho Brahe made a living, it was because they sold to naïve kings predictions founded on the conjunctions of the stars. If these princes had not been so credulous, we should perhaps still believe that nature obeys caprice, and we should still wallow in ignorance (497, p. 295 f.).

Granted that we can not control the exigencies of scientific development, and further that scientific progress has been made despite missteps and flagrant error, must we not still designate false beliefs as such after we unmask them, and further, avoid them, even if by accident they have led to good results? May we not expect better discoveries by substituting more valid hypotheses for poorer ones when contacts with events permit us to do so?

SECTION II

ANALYTIC SURVEY OF THE DATA
AND CONSTRUCTIONS OF
PHYSIOLOGICAL PSYCHOLOGY

CHAPTER 9

ANALYSIS OF SCIENTIFIC PHYSIOLOGICAL PSYCHOLOGY

IN this section we analyze P.P. as a scientific enterprise. Essentially we want to know the significance of the laboratory findings or other work done, including the resulting available constructions in P.P. Since it is possible in science for ascriptions and interpretations to be inversely related to the work performed we intend to investigate this relationship carefully.

Such an analysis involves the isolation of data factors and their scientific treatment. At the very least we must consider the materials worked upon and the techniques employed. For instance, what problem has the worker set himself? What are the assumptions basic to the work accomplished?— whether or not acknowledged.

Several hampering obstructions must be cleared away upon first approaching our task. Even if we limit ourselves to rigidly selected samples of P.P. researches, it is a formidable enterprise to achieve a proper coverage of the field. Also, taking into account the historical fact that P.P. has been the name for experimental psychology, and that it is articulated, even if not identified, with most of psychology, it is fairly impossible to draw effective boundaries for our study. Both of these difficulties we shall attempt to escape by (a) choosing for consideration nine general classes of problems (p. 124), and (b) examining books and articles not particularly classified under the P.P. heading.

TOOLS ESSENTIAL FOR SCIENTIFIC ANALYSIS

Before proceeding directly to our analysis it will be helpful to develop some significant tools. For this reason we suggest a brief examination of the important factors and procedures in scientific work.[1]

Crude or Preanalytic Data. All scientific investigation begins with some primary contact with crude data. A scientist becomes interested in some circumstance or event which involves a problem of existence, identification, quantity, analytic or synthetic constitution, relation, etc. A frequent and important sort of interest is the establishment of the existence or nonexistence of some alleged object or entity, as for example, an electromagnetic ether or an ether-drift. In some cases the crude data may stimulate the investigation of the identity of some object accidentally discovered, such as the mixture which Perkin afterwards identified as an analine dye. Or the problem may concern some later-to-be-identified object, organism or condition involved in some disease, a virus, or some sort of plant or animal organism, for instance. In psychological situations, of course, these crude or preanalytic data always consist of some interaction between an organism and a stimulus object.

Although the psychological interaction is in all general respects similar to any other kind of interaction isolated from the general continuum of events, there are obviously fundamental differential characteristics. It is these specific details which are of basic interest to the psychologist. As the accompanying diagram indicates (Fig. 1), the primary details consist of functions or operations of objects, organisms, and other event or field factors.

Scientific Investigation. Contacts with crude-data situations, the first step in the scientific process, are at once followed by various sorts of operational interactions. Some of the earliest of these investigative processes consist of the analytic isolation, arrangement, and classification of the crude data. From these contacts are derived the analytic data, which are then subjected to additional study. Further contacts with the analytic data are described as manipulation,

[1] Most of the material of this chapter has been taken from a previously published article (298).

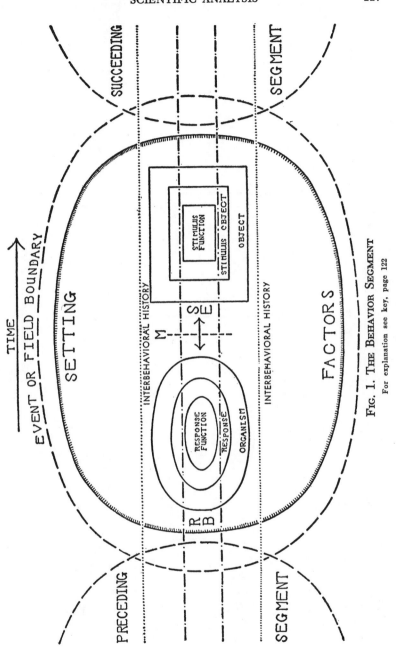

Fig. 1. The Behavior Segment
For explanation see key, page 122

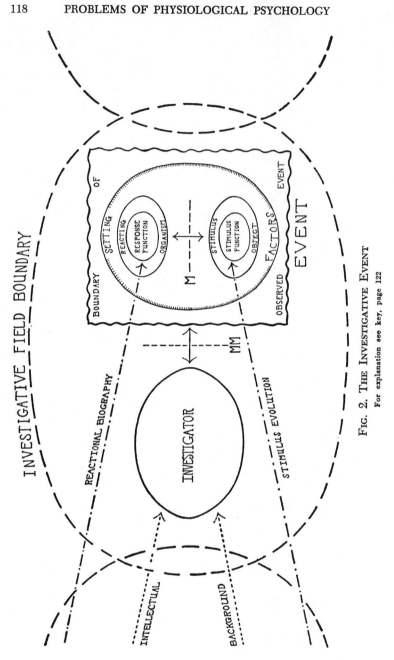

Fig. 2. The Investigative Event
For explanation see key, page 122

observation or examination of events, or their experimental handling either *in situ* or in the laboratory. Naturally the particular operational procedures (dissection, calcination, calculation, solution, weighing) depend upon the worker's type of interest, crude data, hypotheses set up, apparatus available, and general investigative equipment. The results of such investigative contacts with crude data form the content of the scientific protocol.

In short, the investigative phase of science may be summarized as a scientist's interbehavior with an event. For the psychologist it constitutes a scientific field in which the investigator interbehaves with the interbehavior of an organism and a stimulus object, which may, of course, be another person. The investigative event or field is illustrated by the diagram (Fig. 2) on the opposite page.

Scientific Construction. On the basis of such investigative contacts the scientist next constructs in series: (a) simple and complex descriptions of the events studied, and later, (b) interpretive and explanatory theories concerning these events in their interrelationship with still other events. It is hardly necessary to mention that from the event continuum one may isolate for study either (a) a unit event, (b) a thing, or (c) a cause or condition factor of an event.

Carefully to follow out this design for scientific work will aid in differentiating between (a) data or events, (b) investigative operations and procedure, and (c) various constructions, whether statistical, descriptive or interpretive. But there are also more specific advantages. For example, such a blueprint may assist in determining to what extent events are original or patinated—that is, endowed with the results of previous contacts with them. Since scientific contacts with events are generally preceded by various casual contacts, the question always arises how much the original events have been overlaid with properties attributable to such prior contacts. Obviously when possible such patination may be removed by various instruments and techniques. We should not overlook here the difficulties engendered by the properties accru-

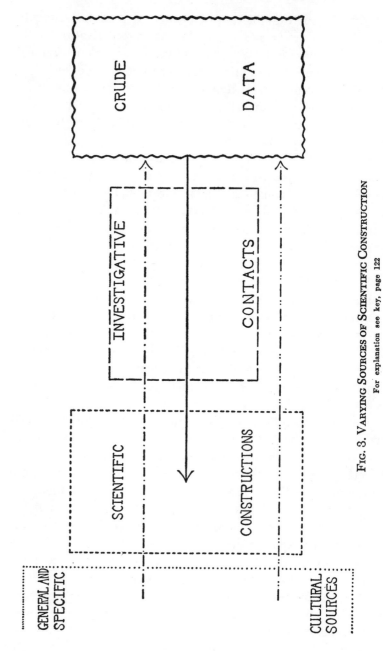

FIG. 3. VARYING SOURCES OF SCIENTIFIC CONSTRUCTION

For explanation see key, page 122

ing to data because of the types of apparatus and the techniques employed in specific investigations of events.

Perhaps a more important advantage is the service such a design renders in avoiding errors involved in the ascription of characteristics to events by custom and tradition whether or not complicated by actual prior contacts with them. In discussing the brain and nervous system we considered this point. In short, the scientific constructional problem is whether the descriptions and explanations are derived from the events through investigative processes, or whether they are imposed upon the events from sources partially investigative and partially or entirely traditional. Figure 3 illustrates these inexhaustive possibilities.

On the whole, constructions derived from events are likely to be legitimate, whereas those imposed upon events will only by the merest chance be anything but illegitimate and useless. When astronomers construct their descriptions on the basis of star and comet movements they are more likely to assert that their orbits are oblong or elliptical instead of circular, as they do when they start with the tradition of the perfect figure. When the physicist begins with falling bodies he is more likely to develop a law of the interaction of bodies in a field than when he simply applies to them the principle that bodies always act as they do because it is their inner or teleological nature to attain a prescribed goal. When psychologists construct their descriptions and theories from their observations of organisms interacting with objects they will hardly have a basis for the illegitimate concepts of psychic or physiological forces.

Applied to P.P. problems, the question is asked when observing a person acting whether it is a psychological or a physiological action or whether we merely ascribe the name to it. Again, how much do we endow the action by naming it in a certain way or by placing it in a certain class or group? Naming an action is a process depending upon direct or indirect interaction with it; thus we may be influenced in our studies by having previously named the crude datum.

KEY TO FIGURES

FIG. 1. THE BEHAVIOR SEGMENT

Although every factor in an event is equally important it may still be said that a psychological event or psychological interbehavior centers about the mutual interaction of stimulus and response functions, represented by the double headed arrow. These functions localized in the responses of organisms and stimulations of things (stimulus objects) become factors in psychological events when organisms and objects become interrelated in a behavioral field. This coming into contact of the object and organism marks the beginning of the interbehavioral history of the two. Under specific setting and mediating (M) circumstances this contact eventuates in the building up of response functions by the organism and stimulus functions by the object. This reaction evolution called reactional biography (RB) and stimulus function evolution (SE) may result in the unchanged successive reoccurrence of events or fields in time, or disappear through various interbehavioral conditions. In many instances it is proper to say that the original functions give place to other response and stimulus functions. While in the diagram both the interbehavioral history and the RB and SE lines continue through succeeding psychological events or behavior segments, at least the RB and SE lines should be broken off past the current behavior segment or interbehavioral field or event when particular response and stimulus functions disappear.*

FIG. 2. THE INVESTIGATIVE EVENT

Fundamentally the psychological investigative event constitutes the interbehavior of the investigator with a behavior segment or psychological event as diagrammed in Fig. 1. Just as the event investigated is conditioned by the interbehavioral history of the organism and object, so the investigator is more or less influenced by his antecedent intellectual background. This interaction of the investigator and the crude event is represented by the double headed arrow, an interaction which is further influenced by other factors in a field such as the general conditions prevailing in the investigative milieu as well as by MM, the particular instruments and techniques of investigation.

FIG. 3. VARYING SOURCES OF SCIENTIFIC CONSTRUCTION

The solid line with the arrow pointing to the left represents scientific construction derived from the crude data through investigative contacts. The other two lines indicate that the constructions are imposed upon the original or crude data either in conjunction with investigative tests or bypassing investigation altogether. In the former of these two cases some resemblance to scientific hypothesis is maintained, but none in the latter. Instead, the exclusive source of the constructions is the general and specific cultural background of the constructor. These three extreme possibilities suggest various constructional combinations resulting from varying components of investigative contacts and cultural influences.

* For a comprehensive treatment of the behavior segment in particular, and interbehavioral psychology in general, consult Kantor (289, 292, 297).

In general the value of this scientific model lies in the control it affords over the arbitrary factors in scientific work, whether in the (a) selection of data and problems, (b) setting up investigative techniques, or (c) constructing interpretations and theories. Basic to this entire design with respect to P.P. studies is the accent on specificity of observation and construction which leads to the following results.

A. On the side of Data.
    (1) Making certain of a definite event.
    (2) Distinguishing events from constructions.
    (3) Separating crude from analytic data.
    (4) Distinguishing between psychological and nonpsychological data, for example separating events belonging to the domains of psychology, biology, and physics.
    (5) Keeping psychological events or interactions distinct from phases of such events.
    (6) Specifically separating events from conditions.
B. On the side of Investigation.
    (1) Distinction between protocols obtained from psychological interbehavior with biological or psychological events.
    (2) Distinction between operations upon data and setting up demonstrations of accepted constructions.
    (3) Distinction between types of investigation and results of (a) biological and psychological studies, and (b) other events similarly named.
C. On the side of Construction.
    (1) Separating description from ascription.
    (2) Separating analogical statements from description of events.
    (3) Extrusion of constructions involving forces and powers, in favor of the interrelation of factors in a field.

With this brief sketch of the scientific enterprise before us we proceed to examine P.P. studies considering data, investigation, description, interpretation, and explanation.

We have already raised the question: How can we have irrelation between investigative work and constructions? Our scientific model provides an answer. The investigator may actually occupy himself with crude data or with the refined data of experimental investigation but still not employ his results in his constructions. For example, in studying a learning problem one is concerned with an organism in contact with numerous objects and conditions as field factors. Instead of building constructions, however, on such factors as a basis one builds around hypothetical traces or neural constructions.

TOPICAL ORGANIZATION OF THE PHYSIOLOGICAL PSYCHOLOGY FIELD

Because of the expansiveness of the P.P. field it is advisable to set up a series of departments for convenience of examination. The following arrangement of topical divisions may serve as a basis for examining the data and constructions involved. Needless to say this is only one of the many arrangements that might be employed. Certainly it does not avoid overlapping materials. Nor does it obviate stepping beyond the bounds of conventional treatments.

1. General Physiological Psychology

2. Sensory Physiopsychology

3. Psychophysiology

   a. Psychomotoric situations

   b. Psychovisceric situations

4. Psychoneurology

   a. Cerebrology

   b. Psychoneuropathology

5. Experimental Psychoneurology

6. Clinical Psychosurgery

7. Psychochemistry

8. Psychobiology

9. Psychosomatic Medicine

CHAPTER 10

GENERAL PHYSIOLOGICAL PSYCHOLOGY

THE DOMAIN OF PHYSIOLOGICAL PSYCHOLOGY

IT is our purpose in this chapter to survey critically the general field of current P.P. in order to ascertain: (1) the events studied, (2) the techniques of investigation, (3) the results achieved, and (4) the consequent interpretative constructions.

In the opening pages of this work we referred to the lack of clear-cut boundaries marking off P.P. as a distinctive domain. Certainly from a reading of the literature one can only conclude that the variety of investigations and array of constructions are not held together by a unique sort of event but by classical psychophysiological assumptions. Let us test our conclusion by attempting to locate the boundaries of P.P. on the basis of the outstanding criteria of a scientific enterprise.

The Data Criterion. At first glance there appears to be considerable merit in the view that P.P. is the study of the biological mechanisms of behavior. But since the nervous system for the most part is regarded as constituting the behavior mechanism, this view becomes inappropriate because it excludes investigations of drug effects, fatigue, hygienic conditions, and other data concerned with the relations of biological and psychological events. Again, the large place brain-extirpation studies with their negative findings occupy in the literature really indicates that P.P. is the study of what are *not* the mechanisms of behavior.

Other writers, influenced or not by the implication that the mechanisms idea still contains dualistic germs, emphatically declare that P.P. reflects a shifting toward objective and verifiable problems of action—in other words, "the organism's performance in relation to changes in the internal and external environment" (75, p. 453). If this were true, the data of P.P. would not be differentiated from those of any other branch of psychology. Cameron, the writer just quoted, goes on to say, however, that two of the most active P.P. fields are the major behavior disorders and central nervous-system functions. Aside from the classic neural-mechanisms conception it appears that the psychologist's interests or lines of work rather than definite type of data determine the scope of P.P.

The Methodological Criterion. Psychologists certainly can no longer accept Wundt's methodological definition of P.P. as experimental psychology, thus making the whole of psychology consist of two provinces, namely, P.P. and its counterpart, social psychology. Wundt's attempt to mark out the boundary of P.P. antedates such developments as (1) the view that all psychological science is experimental, and (2) the elaboration of a number of new specializations—for example, animal- comparative- abnormal- child- conditioning- and educational-psychology among others.

At the same time the growth of so many new areas of psychological investigation makes it impossible to mark off P.P. as a distinctive province on the basis of the criterion of pure and applied science. It is now generally recognized that investigation of events and use of achieved results are only reciprocal phases of one and the same enterprise. These two phases can not be held far apart on the assumption that one departs widely from the original events studied toward some remote domain of pure principles.

The Construction Criterion. Though we might expect that by employing the construction criterion we could adequately differentiate the P.P. province from others, this is not the case. On the contrary, in delineating the scope and boundary of P.P., current writers are more influenced by their general ideological presuppositions than by their contacts with specific kinds of events. Even though writers today no longer explicitly avow the ancient mind-body theory, the results of experimentation are presumed to illustrate some one of its many versions. In the meantime, the gross admixture of data and construction in P.P. literature prevents any clear-cut isolation of a characteristic investigative province.

How physiological psychologists avoid the old issues without really developing a new approach is exemplified by Liddell's recent introduction to a review of current P.P. literature.

Beyond a formal recognition of the philosophical problem of mind and body the chapter heading, Physiological Psychology, serves no purpose in what is to follow. In reviewing some of the many psychosomatic problems now being explored by physiologists, psychologists, and clinicians representing almost every medical specialty, no need arises for sorting out mental processes from various physiological functions observed in the same experimental situation (368, p. 487).

Notwithstanding the traditional influences which have brought about an unwholesome admixture of events and constructions it is still possible to discover the authentic province of P.P. After all, the tie that binds the domain into a distinct unit can be found in the relations of actual biological and psychological events. Although an examination of books and articles bearing the P.P. titles and a review of investigations obviously regarded as belonging to the P.P. domain do not lead us straight to our goal, they still make available the materials, which when refined provide the furnishings for an adequate P.P.

THE CONTENTS OF PHYSIOLOGICAL PSYCHOLOGY BOOKS

Students who vainly seek a strict formulation of the nature of current treatises fail because much of the contents of P.P. books consists of the same material as that contained in biological treatises. As much as two thirds of P.P. volumes are devoted to details which are in no sense integrated with the description of psychological events (151, 203, 332, 603). In short, the biological material comprises the facade for a building which does not exist.

There is, of course, the implication that these biological materials constitute mechanisms of psychological behavior, for example, when the nervous system is presumed to mediate the organism's adjustments to its environment. Such statements hardly conceal the intention to substitute neural mechanisms for mental causes and powers of action. Sometimes authors assume that the mechanisms are merely the organic factors of action. But the overwhelming stress of neural mechanisms does scant justice to the total organism. Skin, bones, and viscera, for instance, are not accorded their proper place in the entire behavior situation.

On the whole, such borrowing is motivated by the traditional philosophical conception that somehow the psychological (psychic) is rooted in or connected with natural things. In addition, there is the economic principle of supplying a demand. Since on the whole, P.P. is not really concerned with actual interactions of organisms with stimulus objects, and since psychological facts are considered unavailable because they transcend natural events, one provides what one can in the form of biological substitutes which are presumed to be just as good or better.

Possibly the inclusion of so much anatomy and physiology may be urged on the proper ground that students of psychology should know physiology. But does not this argument conceal the underlying mind-body bias? By all means, students of psychology should know mathematics, physics, biochemistry, and anthropology also, but such materials are not accorded the same importance. P.P. writings hardly give the impression that psychology is an independent science, the data of which do not require substitution by anatomical and physiological facts. One is forced to conclude that the preponderance of anatomy and physiology in P.P. treatises suggests that psychologists are not yet sure that psychology deals with authentic, natural events unencumbered by psychic states. Possibly psychologists are still dubious about the scientific nature of psychology (43, p. 314).

INVESTIGATIVE REPORTS IN PHYSIOLOGICAL PSYCHOLOGY

By contrast with P.P. books which cleave to the line of traditional psychology, and at least by implication reveal an acceptance or rejection of the perennial psychophysical dualism, investigative reports are more closely in tune with the events studied. Though the writers of such reports do not basically depart from traditional doctrine they do not let it obtrude too prominently. This fact is symptomatized by the larger coverage of topics than found in P.P. treatises, such as conditioning, learning, abnormal reactions and pathological personalities, sleep, pain and headaches, effect of menstruation, extirpation, electroencephalography, drug and hormone effects, etc., etc. The range of materials is well illustrated by various annual P.P. reviews (11, 493).

The more favorable aspect of investigative reports may be ascribed to the tacit acceptance of the hypothesis that, after all, P.P. is really the study of the relationship between biological and psychological events. Not that this hypothesis is ignored by book writers, and in fact is offered as a definition (151, 203), but in the end the events lose their influence in favor of basic presuppositions.

Here it is only fair to say that current P.P. treatises as well as research reports mark a general advance over their historical predecessors. Unfortunately this advance is largely owing to the neglect of basic presuppositions. Naturally the negativistic attitude of ignoring theory in both books and articles can have but limited scientific value, since theory is not only the guide to research but also a prerequisite for organizing and analyzing data. Now that many physiological psychologists have turned toward a behavioristic interpretation of psychological happenings, physiological materials are relatively better oriented in P.P. writings. For one thing, the descriptive functions of biological (especially neurological) processes are separated from the explanatory functions. Although current P.P. is still an assiduous industry designed to work out biological mechanisms, the claims of the original events are not so completely set aside as was formerly the case.

Howsoever faulty the neural-cause and determiner constructions may be, the constructors do not directly endow the events with nonnatural factors. The psychic processes earlier regarded as the determiners of psychological events are now substituted for. Today, neural factors or mechanisms are looked upon as intervening variables between the stimulation and response phases of the organism's action. Such intervening variables take the place of psychic causes as internal principles.

COALESCENCE OF NEUROLOGY AND PSYCHOLOGY

So elaborately do psychologists carry physiological materials into their domain that they even propose a union or coalescence of psychology and neurological physiology (353, 369). The following is a typical statement of this view.

The investigator of conditioned reflex action, unlike the neurophysiologist, is primarily concerned with the experimental animal as an individual and is prepared to expend the time and effort necessary to explore in physiological detail the effects on its behavior of maturation, aging and learning. His data must, however, be referred for eventual explanation to the operations of the central nervous system (369, p. 522).

The same writer however, admits:

. . . the experimenter in the field of animal behavior must derive his theoretical formulations from the data of interofective and exterofective action (369, p. 520).

He nevertheless does not give up his basic hope of eventual neural explanations.

When it is possible, in the same animal, directly to examine the functioning of its nervous tissue and at the same time to record the changing patterns of effector action resulting from conditioning, a comprehensive theory to account for learned behavior in terms of central nervous action and of effector action should be possible (369, p. 520).

Is it not significant that the neural theory requires to be harnessed to a hope, even in the case of animal-conditioned reflex experiments, a domain most favorable to the theory. What other conclusion than that we are here concerned with a dogma! And all the more powerful a dogma because it is derived from a metaphysical source and not from events.

Lashley has copiously demonstrated that behavior is independent of particular nerve cells; still he persists in believing that neural patterning implies a coalescence of neurology and psychology. He bases his argument on the correlation of complexity in behavior and neural functioning, and proposes to demonstrate this correlation by considering motivation and intellectual functions (353).

Motivation he treats as a problem of drives. Three variables contribute to the dominance of a behavior pattern. The first comprises specific hormones, which are presumed to increase the excitability of nonlocalized nervous organization. Granting that the claim can be substantiated, and that the neural factors and not the organism are primarily modified, would this be an adequate coverage of the motivation field?

The second variable he takes to be the changes induced by cortical destruction. Intensity of the sexual drive is reduced in proportion to the mutilation. This, of course, is a high-handed procedure, revealing no interest in or comparison of relative effects of neural and nonneural tissue destruction. Is there then sufficient evidence for a proper generalization?

The third variable is the adequacy of the stimulating situation. A rat rebuilds her nest after she has weaned her litter and returns to the nest a newly born rat if presented to her. In this case the description of a variation in intensity and excitability of a drive surely is independent of neural organization except as one chooses to impose neural interpretations.

With respect to intellectual behavior, Lashley presents a transparently arbitrary description of complex interbehavior as functions. What possible justification can there be for reducing thinking and intelligence to functions? As to neural action, doubtless there is some justification for assuming a corresponding complexity of neural action, as part of total complicated behavior, when comparing more and less elaborate performances. But what evidence of neurological and psychological coalescence do we have here? Instead, why not construct a coalescence of complexity of behavior with complexity of behavior situations including stimulus objects, settings, and behavior media?

Most assuredly, when all the factors of behavior situations are taken into account it is unnecessary to reduce complex action to neural patterns or to explain the organism's behavior or all interbehavior by physiological parts. If a mutilated animal performs less well than a normal one we must neither regard the unmutilated part as the cause of the better performance nor the mutilation as a destruction of resident powers or determiners.

Not only do internal neural principles not allow for the complex interoperation of organisms and stimulus objects, but they also exert a deleterious effect upon investigation. Recall merely the cerebral argument in conditioning.

Because Zeliony who worked in Pavlov's laboratory in 1912 (657) could not establish conditioned reflexes in decorticate dogs, Pavlov was certain that the seat of conditioned action was located in the cortex. Nor did he give up this belief when Poltyrev and Zeliony (499) did condition motor responses to auditory and visual stimuli in dogs, and Lebedinskaia and Rosenthal (361) achieved salivary responses to a metronome, because at autopsy small remnants of cortex were found. That this obdurance was not so much based on data as on theory is indicated by the fact that Pavlov's basic processes of irradiation and concentration could hardly have had scope for their operation in the small amount of remaining tissue.[1]

Today, it appears well established that decorticate dogs

---

[1] Pavlov's irradiation doctrine has been severely criticized by Loucks (382, 383).

and cats perform conditioned responses. Evidence of this sort has been presented by a long list of workers, for example, Ten Cate (592), Culler and Mettler. (100), Poltyrev (498), Girden, Mettler, Finch, and Culler (177), Zeliony and Kadykov (658), Dusser de Barenne (130), Bard (23), etc. The brain interpretation nevertheless is paramount. Hilgard and Marquis who very critically discuss Pavlov's general theory of cortical function still hold:

> The cortex remains important in normal conditioning, and, according to the principle of functional encephalization, its importance increases throughout the phylogenetic series to man (232, p. 335).

In abnormal conditioning, of course, the locus is generally regarded as still cerebral, though subcortical.

Psychological and Biological Events Compared

Despite (1) the fact that psychological events are always derived from a source which simultaneously also yields biological events and (2) the traditional identification and confusion of these two types of happenings, there is still no warrant for the coalescence conception. Instead, we need a careful differentiation of these two types of interbehavior.

Biological events always center about: (1) the operation of morphological organizations of cells and conditions which activate them, and (2) the interaction of organisms with their environing circumstances. The former type of biological event we may characterize as structure-function interaction, the latter as bioecological. By contrast, psychological events constitute forms of interbehavior evolved beyond or at a later level than the phylogenetic and ontogenetic evolution of organisms (293).

Structure-Function Interbehavior. Investigations of structure-function or physiological and embryological interbehavior are concerned primarily with tissue, organ, or system structures which operate on the basis of their organic evolution. Thus glandular cells secrete, muscle cells contract, bone cells support, etc. Clearly such investigations, though of the utmost importance for the understanding of the details of total organismic behavior, are best conducted on isolated preparations. Although organisms always act as total units, it is not only permissible but necessary to study particular structure-function operations to the neglect of other aspects.

The other factor of the biological interbehavioral event, called the stimulus, is described as the condition which is involved when the structure functions. No better definition of a biological stimulus exists than the one formulated by Adrian:

> Any change in the environment of an excitable tissue, which, if sufficiently intense, will excite the tissue, will cause it to display a characteristic activity (3).

Structure-function stimuli are general or indifferent; they may be thermal, mechanical, or electrical, requiring only that the intensity be adequate. In turn the structures do what their particular evolution demands. What variations in operation occur are conditioned by added circumstances such as fatigue or narcosis. The emphasis is on a discharge of energy, as exemplified by the all-or-none rule of nerve and muscle action.

Structure-function interbehavior is characterized not only by a definite specificity, but also by (a) relative automaticity, (b) constancy or invariability, (c) permanency, and (d) locality when the anatomy of the whole organism is taken into consideration.

Bioecological Interbehavior. The interbehavior of the total organism with environing conditions constitutes a series of adjustments on the basis of evolved structures and favorable or unfavorable survival conditions. Investigations of bioecological interbehavior yield data concerning the movements of animals corresponding to contrasts and changes in temperature, topological contours, presence or absence of food objects, adequate and inadequate respiratory conditions, etc. The emphasis in these instances is upon contingencies and variabilities in commutual organic and environmental relations.

Bioecological stimulation, therefore, can not be described as qualitatively indifferent (though quantitatively sufficient) conditions, but should be regarded as comprising complex factors. Respiratory conditions, for example, consist of definitely ascertainable compositions of air, and are not merely indifferent tissue excitants. Food objects bear a close relation to the various assorted tissue needs of the complex organism. Also to be taken account of are all sorts of organic modifications, habituations, and adaptations.

Psychological Interbehavior. The primary contrast between biological and psychological events is found in the historical development of psychological interbehavior in the life history of individuals. Psychological reactions, except in the comparatively rare and simple reflex actions, are not closely interrelated with biological structures, on the one side, and properties of things, on the other. For the rest, psychological events consist of more or less complicated interbehavioral fields (296). Responses are simply the locus of reaction functions of the total field. Similarly, stimulus objects operate functionally in the field. In addition there are the factors which mediate the entire interoperation, and also the setting factors corresponding with the specific response and stimulus functions.

The significance of response-function and stimulus-function constructions stands out when we realize that any response or stimulus may harbor many reaction and stimulus functions. Take the case of word responses in speech contexts. Such words as *stone* and *fast* have many response functions. Similarly, phrase and sentence responses operate differently in their uniquely appropriate situations. Again, with the same object may be connected many different sorts of stimulus functions according to the operational field. This is the case when the words just mentioned operate as stimulus objects. Is further evidence needed that psychological events are far less conditioned by structural organization than are biological events?

As in every scientific distinction the clearest case is presented by the extreme points on a continuum. In distinguishing between biological and psychological events, however, we must not overlook the indifference point—namely, those events where the criteria can not be unambiguously set up, such as in complex bioecological happenings. Such events, however, are not to be interpreted as neutral, that is, neither biological nor psychological. On the contrary, they are best described as an intermixture, viz., in part biological and in part psychological.

INDEPENDENCE OF PSYCHOLOGICAL EVENTS

Howsoever far P.P. has come toward the desirable goal of correlating biological and psychological events there still remains the view, as we have seen, that somehow psychological events are *subservient* to biological ones. Because all psychological events involve organic factors there is, to be sure, a genuine recognition that proper P.P. constructions adequately interrelate biological and psychological events. But what is further required is the realization that psychological interbehavior constitutes autonomous and independent events. While we must applaud those who on psychic grounds reject the plea of independence, we still condemn the solution resting on the coalescence or identifying principle. The independence of psychology is an obvious fact based on the nature of the crude or preanalytic psychological events, as Kantor (286, 289, 291, 292) has suggested. Upon somewhat other grounds Skinner has presented reinforcing evidence (561, 562) in defense of psychology as behavior independent of neural theory. There have likewise been suggestions for relieving learning theory and other specific phases of psychology from neural doctrine.

The independence doctrine has been sharply attacked, though in a curious way, by Loucks (384), who contrasts neural theory as internal with externalistic theory consisting of behavior. Though he admits that in learning studies the internal theory has not won its way unequivocally, he argues that in the case of emotions and delayed-reaction experiments, behavioral movements or overt responses do not yield differentiable or explanatory results; thus the internalistic view can not be discarded.

Louck's conclusion may be evaluated both as probable on his premises and beside the point altogether from the angle of the events involved. His premises imply that psychological actions must be described or explained as actions of the organism. He wants to correlate or contrast the central and peripheral phases of that action. It is questionable whether he is at all concerned with psychological behavior, which can hardly be minimally handled otherwise than as responses to stimulation.

We hope it is scarcely necessary to dissociate the sort of independence construction we have been discussing from that implicit in older physiological psychologists such as Bain, Spencer, Wundt, etc. As we have indicated before, it has always been realized that actually no evidence was forthcoming that psychological processes could be connected with physiological ones. This idea was based, of course, on the uncrossable chasm between the psychic and the physical, a clear expression of which is found in Titchener (599). But, as we have also seen, mentalistic psychology has always been obliged to resort to the nervous system to anchor mental states and keep them from floating off into diaphanous realms represented only by words.

We are forced to return to our original conclusion (p. 2 f.) that the general constructions of P.P. are dominated by philosophical theory. Of course, this philosophical theory is not a wittingly-adopted feature of some technical system, but rather a series of culturally-assimilated attitudes. If physiological psychologists free themselves from the charge of direct adherence to animistic doctrine they still are fettered by the tradition of internally and externally localized causes of the organism's behavior (449, 621-623).

CONSTRUCTIONAL CORRELATION OF BIOLOGICAL AND
PSYCHOLOGICAL EVENTS

Granting that we can properly distinguish biological and psychological events, we may then construct conceptions concerning their relation. It is to be expected, of course, that any construction depends upon the constructor's prior conceptions concerning the factors to be related. The following four constructional types represent the predominant ways in which psychologists treat this problem.

Analogic Constructions. The most general and freest conception of a relationship between biological and psychological events treats them simply as analogous. Descriptions are made in the form of diagrams which are presumed to map and represent psychological events. The correlation is based primarily on the fact that organisms are concerned in psychological situations. The numerous diagrams presumed to describe the biological analogues of conditioning and learning exemplify such constructions.

Excellent examples of such analogies are found in the attempts to relate summations and inhibitions of behavior with synaptic mechanisms worked out with physiological preparations. The most recent instance is the use of Lorente de No's (379) findings concerning the recurrent nervous circuit to describe complexities of total organismic psychological behavior (353).

The most serious criticism of such analogies is that the constructors talk biology whether actually descriptive or hypothetical, with the presumption that there is somehow a relationship with psychological events. The most favorable conclusion concerning such analogical construction likens it to the process of fitting a curve to data. Recent attempts to develop mathematical descriptions of biological occurrences with the assumed implication for psychological events constitute the extremes of such analogizing effects.

Propinquity Constructions. Less creational constructions are those based on a simple association or correlation between the two types of events. In one phase it is believed that what happens to biological events also happens to psychological. But there is another aspect of propinquity constructions which assumes that one type determines the other. The best examples here are drug and fatigue effects which match decreased efficiency of psychological performance. These examples illustrate the correlation of whole biological and whole psychological events. But sometimes isolated biological facts, such as those primarily concerned with neural action, are presumed wholly to determine psychological performances.

Symptomatic Construction. In this type of construction some sort of identity between the two kinds of events is assumed. Whatever biological facts are handled are regarded as factors abstracted from the total. Thus neural or muscular incidents are taken as symptomatic of the larger total event, and are presumed to give a descriptive or predictive insight into the whole psychological happening.

An important implication of the symptomatic type of construction is that psychological events are somehow interpreted as complications or integrations of biological events. When one is concerned with simple and localized physiological happenings, then they are regarded as biological. When these are highly integrated they are presumed to become psychological. In a broad and general way the constructors of such correlations assume that complex voluntary, intellectual and thought happenings are complicated integrations of simple bodily reaction.

Participative Construction. Such a construction centers around the participation of biological factors in total psychological-field events. Basic here, one recalls, is the interbehavioral principle that psychological events are not localizable alone in the activities of organisms but constitute field situations in which there are many other factors. Biological activities are thus localizable as factors in the organism's contribution to the total event. There is no implication that the organism operates only in psychological fields; the participative construction, however, concerns only such fields.

CONSEQUENCES OF SYSTEMATIC CONSTRUCTIONS IN PHYSIOLOGICAL PSYCHOLOGY

Up to this point we have considered the detailed features of P.P. But what are the overall or systematic results of such a survey as we have been making? The literature on P.P. points to the evolution of systematic constructions, which, unfortunately, do not redound to the advantage of the science as a whole. Because P.P. originated as the experimental side of dualistic psychology, and because it has since developed with a strong dependence upon biological factors, it has increasingly become a body of limiting and determining principles rather than a department of work concerned with a particular type of data and investigative techniques.

An outstanding consequence of the systematic constructions of P.P. is the overemphasis of animal investigation, with a corresponding lack of development in the study of human behavior. Even when human activity is handled, the emphasis is upon simple actions which can somehow be attached to physiological processes.

These consequences are already inherent in Wundt's *Grundzüge*. Because experimentation began under physiological auspices and perhaps (in the early days of experimentation) was facilitated by adherence to physiological processes, Wundt, as we have seen (p. 126) drew a sharp line between physiological and social psychology. All complex human behavior was relegated to the latter department. For such an animistic psychologist as .Wundt, complex human activities could readily be considered as only distantly related to the organic. His argument was simple. There is no social mind because there is no social body to connect it with. Nevertheless, his thinking was shot through with the psychophysiological bias. This bias, supported by the historical fact that early experimentation concerned sensory processes, is responsible for the neglect of complex human behavior.

In our historical review we suggested that although Wundt was mistaken about our inability to experiment on social-psychological problems, he also erred in believing that experiments somehow made psychology scientific. The difficulty here is that experiments conditioned by a certain time period, in this case the experiments of the physiologist, are made a criterion for psychological activities. This view may be described as experimentation *a outrance*. From Wundt's time to the present, psychologists have overlooked the fact that experiments must be made for psychological events and that psychological events should not be contorted to fit the experiments.

How else account for the unhappy result that psychologists rule out a great many psychological events from the program of laboratory attack simply because such events are not subject to traditional experimentation based on sensory physiology or conditioning. Aside from the usual fashions in scientific work, the stress of "biological" principles has been responsible for the view that all learning consists of conditioning.

SPECIFIC SURVEY RESULTS: SUMMARY

The general undesirable sequelae of systematic construction in P.P. stand beside the more specific difficulties which we have pointed out from time to time. By way of summarizing the situation in general P.P. we indicate some points concerning data, investigation, and interpretation which require emendation.

Data. The literature of P.P. certainly shows lack of clarity concerning data. Physiological data are not distinguished from psychological data, nor are P.P. data separated clearly from other psychological types. Now where data are not distinguished they are, of course, confused. Not only are crude and refined data mixed, but crude data of psychology are confused with refined data of physiology or other sciences. Confusion of crude and analytic data, as well as the admixture of psychological and physiological data, is well illustrated in a statement of Woodworth's designed to show the relations between physiology and psychology and to avoid a mind-body problem.

> Where the psychologist speaks of eating one's dinner, the physiologist, more analytically, speaks of the contraction of certain muscles under the excitation of certain nerves, etc., but he is describing the same identical process as the psychologist. When the psychologist speaks of seeing the color blue, the physiologist speaks of processes in the retina, the optic nerve and its brain connections. There is no doubt, to my mind, that seeing blue is identically the same process as that which the physiologist describes. If he were able to give a much more complete analytical description than is possible today, he would not, to be sure, ever find the color blue as an experience, just because that experience is the total process which he is breaking up into parts (639, p. 335).

When the psychologist speaks of eating one's dinner and seeing blue he is merely speaking *non ex cathedra*. Surely both physiologists and psychologists start at that level. But as scientists, both must proceed at once to develop more precise descriptions on the basis of manipulation and analysis. What then in the psychologist's description corresponds to the physiologist's analytic handling of muscle contraction and nerve conduction? If the psychologist stands by experience as total processes he has no refined data. But if sensations of blue are taken as refined data, as is actually done, they are treated as psychic results of what the physiologists have analyzed (286).

Investigation. Similarly, there are numerous confusions on the investigative level. Many studies which throw only vague light on general behavior—such as no action vs. action in the case of anesthetics, or when convulsive or tetanic action is induced—hardly qualify as psychological projects. At best they are bioecological. Surely a number of such investigations in the animal domain can only be classified as psychology on the basis of putting both psychological and physiological actions under the rubric of behavior.

Construction. Bad assumptions in science are seldom as damaging as uncritically accepted assumptions. When investigators insist upn maintaining contact with original events uncontaminated with tradition, their errors in the end are self-corrective. Examples of permanently harmful presuppositions in P.P. are the persistent traditional postulates concerning the biological basis of mental life and the supremacy of biological or cortical factors in psychological performances.

Chapter 11

SENSORY PHYSIOPSYCHOLOGY (I)

Sensory Physiology and Discriminative Interbehavior

THE inordinate amount of P.P. literature devoted to the physiological and psychic character of sensory processes —the latter euphemistically labeled experience—can be accounted for on several grounds. In the first place, sensory physiopsychology has always been the central motif in the pattern of psychophysical tradition. We have learned from our historical survey in Chapter 2 how this pattern originated from the epistemological problems of spiritistic philosophy. Precisely because sensory physiopsychology is so deeply rooted in our intellectual culture and is also the oldest branch of P.P., it is the most standard and presumably the most solidly established.

It is undeniable, however, that this branch of P.P. encompasses many more troublesome problems than acceptable facts. This situation prevails because, although the constructions of sensory physiology are universally assumed to be derived from the crude data of object discrimination, actually they stem from metaphysical origins.

Illustrations of the serious problems of sensory physiology are found in the following questions. Do the descriptions and interpretations of P.P. articulate with the data of actual perceiving? Can the construction of sense avenues, with all that it implies, be interrelated with the objective events comprising discrimination adjustments? Another problem concerns the relationship of psychology and physiology. How can local physiological processes be connected with psychological events?

Of course, such well-established physiological constructions as the all-or-none law of neural and muscular discharge and the refractory period of neural conduction can be harmoniously integrated with objective constructions of sensory

144

discriminations. But in other respects the incongruities are glaring. So troublesome are the problems that it is even hard to allocate the data and investigative task. Some psychologists assert that sensory physiology is mostly psychology (128, p. 67); others interested in reducing psychology to physiology declare that it is indifferent whether we call sensation (sensory) studies physiological or psychological (501, p. 132). It follows, therefore, that an important expository feature of this department of P.P. comprises the anatomical description of receptors or end organs and a discussion of the hypothetical functioning of the anatomical parts.

In addition, sensory physiopsychological discussions are heavily loaded with philosophical theory concerning the localization, mediation, and production of psychic processes. Behavioristically-inclined writers, of course, simply omit the psychic, though they do not in any important particular vary their expositions. Certainly a complete working over of this area is necessary. For one thing, we should attempt to eliminate such a paradox as the declaration that while "there is almost no satisfactory physiological theory of sensory quality" (47, p. 503) sensory physiology is one of the most scientific departments of psychology. A basis for this paradox we find in such a statement as the following:

. . . when an organism is making a qualitative discrimination it is distinguishing between the excitation of one system of nerve fibres and another system (47, p. 503).

Sensory physiopsychology constitutes a complex system of particular elements. These elements consist of special constructions for describing and interpreting the details of interaction. Since the elements are abstracted from both the organism and the stimulus objects, a pattern for examining physiopsychology can be found in the following arrangement of topics: (a) the stimulus, (b) the receptor, (c) afferent conduction, (d) central conduction and termination, (e) efferent conduction, and (f) effector action.

The Stimulus and Stimulation

In spite of the fact that psychologists employ at least four widely different stimulus constructions, we may still refer to a standard P.P. concept of stimulus. Briefly, it is physiological in character. The general assumption is that the organism's receptors are impinged upon by various conditions or energies which result in certain psychic effects. In line with tradition, P.P. writers are primarily concerned with electromagnetic radiation for vision, air waves for hearing, chemical substances for smell and taste, and mechanical contacts for touch and pressure.

In the P.P. domain, stimuli are primarily regarded as excitations of sensory qualities and conscious processes or experience. So far as the response is concerned, physiological psychologists must, of course, depart from the general physiological viewpoint which stresses tissue action such as contracting, conducting, secreting. Though physiologists are not professionally called upon to talk about corresponding sensations or psychic processes they nevertheless indulge in such behavior. Physiological psychologists, however, universally look upon stimuli as radiation or physical conditions correlated with sensation or sensory quality. The stimuli are presumed to induce changes in the nervous system, especially the brain, which result in sensory qualities. For example, color:

. . . does not come into being until physiological processes have been aroused in the nervous system (506, p. 523 f.).

Likewise in a recent treatise on vision we find an exemplary statement concerning the alleged operation of the nervous system after stimulation.

Although much accurate information has been accumulated with reference to color, very little as yet can be said with regard to what must happen in the nervous system to produce color (26, p. 15).

Physical Stimulation and Sensory Qualities. What factual

basis is there for simply correlating physical stimulation and sensory qualities? Nothing more than the general biological correlation of organism and environment. This simple fact, which lends no ground whatever to any conception of sensory qualities aroused or produced in the organism, has under the influence of traditional philosophical assumptions been violently distorted to yield sensory physiopsychological constructions. The attempt to correlate physical factors such as vibrations or energy changes with sensory qualities is obviously designed to coordinate mental and physical existents. Visual-discrimination interbehavior involves light; auditory interactions require air factors, but these facts can be completely taken into account without the transformative procedure of making such physical factors into simple conditions for creating sense qualities through the excitation of anatomical tissues. The physiological-stimulus construction at once reveals its autistic character and its total lack of descriptive and interpretative value for handling the events of organism-environment interaction.

Discoordination of Physiological Stimulus and Sense Qualities. Scientific investigation reveals no fixed correlation between any sort of energy stimulus and sensory quality. If we consider only the most favorable field—namely, visual behavior—the homogeneous light rays which the physiological-stimulus construction calls for are lacking. The idea of monochromatic light is a pure construction.

Light in which we have but a single wave-length is said to be monochromatic. It must be remembered, however, that strictly monochromatic light involves an infinite train of waves, such as would emanate from a particle the vibrations of which were subject to no sudden or gradual change of phase. Arbitrarily homogeneous or monochromatic light is something that has no actual existence, though we are accustomed to speak of light that the spectroscope shows as a single narrow line as monochromatic. The color depends upon the wave-length, but the color cannot always be taken as an indication of wave-length, as certain colors can be imitated by the simultaneous action upon the retina of two trains of waves, either of which action alone would give rise to a totally different color from that perceived when both act together. For example, a yellow scarcely distinguishable from the yellow of the sodium flame can be produced by a mixture of red and green light in the proper proportions. A screen can be easily prepared which transmits red and green only and in about the right proportions to produce the sensation of subjective yellow, as it is called (638, pp. 11-12).

Again, physiological psychologists have had forced upon them that the stimulus even in the case of vision can not be described in terms of wave lengths alone but must include energy value. The fact that the quantity of radiant energy reaching the unit area in a given time is so great suggests the complexity of the stimulus. And indeed the stimulus is always so complex that we really have no definite factor with which to correlate anything. Consider how the difficulties are magnified when we think of reactions to a multicolored painting. Adding the textual and compositional factors we leave far behind any possible retinal-point stimulation construction and come to objects. Here the simple analogical stimulus construction is of no possible value.

Actually the facts originally supposed to be explained by the physiological-stimulus construction have fallen away. We have just indicated that there is no universal one-one correlation between color qualities and wave length. For example, there is no single wave length for the purples, whereas orange can be correlated with one wave length or a combination of several. Nor may we lose sight of the fact that correlations of light rays with qualities are predicated upon focussed light, while the eye is always stimulated in light reactions by stray or scattered light as well. Though this fact does not affect the construction of simplified correlations between colors and wave lengths or frequencies it certainly lends no support to the physiological-stimulus construction. On the contrary, it exposes the great gap between this abstracted and over-simplified construction and the facts it is designed to describe.

As a final consideration of the physiological-stimulus construction we confront it with the evidence from electrical recordings of retinal responses. Working with various animals, physiological psychologists (188-190) have observed that the potential records taken from the retina when stimulated by various wave lengths show no differences. The conclusion therefore seems warranted that the retinal end-organs indicate no qualitative differences of excitation by different wave-length stimulation. That such results if established, as against others showing opposite effects (323), make no dent in accepted P.P. theories, is one more tribute to the power of scientific tradition. What physiologists and physiological psychologists do is to assume that quantitative differences must be available, which though not in line with the findings of neural conduction are correlated with psychic qualities mediated by the cortex (211).

Sources of Sensory-Quality Construction. An analysis of P.P. doctrines yields two sources of sense-quality construction. The first is the abstractionistic operations upon things and organisms and the second the wholesale borrowing from other sciences.

(a) *Abstractions from things.* In view of the obvious fact that the psychologist begins with the crude data of interaction between organisms and objects, he derives sensory qualities by abstracting from things such qualities as colors, shapes, sizes, sounds, intensities, contrasts, etc., and putting them into the psychic domain. Instead of describing the organism's interaction with objects possessing such qualities and properties he reduces the objects to vibrations and energies. Hence the qualities can only be recovered by having them produced or created by the brain.

(b) *Abstractions from organisms.* Constructions of psychic-qualities are also derived from the activities of the organism itself. The procedure is to place pain, pressure, nausea and other so-called organic qualities on a continuum with color, sound, etc. As we shall see (p. 280), this procedure has influenced physiological psychologists to reduce things to stimulations.

(c) *Scientific importation.* A second important source of

P.P. construction is borrowing from other sciences. The physicist, for example, isolates spectral colors and correlates them with wave frequencies, sounds with air waves. While such isolations and correlations are in strict line with scientific procedure and of greatest importance they cannot be carried over into the psychological domain. This is always done by associating such borrowing with another type of free construction, so that the brain and nervous system are made to create the qualities.

Stimuli and Interactional Media. Actually the proper description of the interbehavior of an organism with stimulus objects is far removed from the physiological-stimulus construction. It implies a treatment of the organism's activities and of the objects in a field. As the writer has pointed out elsewhere (286, 289, 292, 297) what is called the stimulus in P.P. constructions really constitutes media of contact between organisms and objects. The physiological-stimulus construction as a result has nothing to do with the perception of objects, but is concerned with a correlated construction of sensation or sensory qualities. For this reason even structuralistic psychologists are beginning to realize that there is no distinction between perception and sensation (44, p. 6). Though the physiological psychologist increasingly acknowledges that he is working with an interaction between the organism and stimulus objects, even when those stimulus objects are simple color patches, he still fashions his constructional tools on the basis of the borrowed abstractions we have mentioned. There is, in other words, a constant reversion to atomistic sensations.

Stimulus and Stimulation. An interesting variant of the physiological conception of stimulus localizes the stimulus in some physiological process. Stimulus becomes, then, stimulation or excitation, a phase of the individual's activity (522, p. 29). This type of construction, briefly considered in paragraph (b) above, may be traced back directly to the Fechnerian conception of inner psychophysics.

Stimulus and Object Constancy. If, as we claim, psychological events as crude data consist of interactions between organisms and objects, is it possible then to relate these data to a description of how energy-changes cause the creation of qualities? For the most part, of course, physiological psychologists are content with the purely analogical function of their descriptions. But there are many instances when they can not escape being troubled by their analogies. The problem of stimulus constancy is a notable instance.

Actually, organisms interact with *objects* and their *properties*, instead of the way they should on the basis of the "stimuli they receive." The discoordination of stimulus construction and the facts of interaction comprise, of course, an old problem. Recall the paradox of inverted retinal imagery, the tridimensional perception of bidimensional retinal distribution, etc. Nevertheless, the improbability of the physiological-stimulus construction is not recognized. In fact, spiritualistic epistemology has influenced psychologists to turn more and more to the brain-creation view.

The ineptitude of the physical-stimulus construction is similarly revealed in illusion facts, in which the objects are reacted to not as they are, but as they seem to be. The difference between constancy and illusion obviously does not show any more correlation between physical stimulus and response, but it does bring to light setting factors and their influence on interbehavior.

Even before modern technical psychologists became interested in the problem, philosophers made much of the facts that varying illumination, angle of vision, change in relative position of perceiver and object, which presumably result in different stimuli, do not do away with or alter the object reacted to. Who could ask for a clearer demonstration of the different types of construction and the obvious inferiority of the physiological-stimulus conception!

We have already referred to Helmholtz's invocation of unconscious judgments to account for object constancy. In more recent times, psychologists have resorted to such *ad hoc* theories as the regression of phenomenological objects to or toward the real objects (595) to account for size and shape constancy. Aside from the introduction of the phenomenological construction such theories are only verbal descriptions of the original fact that persons are interacting with things. Since such psychologists can not depart from the traditional stimulus theory, they constantly interchange their technical descriptions with descriptions of crude data.

As a final comparison of the datum and tradition influence on stimulus construction we consider the studies of the Gestalt psychologists on form and shape objects. Their experiments obviously concern interbehavior with objects on the basis of definite interdependence conditions, but they do not depart from the elementaristic construction of sense avenues. They simply invent autistic organic constructions concerning the totalitarian operation of brain configurations.

The only conclusion to be drawn concerning standard P.P. stimulus construction is that it originates from a purely philosophical and not an investigational source. The physiological psychologist has built up this construction on the analogy of the physiological stimulus in order to bolster up some sensation or phenomenology doctrine. Now since psychic-process doctrines constitute special types of abstraction with no counterpart in nature, the analogical borrowing adds nothing to the advancement of psychology as a science, and in itself is futile.

RECEPTOR ACTION

The Receptor Construction. The sole crude-datum basis for the receptor construction consists of the fact that organisms have evolved special contact structures for interacting with particular aspects of things. But such crude data are ignored in favor of traditional ideas of sense avenues with specific mediatory functions. As the name implies, the nervous system is presumed to be fitted with end-organs which receive isolated and specialized stimuli. Instead of considering the organism as the unitary animal that it is, sensory-physiopsychological constructions imply that it is a system of points, each with its own specialized function.

But what does the end-organ receive? The conventional answer for vision is specialized radiation or energy which is transmuted into a neural process presumed to result in some sensory process, after transmission to a cerebral center. By the operation of a number of such receptors and their related neural elements, the isolated qualities somehow become synthesized to form phenomenological or psychic objects. Though psychologists are wary in their statements, physiologists do not hesitate to say that the qualities called sensations are projected:

> . . . either to the exterior of the body or to some peripheral organ in the body, the effort being apparently to project them to the place where experience has taught us that the acting stimulus arises (240, p. 272).

For the most part, psychologists are content to assert the existence of the objects.

Such elementaristic conceptions persist despite all lack of correspondence with behavioral data. In the case of the retina, for example, one may assume a bombardment by longwave lengths of light—say, those corresponding to red—but while no other receptors are operating one is interacting with a red ball. How much more complicated and unaccountable is the interaction with a catalogue picture of a varicolored and varishaped tulip field! Apparently the cones and rods of the visual receptor do far more than traditional concepts allow.

On the other hand, where are the specialized receptors for particular wave lengths? Writers like Hecht (211) and Troland (602, 603) who adopt a three-component color theory can not find, but only assume, three kinds of cones, each differentiated for one hue. This they do because while one optic fiber may be connected with several cones, no cone has more than one fiber. Unfortunately this heroic attempt to hypothesize anatomical structures, that will receive sufficiently little stimulation, is frustrated by the lack of differentiation in the impulses traveling away from the retina. As usual, a way out is sought in the magical operation of the brain. Such is the final compensation for all the effort to construct physiological mechanisms for sensory processes!

Lack of correlation between visual receptors and stimulation or sensory qualities is similar in all complex or distance avenues or modalities. While the organ of Corti is complex enough to assume a selective differential response with many air-wave frequencies, it is still impossible to correlate the receptor with complex sounds. And, too, for all receptors there is the afferent-conduction difficulty.

No one can object to various isolated correspondences between hue and wave frequency or between pitch and air-wave frequency, but when the operation of receptors as mediators and gateways of sense avenues are in question, we are more involved with traditional ideas of specifically anatomical and physiological action than with actual inter-behavioral data. Take the case of the comparatively simple cutaneous senses. If anywhere, we should be able to discover satisfactory facts of correlation between pain, temperature, pressure, and receptor organs. That this is impossible is indicated by the following detailed items.

(1) Von Frey's original classical establishment of the correlation of cutaneous sensation and receptors was obviously made on the basis of epistemological theory. To begin with, he never considered the interbehavioral events, but drove straight for physiological and psychic elements. Thus he selectively reduced cutaneous qualities to four—warmth, cold, pressure, and pain. Then by various indirect arguments he correlated each with some anatomical organ (48, p. 470).

As Boring (48, p. 471) points out, Von Frey's correlation of warmth and cold with Ruffini and Krause structures respectively had already been obviated by the findings of Donaldson (122) and Goldscheider (179, 180) that only free nerve endings could be found beneath touch and warm-skin spots. Since that time a series of workers (103, 198, 340, 482) have adduced histological evidence confirming the non-correlation of specific receptors with warmth and cold. These findings, however, are not undisputed. Weddell (619) is convinced on histological grounds that Krause's end-bulbs are correlated with cold.

(2) For pain, regarded as unique sense qualities, there are no organized receptors. Free nerve endings are themselves considered as receptors. On the other hand, various workers doubt whether the facts of pain indicate any single isolated sensation qualities such as tradition has ascribed to the mediating action of organized receptors. Livingston (373, p. 42), on the basis of a large clinical experience, asserts that pain like all "sensation" is a perception, and that no matter how pure a "sensation" may appear to be, its underlying impulses represent a composite arising from more than one end organ.

(3) Where only free nerve endings are found, as in the central portion of the cornea of the eye, there is not only a locus for pain but for touch or pressure also (180, 373, 459; 460, p. 38). This fact is a powerful obstacle to the correlating tradition, and suggests also that the work on physiology and psychology of the senses has been unduly influenced by the elementaristic dogma of sensations and anatomical organs.

(4) From the histological standpoint it is interesting that the gradations between the most widely separated end organs are such as to exclude the kind of structural differentiation necessary for specialized functions. Sheehan writes:

Between the largest Pacinian corpuscles that are plainly visible to the naked eye and those of Golgi-Mazzoni which can be detected only with the miscoscrope, there is an uninterrupted series of intermediate and transitional forms. And from the so-called genital corpuscles there is a further gradual transition to the more elaborate corpuscles as described by Golgi and Mazzoni. Thus we have to remember, in ascribing any particular function to one type of end-organ, that there are all grades of corpuscles between the typical Pacinian and the other similar lamellated corpuscles (545, p. 411).

(5) Even those who accept the hypothesis of punctate distribution and the generally sharp differentiation between receptor action can not agree concerning the correlation of quality and receptor. Thus Waterston (616) regards Meissner's corpuscles as subserving pain as well as touch, while Fulton following Woolard, Weddell, and Harpman (643), argues that pain can not be evoked from them.

Indeed one can insert a needle into one of these corpuscles and so cause internal stimulation without evoking conscious sensation other than that of touch and pressure (161, p. 6).

On the other hand, in a recent review of cutaneous research Stone and Jenkins (584) report that Bourgignon (51) for the first time in history connects Meissnerian corpuscles as well as free nerve endings with temperature sensitivity. Fulton (160, p. 6) writes of the principles of specificity of sensory perception from individual end organs as though that were Bell and Müller's theory of specific nerve energies, though it is clear that these writers were not so elementaristic as not to include the nerves and brain. In dealing with the specific-energies doctrine it is probably well always to stress the organismic view implied in these early writers. Certainly it is helpful to emphasize the analytic procedure to which the physiologist always resorts.

(6) Though cutaneous quality correlations have been developed on the basis of correspondence of receptor action and general external-stimulus conditions as well as organic action (pain), the former sort of correlation is not agreed upon. Thus Woolard, though a believer in end-organ specificity, comments:

It is difficult to imagine why there should be separate receptors for heat and cold, since these differ only in molecular velocity (642).

Dallenbach (104), however, does not regard molecular velocity as the direct stimulus for cold and warmth but rather a change in the temperature of the receptor.

To be mentioned here also is Nafe's hypothesis that cutaneous sensations are mediated not by specific end organs in the skin, but by the discharge of patterns of sensory nerve endings under the influence of the smooth muscles of peripheral blood vessels. For example, sensations of warmth depend upon relaxation and cold upon contraction of vascular muscles of the skin (457, 458).

(7) Writers on the historical development of sensory physiopsychology point out that despite the undisputed evidence which Head's cutaneous nerve-section experiments (204) show in favor of patterns of afferent excitation instead of discrete reception, the latter view remains the favored doctrine. This is, of course, nothing but expansive tribute to traditional philosophy. Nerve regeneration signifies that warm and cold reactions as well as pain and touch are temporally differentiated. Whether or not one should adopt Head's two systems of protopathic and epicritic fibers, his evidence certainly demands a serious questioning of the conventional constructions concerning cutaneous qualities and their receptorial mediation.

It may not be inappropriate to suggest that the slight effect which the work of Head and his collaborators has had upon psychological thinking concerning cutaneous sensory events is in some part, at least, owing to the fact that these workers, after all, adhere to conventional psychophysical tradition. Head's theory concerns only peripheral mediation mechanisms for psychic qualities. He denies special peripheral physiological activities corresponding to primary sensation (204, p. 831). For him, the qualities of pain, heat, and cold are abstractionistic sensations which are modified by the central nervous system. Though he approaches the view that cutaneous facts are ways in which the organism responds to things and conditions, he does not escape the dualistic prejudice of mental or psychic qualities.

(8) So confused and contradictory is the literature on receptor action as to lend special point to Nafe's conclusion.

After fifty years of investigation we have no demonstrated correlation between any particular type of sensitivity and the specialized end-organs and fibres that subserve it (458, p. 1041).

AFFERENT CONDUCTION

The facts and problems of neural conduction constitute excellent criteria for examining sensory physiopsycholoigcal constructions. Physiological psychologists make a great effort to correlate the atomistic and specialistic elements of centripetal conduction with sensation qualities. On this basis they elaborate constructions for the interpretation of the complex interbehavior of all sorts of organisms including the human. In the latter case they concern themselves with the problem of how neural fibers convey experience (444, p. 265). Unfortunately, even in the purely physiological facts of conduction—that is, facts elicited from preparations employed in the study of the lower organisms—we find strong evidence of the impropriety of attempting to correlate qualities with neural impulses.

Two procedures especially characterize this kind of correlational construction. In the first place, the constructors set aside the complex activity of organisms, and in the second, they push at all cost and with disregard of evidence the philosophical theory of specific energies. The magnitude of their efforts may be easily gauged by the paucity of proof for any functional differentiation of neural conduction.

In view of the great complexity of neural organization we should expect great anatomical and physiological variations in neuron units as well as in neuron systems. With the aid of recently developed electronic techniques, these variations are being isolated and described. In 1911 Ranson (510) showed that there are nonmedulated fibers in spinal sensory nerves, and in 1931 (513) demonstrated that they exist in large numbers in most cutaneous nerves. Since then, Gasser, Erlanger and others (134, 134a, 135; 161, ch. 4; 170) differentiated between sensory fibers on the basis of size, rate of conduction, and sensitivity to stimulation. The smaller the fiber the slower the conduction and the greater the stimulation required to activate them. This differentiation has been elaborated, so that in the cutaneous nerves three types of fibers named A, B, and C are recognized. The A fibers are the largest and most thickly myelinated, most rapid in conduction, carry a longer impulse, and are most sensitive. The B fibers are less thickly myelinated and more moderate in the other characteristics as compared with the A fibers. C fibers are unmyelinated and show the slowest impulses. Similar differentiation of fibers has been described for the optic and other nerves (36).

Moved by the force of the philosophical tradition that the nerves mediate or produce qualities, physiological psychologists and physiologists have attempted to correlate such differences with sensory "functions." The results are disappointing. It is inevitable that the focus of interest should be cutaneous, and especially pain, functions. In the early days of fiber differentiation it was believed that correlations could be made between fiber size and sensation. For example, Ranson in 1933 wrote:

It is also becoming clear that the four varieties of sensations are mediated by different types of fibers—touch by the large myelinated fibers, temperature sensations by those of intermediate size and pain by the fine myelinated and unmyelinated fibers (511).

But even at that time the evidence appeared inconclusive. In 1932 Adrian (4) declared that since there is no sharp grouping of cutaneous fibers and that the branches of particular fibers are smaller than the parent fiber:

It is therefore unlikely that there is any sharp division of fiber size corresponding to muscle sense, touch, and temperature (4, p. 58).

Data have accumulated indicating that there is considerable overlapping in the various characteristics and functions of the fibers (373, pp. 45 ff.; 135, pp. 68-78). Hence the definite correlations hoped for are not available. Moreover, as Erlanger and Gasser point out, what connections one might find in the peripheral nerves might not hold for the central nervous system.

It is necessary to realize in this connection, however, that each of the branches of the terminal arborization of a fiber in the central nervous system is going to exhibit properties characteristic of its own size, not those of the axon from which it springs. Therefore, it is impossible to tell from the size of a peripheral fiber what its central characteristics are going to be. All that we can assume is that large fibers will probably have extensive arborizations and produce correspondingly large or extensive central effects (135, pp. 74 ff.).

Gasser (169, p. 171 f.) definitely asserts that the possibility of a relationship between the elevations in the action potential and the modality of sensation has not proved compatible with experimental evidence. Here we might ask whether the notion that such a relationship existed was not based on the kind of presence-absence observations employed to localize brain functions.

Turning to the so-called special senses we run into a hopeless situation from the standpoint of specific conduction. The problem is to locate specific discharges for an enormous number of qualities and not just one as in the case of each cutaneous avenue. Even if one accepts the theory that color qualities, for example, are compounded of three or four elementary types there seems no point in attempting any correlation, in view of the accepted physiological principle that even sensory and motor impulses may have the same quantitative properties (211, p. 706). The notion of specific conduction meets with such an obstacle as the contracting of vaso-motor tissues by impulses which normally operate as cardiac inhibitors (338). Physiologists since Müller cleave to the idea that it is really the tissue of final termination, the brain, for example, which produces the ultimate effect. This probably explains their use of the term "message" for neural impulse.

Who deciphers the messages? No doubt some sort of anthropomorphic idea is implied here, since it is not merely a style of expression. This message construction is part of a system of thought which involves a report to the sensorium.

The term *sensorium* is certainly reminiscent of the term *soul*. To call the brain a sensorium, however, does not remove the odium from the construction. In fact, it makes matters worse. To carry on a soul commerce is a frank procedure and does not involve any misinterpretation of the plain facts of neural nature.

Physiologists (169, p. 171 f.) are sensitive to the differences between facts analytically worked out in the laboratory and the unitary and total operation of the whole nervous system in actual behavior. Certainly laboratory data can not be overestimated as parts or phases of the operation of organisms. But such data, we may be certain, must always be treated as biological. Constructions concerning the partial working of an organism should indeed be amenable to incorporation in constructions designed to describe and interpret the operation of the entire organism. But such part or whole constructions must not be taken to tell psychic stories. Even here we may be sure that valid physiological constructions can only be parts of a psychological construction as we discussed at length in the previous chapter. In short, the biological facts of neural conduction have to do with the integration and coordination of the organism as it interacts with stimulus objects. This is as true for pain, touch, and temperature situations as for visual and auditory inter-behavior.

Effective testimony against the quality-conduction construction is the fact that afferent conduction is never an isolated event with a consequent series of separate efferent or visceromotor happenings. We may attribute this separation of the different aspects of the total organismic action to those philosophical ideas having to do with excitation of knowledge and consciousness which leads to some further action. Also the physiological-conduction construction must always be considered in connection with the physiological fact that impulses or messages are never isolated from other impulses (94). Separation for local investigational purposes is another matter. Speaking of visual activities Graham writes:

The discussion has given abundant evidence to show that the visual response is not a direct representation of the excitation in the end-organ or afferent pathways. Trains of impulses which reach the central nervous system by way of the peripheral nerve fibres are modified by and combined with impulses from similar and dissimilar end-organs (187, p. 874).

The conventional construction concerning afferent propagation includes also the notion that in physiological and psychological action the neuron or conduction systems start from a resting condition. The assumption is made that a stimulus starts off some afferent conduction correlated with some quality or experience. The most charitable criticism of such constructions is that physiological psychologists attribute to the activities of the integrated organism events observed only in laboratory preparations.

Moreover, since there are no sensations, the attempt to correlate impulses with sensations is to correlate some definite biological event with something which exists only as a purely philosophical construction. It is no accident that physiologists and others who try to correlate either afferent conduction or central termination or both with sensations are pulled up sharply at uncrossable chasms.

CENTRAL TERMINATION

Though it is an obvious and acknowledged fact that the structure and function of the brain are in all respects continuous with the remainder of the nervous system, physiologists and physiological psychologists still persist in setting it up as a unique and regnant organ. That the brain occupies a central position in the organism's anatomy and that it possesses a complex cyto-architecture certainly suggests nothing more than an observable evolution of morphological detail.

Still, the brain is made into a super train dispatcher who receives messages concerning what goes on in the world outside and evolves "a plan suitable to the occasion" (5, p. 276). So far as the problems of sensory reaction and perception are concerned, the brain is made the locus for all sorts of imaginary processes and functions. Everything that can not be otherwise accounted for on the basis of the philosophical system of mind and body is attributed to the brain. When the assumed differentiation of end organs for stimulation appears lost in the common character of afferent conduction the brain terminal is said to mediate the qualities.[1] The domination of P.P. and physiology by the brain dogma is no better shown than by a quotation from Ranson:

I shall leave out of account entirely the most difficult part: how when these propagated disturbances reach the brain they give rise to conscious sensation, which appears to be something of an entirely different order than a neural activity. I can not understand how such a thing as a sensation of warmth makes its appearance as a result or as a comcomitant of the activity of certain nerve cells in my brain. I *can only admit the fact* and leave to the future, perhaps the far distant future, the problem presented by the relation of brain and mind (511, p. 395).

As the above quotation indicates, what is really nothing but a traditional philosophical construction is regarded as an unquestionable fact.[2] Why can not the physiologist be content with the ascertainment of the events in the entire organism or its anatomical parts when it is interacting with a warm object? Is not this an instance of many problems "not amenable to investigative procedures" and "requiring distant futures for solution" which are spurious issues altogether?

A critical approach to the sensory physiopsychological problem with its available historical perspective allows no other conclusion than that the futurity invoked is simply past tradition. Problems of sensory neuropsychology are founded

[1] It is interesting to note here that bilateral ablation of the temporal lobes increases "smelling behavior," whereas such behavior disappears with the additional destruction of the olfactory tracts (62).

[2] Compare this statement dated 1933 with Bonnet's, written in 1769. "The philosopher does not investigate how the movement of a nerve causes an idea to arise in the soul. He simply admits the fact and readily renounces the attempt of discovering the cause. He knows that it springs from the mystery of the union of two substances, and that this mystery is for him inscrutable" (509, p. 332).

on the venerable presupposition that the organismic structures and functions are connected with and operate in the
service of the soul. A quotation from a physiologist, who
unlike current psychologists is not sensitive to the objections
that his science is concerned with such diaphanous materials,
makes this plain.

The final explanation of the differences in quality involves a
study of the nature and properties of consciousness itself,—a subject which as yet has not been undertaken by physiology. At
present we accept the fact of consciousness and the fact that there
are different kinds of qualities of consciousness, and our investigations are directed only toward ascertaining the anatomical,
physical, and chemical properties of the organs involved in the
production of these subjective changes (240, p. 272).

Corresponding to the autistic construction of correlations
between "stimuli" and psychic qualities or experience is the
invention of marginal centers surrounding the sensory projection terminals, which serve to associate, really to create,
objects on the basis of the qualities mediated by sensory
terminal centers. A clear and straightforward statement of
this type of autistic and factually unwarranted speculation
appears in the following:

At the present time very little that is positive can be said concerning the relations of particular visual attributes or dimensions
to the cortical process; the calcarine region evidently contains
neural mechanisms for the synthesis of similar impulses received
from the two eyes; it is the seat of the primary activities of binocular discrimination. That it contains processes corresponding specifically to brilliance and chroma, we can scarcely doubt. Pathological changes in the occipital cortex can effect chroma independently of brilliance and may yield highly specific chromatic
effects, such as red vision or erythropsia. The cortex seems to
carry out a series of neurological operations upon the incoming
optic nerve-currents, gradually putting them into shape for the
coordinated control of efferent cortical innervations and the
determination of the visual experience. Such operations include
the introduction of memory records, which seem to be carried
largely in the so-called visuo-psychic areas, immediately surrounding the primary projection zones (602, p. 698).

Not all physiologists and physiological psychologists are complacent about the difficulties of connecting souls and brains. An admirable example is provided by Sherrington in his discussion of the brain and its mechanism (550). Though this eminent physiologist does not disbelieve in psychic processes, in fact regards it possible that such processes can, with the energy of electrical potentials, coexist in space and time, he is strongly aware of the impossibility of connecting the psychic with brain processes. Thus he asks and answers:

> But indeed, what right have we to conjoin mental experience with physiological? No scientific right; only the right of what Keats, with that superlative Shakespearian gift of his, dubbed "busy commonsense." . . . To many of us a mere juxtaposition of the two sets of happenings proclaims their disparity. On the one side changing electrical potentials with thermal and chemical action making a physiological entity held together by energy relations; on the other, a suite of mental experience, an activity no doubt, but in what if any relation to energy? . . . We admit that the physico-chemical, to which we here seek to correlate the "mental experience," is for us itself at long last mental, a thought, an idea. But that does not help because, at least to me, neither of the two appears related to the other. As mental events I should suppose them aloof. Science, nobly, declines as proof anything but complete proof, but common sense, pressed for time, accepts and acts on acceptance (550 pp. 23-24).

The common sense here referred to is nothing but cultural tradition, the very same that decrees man to be the end and acme of creation. But the interesting thing is that we already know, by as complete a proof as we require, that the whole problem is devoid of scientific sense.

It is not a far-fetched estimation of the present situation to say that the emphasis of the brain as a master organ simply shows the combined power of cultural tradition and scientific professionalism. This estimate is supported by a statement of Adrian when referring to human behavior in general.

> . . . from one aspect human behavior is an affair of networks and impulses; it may be useful to picture it in these terms in

spite of the fact that we know far more about our thoughts and actions than we do about the mechanisms in our brains (5, p. 276).

EFFERENT CONDUCTION

Admittedly the facts of efferent conduction superficially present few problems; still such facts are of the utmost importance for any precise interpretation of P.P. It is certainly proper for anatomists and physiologists to localize their interest in the role of neural conduction in motor and sensory activities. But the important question concerns the further steps to follow.

In the first place, is the atomistic separation of the parts of complex actions a basis for constructing machinery for the control of peripheral parts of organisms by some central mechanism? If so, the construction does violence to the actual operation of organisms as integrated units. On the other hand, there is little to object to here if the construction merely implies the study of integrated actions on an analytic and partial basis.

In the second place, does the atomistic procedure imply that in addition to dividing the organism's action into the reception, redirection, and transmission of messages there are also psychic processes determining what direction messages are conveyed for execution into muscular and glandular elements? In the latter case the atomistic procedure can not be too severely condemned.

A third question is how closely does the anatomist and physiologist connect centrifugal conduction with discriminative or cognitive behavior? Quite correctly the centrifugal conduction is related to elaborate cortical as well as reflex action, but the mental correlates of the former are presumed appreciably to antedate the efferent conduction and the final action. Our question concerns the place of efferent conduction in the actual discrimination or perceptual action.

On the whole, physiological psychologists follow the atomizing lead. What really are always complex unit actions are divided off into sensory, central, and motor parts. In dealing with the behavior of an organism, however, it is impossible to separate the afferent, central, and efferent phases of its total action. And this holds even if we confine ourselves to the operation of physiological actions. Centripetal can not be set off from centrifugal conduction or from the operation of numerous internuncial neurons in the various tissues of the central or axial nervous system. This is likewise true when the organism interbehaves with simple stimulus objects such as color surfaces, tones or odors.

EFFECTOR ACTION

P.P. has progressed a long way from the early conception that sensory physiopsychology is primarily concerned with the mediation of sensations by the end-organs, conduction, and central termination factors. Current writers on P.P., more sympathetic to the notion of the organism as a whole, may not object to vague references to muscle and gland action. Anyone interested in complex interbehavior with stimulus objects, whether located within or without the organism, must include in his descriptions and interpretations the positive and complex operation of muscular and glandular structures. This is as true of perceptual as of the more intense manipulative and locomotor actions. It is hardly necessary to reiterate that this view does not clash with the particularistic study of the physiologist who limits himself to the actions of the isolated organism. All the findings of the latter may be comfortably fitted into the psychologist's construction of biological participating factors in a complex field of interbehavior.

The necessity to include in our descriptions of perceptual behavior all the numerous features of the interbehaving organism is made clear when we compare the traditional view of perceptual reactions with one based upon the crude data which set the investigative and constructional problem. The traditional view is well illustrated by the Berkeleyian idea that when:

Sitting in my study I hear a coach drive along the street; I look through the casement and see it; I walk out and enter it. . . . There are three coaches, an auditory, a visual, and a tactual object respectively (33, p. 33).

The three coaches are, of course, "psychic" experiences, which the modern physiological psychologist has attempted to correlate with the workings of afferent and central neural actions. This view still prevails despite the fact that even in Berkeley's description the individual in each case is described as acting.

By contrast, the interbehavioral description does not separate perceiving as an act different from other acts involving muscular performance. Rather, there is a distinct form of interbehavior with a coach. That the heard, seen, and touched object is reacted to as one in all instances, is a matter of prior interactions of the total organism. Effector responses therefore constitute factors in the total field.

CHAPTER 12

SENSORY PHYSIOPSYCHOLOGY (II)

PHYSIOPSYCHOLOGICAL CONTINUITY

STUDENTS of P.P. can not miss the essential continuity in the oldest and most recent physiopsychological investigations. Throughout its history sensory physiopsychology has promoted physiological theories of sensation under the aegis of spiritualistic epistemology. Not that Berkeleyian metaphysics imported into physiological and psychological science by Helmholtz and succeeding physiological psychologists has remained unchanged in constructional detail. Some of these variations, of course, are simply verbal. For example, the original sensory physiopsychological formula that there are anatomico-physiological mechanisms for the creation of sensation qualities or experience has recently been modified, so that instead of *creating* qualities the nervous system *mediates* or *represents* them. Certainly the essential constructional principle is the same.

Probably the most radical constructional variation is the suppression of emphasis on mental qualities. Here the essential modification is to stress the operation of the brain and other neural structures in the differentiation of sense qualities. Presumably the epistemological problem is either avoided or rejected. But since sensory or afferent conduction allows for no quality mediation and there is not one iota of evidence for psychic and even psychological brain functions, how can epistemological issues be set aside unless we resort to the study of interbehavior with actual things?

How the philosophical tradition affects current investigation is illustrated by Bartley's choice of materials for a treatise on vision. He lays aside:

. . . all items which do not rather immediately contribute to a correlation between experience and neurophysiology (26, p. 15).

169

So there is no chapter on color vision, for as an earlier quotation (p. 146) has indicated, very little can be said concerning what "must happen" in the nervous system. This leaves such topics as brightness and visual acuity to be treated. But even for visual acuity the physiological facts are troublesome. Whereas visual acuity requires a high degree of insulation between adjacent fibers presumed to provide point-to-point connections between the retina and the cortex, the neural elements are closely and copiously interrelated. Bartley does not ask whether the neural basis for visual behavior might be questioned, but simply proposes that atomistic physiopsychology should give way to a gestaltistic field view.

> Our next hope, then, is to be able to do in neural terms what has been done in perception itself, be able to use our present physiological information logically in a field hypothesis (26, p. 15).

The implication in all this is that a neural system should be constructed at the cost of original data. And there is not the slightest suspicion that perhaps the facts of vision are such as to break completely through the ring of historical constructions! The organismic treatment of neural elements is, to be sure, a step in the right direction. But it fails to imply that the original events call for a treatment of the whole organism interacting with stimulus objects which are not reducible to excitants of specific neuron elements. Neural events, of course, as partial factors in the total situation should be investigated not only as occurring events but also for their value in handling variations in interbehavior as in pathological conditions. Not one of such factors can fail to find its proper place in the total system. Thus by loosening the hold of the nervous system as the basis or correlate of experience one may expect a more effective attack upon the original data.

An excellent transition from idealistic philosophy to sensory physiology is provided by Ladd-Franklin's (333) trenchant exposition of the problems of color vision. In a clear-cut style she treats the workings of the receptors and the brain terminals.

. . . our early ancestors . . . had no knowledge of light wavelengths, on the one hand, nor of the efficient physiological chain—lens, retina, nerve-fibre, cortex—on the other hand. To them it seemed that the sensation red resided in the rose also as redness (333, pp. 117, 151).

She repeats the conventional doctrine that colors are subjective; they do not exist until the results of the transformation of electro-magnetic waves in the alembic of the retina reach the cortex (333, p. 22).

By early ancestors Ladd-Franklin must mean the predecessors of the spiritistic philosophers, since the doctrine she espouses has been cherished by philosophers for centuries. But it was not only those philosophers who were unsuccessful in explaining color. We have seen that even our present-day knowledge of the nervous system supplies no basis for the doctrine. Why is it that current physiologists or physiological psychologists can make no headway with this theory? Surely because the theory is not derived from an investigation of events. Contrariwise, it is no wonder that physiology can not establish spiritistic philosophy.

Hylas. I tell you Philonous, external light is nothing but a thin fluid substance, whose minute particles being agitated with a brisk motion, and in various manners reflected from the different surfaces of outward objects to the eyes, communicate different motions to the optic nerves; which being propagated to the brain cause therein various impressions: and these are attended with the sensations of red, blue, yellow, etc.
Philonous. It seems, then, the light doth no more than shake the optic nerves.
Hylas. Nothing else.
Philonous. And consequent to each particular motion of the nerves the mind is affected with a sensation, which is some particular color.
Hylas. Right.
Philonous. And these sensations have no existence without the mind.
Hylas. They have not (33, p. 217).

Ladd-Franklin criticizes the Helmholtzians as psychically color blind because, for them, yellow does not exist (333,

p. 115). Actually, for her, *no* colors exist, because, although she refers to the "deliverance of consciousness," nature knows no such consciousness. It is nothing but a word construction. In the above quotation it is interesting to note that she says our ancestors thought the sensations were in the rose. Such is the power of philosophic tradition in resisting the elimination of sensations altogether from scientific constructions, since sensations are only by-products of the conception that the brain is the seat of the soul.

What the spiritistic philosopher has put together let no physiologist or physiological psychologist rend asunder! On the first page of his authoritative volume on the Vertebrate Eye, Walls declares:

We have been discussing light as an objective physical entity; but, just as there would be no sound if a tree were to fall with no one to hear it, so also there would be no light in the physiological sense if there were no photoreceptor upon which it impinged. In this other sense light is a sensation, an experience in consciousness. Like other such experiences, it may be evoked by a limited number of causes (other than physical light). The qualities of a light-sensation bear only a close, not an absolute, relationship to the objective attributes of a physical light which produces it. Thus, different colors may be seen under different circumstances when the corresponding different frequencies of light are not being steadily presented to the eye at all, or the same color may result from totally different mixtures of frequencies. Two lights with the same energy-content may appear different in brightness while two others, equally bright, may differ greatly in actual physical intensity. Color and brightness are thus subjective correlates of the objective frequency and intensity. The former can be perceived but not measured, while the latter can be measured with inanimate instruments but cannot be perceived with the eye (611, pp. 1-2).

With respect to the specific visual process he says:

Any attempt to depict the events which intervene between the impact of light upon the retina and the registration, in consciousness, of the qualitative and quantitative aspects of vision, must necessarily be largely guess-work, and can be lucid and connected only if it is dogmatic. The following treatment is such an attempt, made for the sake of the reader rather than for the sake of the subject (611, p. 74).

Concerning color in particular, he continues:

Color, or better, "hue" exists only in the mind. No light or object in nature has hue—rather, the quality of hue aroused as a sensation is projected back to the object as one of its attributes, just as the patterns of brightness and darkness in consciousness are projected back into the visual field to endow objects with their size, shape, tone values, and movement. For, we perceive *objects* rather than lights. We can see objects falsely as to size, shape, and motion, and just as falsely as to color since color is purely subjective. The color of a surface depends not only upon its chemico-physical nature, but also upon the kind of light by which we see it, and upon our memory of the impression it may have given us under some more familiar illumination. Thus, a particular dress may look red only in daylight, yet we still call it red under an artificial light when it may actually be reflecting more yellow light and should then be seen as orange (611, p. 81).

Remarkable as it may be to find such a core of metaphysics in scientific description it is still more surprising that the same description contains ideological "genes," which if developed would greatly help to liquidate the metaphysics. It will suffice to refer to only two of these "genes." The first is the point about the chemico-physical nature of the stimulus object. Certainly, if scientists were to take into active account the achievements of chemistry in the analysis of the colors of things, there would be no need for the idea that color is a sensation or psychic experience projected out to hypothetical sources of electro-magnetic vibrations. Instead, we would objectively describe the individual's color interactions with a stimulus object, the properties of which are treated on the basis of modern developments in the chemistry of natural and synthetic color compounds (410). We have already referred to the anomaly of making facts of spectral colors the basis for color construction in general.

The second, which may be called the field gene, is indicated in Walls' remarks about the dress which looks orange but is called red. This brings up the question whether such data as color contrast and color constancy should be treated otherwise than as field situations involving relatively minor variations in the organization of field factors. To blow up the elementary facts of relative interactions between persons and things into a metaphysics of consciousness is absolutely uncalled for by any scientific investigation.

SENSATION VERSUS PERCEPTION

Though no evidence exists that there are sensation reactions in any principle distinct from perceptual ones, the physiological psychologist tries to make such a distinction in order to support the physiological theories of psychological action. Such an attempt is illustrated by the following remarks:

> *Sensation* points to the sense organs with their nerves and nerve centers as the object of study; *perception* points to the objects of the world which we know through the senses (640, p. 450).

Woodworth, who makes this distinction, illustrates it by laboratory experiments.

> In a sensation experiment we apply stimuli that are quite restricted and typically simple, the attempt being to discover what impression or reaction results from these simple stimuli and their variation. In a perception experiment we present objects or objective facts and attempt to discover how well they are observed. In both cases O is keenly attentive to what is presented and in both cases he gives a verbal report. In a sensation experiment we are interested in the correlation of his report with the stimulus, in a perception experiment we are interested in the correlation of his report with a certain objective fact (640, p. 450).

Unless we substitute the word *object* for *objective* we have difficulty in connecting the descriptions with any kind of experiment, since no one can experiment on any but objective facts. In further paragraphs, however, we might gather that the opposite pole of objective is not something psychic but something about the organism. Woodworth asserts that in lifting a loaded pill box in a psychophysical experiment neither the box nor its weight is the stimulus. "The stimulus is the pull of the weight upon the hand, the bending of the joints, the pressure on the skin" (640, p. 450). So far, then, he appears to be discussing the individual's interaction with his own behavior or condition. But no, he goes on to say: "O can be trained to attend to these sensations or in other words to attend to the exact stimulus." Is stimulus another word for sensation? The matter is made clearer by another illustration. In a two-point threshold perception experiment:

> O's task is to distinguish between two points and one. In an experiment on sensation, his attention is directed to the exact impression derived from each application of the stimulus, and he reports whether the impression is compact, elongated, dumb-bell-shaped, or clearly double (640, p. 451).

The exact impression is, of course, the psychic qualities in consciousness. Plainly then the distinction between sensation and perception is made in the interest of psychic states. It is quite understandable therefore why the existence of sensations can only be made plausible by talking about receptors and making receptor actions into stimuli.

Is this not an expensive method for marking the distinction between sensation and perception? In the case of the former one may legitimately be discussing interbehavior with simpler objects than is the case with perception, but this does not allow for any descriptions involving any different connection with end organs. Clearly a scientific handling of these situations requires treating the sensations as phases of reactions (286). What is further necessary is to discover whether we are dealing with the subject's report of what the points suggest (oval, dumbbell, etc.,) or the experimenter's description of the subject's reactions.

It is profitable to note that in the Boring article (42) from which Woodworth inexactly quotes the impression descriptions, the author indifferently refers to the series sharp point, blunt point, oval, elongated oval, double paddle, dumbbell, and two separated points as "mental processes," "process material," and "perceptual patterns." And why not? As long as one deals with psychic processes or impressions there is no way of making a distinction. Incidentally, Boring calls the compass points the stimuli, whereas receptor processes constitute stimuli for Woodworth. Boring refers to receptor processes as excitation, and admits (42, p. 467) they are constructions based on little knowledge.

The distinction between sensation and perception which Woodworth makes is supported he believes by the problem of the stimulus or object error. It is an error in a sensation experiment for the subject or observer to attend to the objects *pill box* or *compass point* instead of the impression or mental state. The assumption here is that when the observer is attending to the stimulus object one is not obliged to take into account the biological factor of his response, whereas in the sensation case this must be done.

The fact of the matter is that if one can abjure psychic states or processes both the simpler (sensation) and more complex discrimination interbehaviors involve the same factors (286).What is studied in each case is an interbehavior with a stimulus object. Depending upon the problem the experimenter sets himself, and consequently the instructions he gives his observer, he obtains different data. In a weight-lifting experiment, if you ask the subject to attend to the pill box you get a different result from that obtained when you ask him to interbehave with the effect of the object upon him (158). But there is no variation of factors.

An additional important point is that in the type of description that Woodworth favors, objects are regarded as meanings, that is, mental states organized out of or added to the sensation states or processes. Now for meanings, Woodworth's statement is clear, that they are not connected with sense organs, nerves, and nerve centers. At this point two fundamental questions arise.

(1) Is it possible to include in scientific psychology any factors disconnected from the operation of the organism, which is a unit evolved with end organs, nerves, etc. The answer might be made that there is a long-distance connection between perception and sensation. This answer, however, involves two difficulties. The first is the methodological mixture of scientific description with simple nonconstructional reference to the crude data, and the second that the whole description is not derived from operations upon crude data or the data themselves.

(2) The second question is whether the sensations point to physiological processes. Surely since an organism is reacting and reporting it is doing so as an animal evolved with end-organs, nerves, etc., but are there any evidences of physiological bases or provisions for mediating isolated qualities or meanings? On the other hand, we have here a clear indication how unsatisfactory traditional P.P. is—namely, a commerce with and a perpetuation of psychic states. As long as this condition prevails, P.P. is not a departure from philosophical psychology, but identical with a spiritualistic form of it.

BINOCULAR COLOR MIXTURE

The literature on binocular color mixture throws considerable light on the basic views of P.P. and the foundations upon which they rest. The data involved consist of the results obtained from placing separately before each eye a red and green or a blue and yellow color filter, mounted in a suitable box with appropriate light sources (129, 210). Woodworth sums up the results in the sentence:

Many competent observers have found it impossible to obtain this fusion, while others have secured it without difficulty (640, p. 575).

A recent example of such data (192) is contained in the accompanying table.

FREQUENCY OF OCCURRENCE OF BINOCULAR FUSION
IN NORMAL AND IN FOVEAL VISION (N=50)

Subjects Experiencing Fusion of	Red and Green		Blue and Yellow	
	Normal Vision	Foveal Vision	Normal Vision	Foveal Vision
Number	33	42	19	45
Percent	66	84	38	90

Now it is typical of the P.P. tradition that some organic or physiological condition should be immediately sought to account for the failure to obtain fusion. Rivers (521) asserted that the facility of obtaining this effect is correlated with the myopic and hypermetropic condition of the eyes. Hecht (210), on the other hand, accounted for the failure to secure fusion on the basis of color-blindness. Grimsley (192), disputing this explanation by his results, offers instead the hypothesis of imbalance or fatigue of the rectus and oblique eye muscles which renders the subjects unable to maintain continuous stimulation of corresponding points on the two retinae. Such explanations are offered as a matter of course and before it is established that there is such a fact as fusion.

Now what about the mechanism of fusion when it does occur? Hecht's answer (211) is typical. With a frank admission of ignorance concerning the underlying physiological processes it is still proposed that the fusion takes place in the brain. He says:

Red and green give a yellow sensation, and several pairs of monochromatic complementaries give white (211, p. 792).

Among the latter, yellow and blue are included. The underlying principle is:

White and yellow are sensations which are produced in the brain out of impulses that come in from the three receptors in the retina (211, p. 792).

Woodworth (640, p. 575) who does not object to the physiological production of sensations is troubled by two questions. First, on Hecht's basis alone does the red-green color-blind individual see only yellow, and secondly, why does not the cortex respond to red-green mixtures by seeing reddish green, as it does in the case of red-blue by seeing reddish blue.

But there is a more profound problem in the magical work of the cortex in producing psychic states altogether, whether synthesizing sensations in mixtures or in monocular or binocular reactions to single colors. There is a peculiar shift on the part of the physiological psychologist. To begin with, his task is to describe if possible what the retina and brain do when the organism differentiates colors, a task he abandons in order to account for the brain's action not merely to produce or make colors but to make psychic colors or sensations.

Has the physiological psychologist been too hasty with his verbal assertions of what the brain does? Has he properly considered whether and what data he is called upon to explain? Recently, Dunlap (129) has repeated the color-fusion experiment, but reaches the conclusion that in the first place there is no such mixture at all and in the second place that the explanation of the disappearance of the two original colors can be accounted for by the psychological principles of (1) color adaptation and (2) the tendency of colors to look white when their intensities are increased. This author adds that the notion of binocular color mixture can be laid away in the museum of curious superstitions. If Dunlap's results stand, is not the prior acceptance of physiopsychological theories open to the charge that they interfere with the scientific investigation of psychological events?

THE RETINAL IMAGE

Throughout the history of sensory physiopsychology physiological psychologists have faced two troublesome situations. First, it has always been apparent that some of the physiological facts employed in description and interpretation were irrelevant to the issues involved. Apparent, that is, from the standpoint of the interbehavior or the crude data but not from the standpoint of the postulates adopted. The second situation was the utter contradiction between the descriptions of physiological facts—which were correct—and the constructions based upon them.

One of the best illustrations is the history of the retinal image. Those writers who adopted the postulate of a mind acting through the intermediation of its body were confused by the reversion of the optical image on the retina. If the operations of the nervous system are the intermediaries of the mind's action how is it that objects are seen upright when their images on the retina are inverted? The history of the struggles of physiological psychologists with this problem is an excellent testimony to the continuity of cultural dualism which has remained unshaken despite all the difficulties encountered. Because of their presuppositions students of sensory physiopsychology have failed to notice the incoordination of optic facts and brain facts.

What is called the newer theory settles this problem by the schema that the mind really does not operate on the basis of physiological factors, which are irrelevant, but on the basis of sensations. The mental image is neither erect nor inverted. As Boring (48, p. 225) implies, the whole problem is one which does not arise from the actual interbehavior of individuals with things, but on the basis of Kepler's scientific description of what takes place on the retina.

But consider the line of experimentation which might have shaken the conventional ideas of sensory physiopsychology but did not. In point here are the experiments of Stratton (586), Ewert (136), Wooster (644) and Gibson (175), which show that modifications and interferences of reactions by means of lenses are quickly and effectively compensated for in actual behavior. All of these experiments indicate that the operation of anatomical physiological elements taken in isolation are irrelevant to facts of perception, and also that reactions to objects and their spatial relations constitute interbehavioral events without the necessity of theoretical intervention of any dualistic processes.

The points made here for visual events may be duplicated

for hearing and other types of interaction. Is it not, therefore, a matter of scientific prejudice to persist in the physiological interpretation of psychological events instead of building constructions more nearly in accord with the demands of the crude data?

THE BLIND SPOT

Even more pointed are the difficulties physiological psychologists experience with the blind spot. Ever since its discovery by Mariotte in 1668 there has been occasion for observing the incoordination between the anatomical fact of the optic disc and the continuity in visual perception. Without sharing our psychological views, Bartley (26) looks askance at those who interpret the behavioral facts on the ground that the optic disc does contain sensitive cells despite the inability of anatomists to find them. Or, as an alternative, that the ganglion-cell fibers located in the optic disc must be sensitive to light. His own theory—namely, that illumination which escapes from the insensitive disc falls on sensitive sense elements immediately and distantly surrounding it gives the continuity of vision—assumes a correspondence between anatomical physiological elements and sensation. Bartley supposes that subjective space as built up from a brain field need not be regarded as containing a gap because of the mechanical accident that sense cells in a small portion of the retina have been pushed aside to form the optic disc. He goes on to say:

> Binocular vision has happened to function well enough that such an incidental event as the production of a tiny insensitive spot in the retina is of little practical consequence (26, p. 115).

Why not count the blind spot as an item revealing the irrelevancy of the optic disc and the lack of conduction for continuous space behavior, as well as an indication for the treatment of sensory physiopsychological facts in general?

ILLUSIONS AND HALLUCINATIONS

Sensory physiopsychology thrives on activities close to

physiological functions. The backbone of its constructional system comprises those activities which are closely related to the evolution of anatomical structures. The elaboration of the eye from a light-sensitive spot and the ear mechanisms from some specialized contact organ form the most likely grist for its mill. That such anatomical characteristics are not too helpful in the general ideological cause, we have seen in the case of the optic disc. When we come to such activities as must be treated as interbehavior with stimulus objects, physiological theory is well nigh helpless.

In the early days of P.P. the great paradox developed that in the case of such events as illusions and hallucinations the discrepancy between stimulus objects and mental processes left little or no room for physiological mediators. False perceptions could only be regarded as purely mental. Of the many theories to explain the popular Müller-Lyer illusion the point of divergence lay between various modes of judgment and such biopsychological factors as actual or incipient eye movements (48, p. 244). On the whole, it is fair to say that by necessity such events were so treated as to suggest some mode of interbehavior based upon previous contacts with similar or dissimilar objects.

Later, with the evolution of Gestalt psychology from the original totalitarian ideas of Brentano and other Thomistic writers, it no longer appeared so serious that things did not correspond to receptoral elements and their physiological conductions. Correspondences were sought not between stimuli and mental states but between those psychic or phenomenal processes and dynamic patterns in the brain. The paradox of illusions seemed to disappear. The assiduous study of responses to patterns of various sorts led to a large number of laws which were based either upon the impelling character of objects or on the dynamic principles located in the individual.

The net result of the Gestalt treatment of illusions which might have suggested constructions based on the reactions of individuals to patterns and objects was the construction of arbitrary forces in the brain to correspond to perceiving powers and tendencies. In one sense this was a rejection of the attempts to deal with psychological events on a basis of physiology. Actually it constituted a procedure of autistically setting up constructions concerning physiological action independently of the facts of anatomy and physiology. It may be concluded that gestaltistic P.P. is the *reductio* of traditional P.P.

Hallucinations, of course, are even more troublesome than illusions. Undoubtedly that is why they have so small a place in P.P. What can be made of events in which no particular end organs or specific neural elements are concerned? But the behavioral events are available, and they force the question whether it is permissible to build up a P.P. system on a principle of including only favorable data and excluding those which are troublesome and thwarting.

If we define hallucinations as reactions to things in no wise present to the organism but reacted to as if they were, we must accept such behavior as not only frequent but of great importance. Clinical neurologists are called upon to deal with a striking condition which they call phantom-limb pain. After amputation of the limb a patient reports fixed and tensed postures of the absent fingers or toes.

Occasionally the fingers or their nails seem to be cutting into the palm, the nails being pulled off, or there is a sensation of boring up through the bones of the fingers into the hand (373, p. 54).

As usual, some neurologists are satisfied with an explanation that the pain is simply psychic. They may call it an obsession. But others, who obtain relief for their patients by injections and surgical treatment, regard such hallucinations as a form of behavior with possibly a substitute stimulation. On this basis hallucinations are made into genuine implicit behavior or into links between illusions or ordinary perceiving behavior. One thing is certain, however, that such events constitute impediments to the traditional forms of P.P. construction.

When we turn to the innumerable facts of anaesthesias, analgesias and other types of behavior subsumed under the term *hysteria*, we encounter a tremendous amount of psychological interbehavior calling for a revision of our P.P. conceptions. Attempts to treat such events on the basis of pure constructions concerning underlying physiological conditions result in the illegitimate simplification of complex happenings and the forcing of interpretations obviously derived from a source other than the data interpreted. For example, Hurst (245) tries to explain anaesthesias and analgesias by the simple procedure of inventing blocks in conduction paths.

DATA AND CONSTRUCTIONS IN PHYSIOPSYCHOLOGY

No development of P.P. points up the issue of crude data and constructions more than the physiopsychological domain. While no observation or experiment has ever started from anything else than an interbehavior of organisms and stimulus objects (191, p. 161 f.; 279, 286), the cultural trend has thrown a veil of presupposition over the materials studied and the interpretations made. Perceptual events are inextricably interrelated with traditional epistemological problems; however, the fact that one is concerned with organisms and objects need not thrust one into speculation concerning knower and known. As we have specified many times, to go on from there and assume further that the known or knowing involves psychic factors mediated by neural factors throws psychology squarely into the metaphysical ring.

The treatment of the facts and problems of visual contrast affords a splendid example of the need for clarity concerning the relation of data and constructions. Obviously visual contrast is an event. When a light and dark surface are put together the immediate adjacent portions of the two look respectively darker and lighter than the portions farther away from the line of junction. Similar contrasts are found in color, temperature, and other perceptual situations. What is the significance of such factors? How can we account for them? The term brightness contrast is used both to refer to this fact and to its explanatory constructions (26, p. 332).

Physiopsychologists who assume that we should have neural causes for everything are not too happy when such a neural explanation is supplanted by a visual-contrast construction. On the other hand, those who seek neural explanations must admit that they are not forthcoming. Consider the case of increased critical flicker frequency when the stimulus area is increased by adding to it a portion of equal brightness and the decrease of c.f.f by an added portion of markedly dissimilar brightness. In the latter case it is assumed that an inhibition of summation has occurred. But as Bartley (26, p. 332 f.) points out, this explanation is entirely arbitrary since there is no suggestion why this occurs in one surface and not in the other.

Those who minimize or reject neural explanations need not be troubled by contrast being at one time an event to be described and at another a factor in explanation. In the former case one merely observes the perceptual effects occurring under various stimulating conditions, whereas in the latter these conditions with their induced effects taken together become a factor useful in accounting for other events. What objection can there be to saying that in the Sherrington disc (640, p. 569) the increase of c.f.f. in the ring is owing to the contrast effect? The important point is to allow the individual's original contacts with the stimulus objects to assume their rightful place as a basis for both a report of what happens and a factor for affecting other happenings.

Bartley (26), who is perplexed by the incoordination of events and constructions, raises the question whether the trouble calls for new types of construction concerning visual problems rather than sheer accumulation of new facts. He suggests a departure from the elementaristic type of construction toward an organismic or field theory. Unfortunately, *field* for Bartley goes only so far as the interrelation of neural elements. Even the concentration of psychological events in the total organism operating in connection with conventional stimulation is insufficient. Nothing less will do than an interbehavioral treatment which includes organisms and objects, media, and setting factors, as well as the historical engendering of event fields. Such a treatment would go a long way toward supplying the necessary new attitude for coordinating facts already accumulated and to be developed.

TRADITIONAL AND OBJECTIVE EPISTEMOLOGY

The interrelation of perceptual events with epistemological problems is probably inevitable and surely not objectionable. To bring perceptual facts into conjunction with the larger question of the nature of knowledge is simply an acknowledgement of the continuity of all behavior events, from the simplest discriminating behavior to the most complex scientific observations. Difficulties only arise when traditional issues are injected into both perceptual and more complex observational events, and when each such contaminated situation is assumed to afford support for another objectionable situation linked with it.

The basic objection to employing epistemological constructions for treating perceptual events lies in the implied physiopsychological postulates involved. We have sufficiently considered these postulates as they have historically dominated both epistemological and physiopsychological thinking. Now we consider the problem as it appears in current thought, especially in the discussion of physicists who have become interested in such problems because of the development of indeterminacy doctrine in quantum mechanics and general relativity theory.

Physicists have emphasized the knowledge problem because of the effect which measuring instruments have upon observations, and hence the necessity to take the observer into account when studying problems concerning the relative positions and motions of bodies (365). Our concern is how physiopsychological postulates are employed and result in improper constructions concerning measurement and things measured. For our purposes we need refer only to the writings of Heisenberg (212), Bohr (38), and von Neumann (461).

The last especially has developed a workable description of the issues centering around the point of partition of observer and observed.

By observer he means some ego or conscious entity which stands over against that which is observed—say, temperature and the thermometer or other instrument used to measure it. The observer is not to be identified with the body, as the observer may also have as part of what he observes the chemical changes of the brain. Thus according to von Neumann the partition between the observer and the observed may be placed between (1) the ego and the brain processes, (2) the ego and the retina, (3) the ego and the length of a mercury thread, and (4) the ego and the temperature. In case of (1), the nerve fibers and eyes are not connected with the observer, whereas in case (4), even the thermometer is.

Von Neumann and the other physicists mentioned accept what they call the psychophysiological principle, which becomes for them the warrant for everlastingly setting an absolute boundary between the observer and the observed. Bohr writes:

. . . Without entering into metaphysical speculations, I may perhaps add that any analysis of the very concept of an explanation would, naturally, begin and end with a renunciation as to explaining our own conscious activity (38, p. 459).

Thus by confusing psychic entities, derived from medieval tradition, with behavior of an individual interacting with temperature conditions and with measuring instruments, physicists perpetuate traditional epistemology. But in no sense is this in line with the work rules of science or any of its findings. There is no difficulty whatever in considering knowledge as a complex form of interbehavior with things and in principle like any other interbehavior to which no one attributes any psychic factor.

Interbehavior constitutes a continuum. In microscopic mechanisms two or more inorganic objects become displaced in a system in correlation with other objects and conditions.

Such fields are called mechanical and are handled by instruments to yield the ordinary L.T.M. dimensions. In studying such fields the observer may regard the objects and conditions as stable and the observational and mensurable operations as slightly or not at all interfering with the isolated events. The factors in the events themselves may also be looked upon as maintaining their identity throughout the changes in their relations.

In the case of radiation events the interbehavior of things involves a mutuality of transformation. In the simple action of light on a photographic plate, changes in both mark great variations in successive time periods. Now since light operates both as particles and waves, and since we can trace an equivalence of matter and energy we may regard these events as more elusive. Though it follows that instruments designed to observe and measure such events play a large part in fixing them for investigative purposes, it is futile to raise fatuous questions concerning their reality or unreality. Doubtless reality is a synonymous term with stability of operation.

Coming to microscopic events the stability decreases to such an extent in fact that physicists have turned so metaphysical as to consider that the observation of subatomic events really creates the events. Actually, however, the difficulties of observation as implied by the indeterminacy principle and the impossibility of accurately distinguishing between the mensuration instruments and the measured object in quantum mechanics leave no room for spurious epistemological questions.

Two conclusions may be drawn from the field-of-physics investigation. The first is that the only genuine partitions must be made on the basis of (1) objects, (2) observer, and (3) means and techniques of observation. Neither one fuses with the other, and certainly the observer never absorbs the thing observed. Whatever difficulties there may be in the stability of the observed, and whatever technique may be required, whether the determination of simple point coincidences, disintegrative analysis or statistical inference, we can always expect to distinguish between data and constructions.

The second conclusion is that however far the development of observation and the range of observed things lead toward hierarchies of construction, the point must still be stressed that all observation begins with something to be observed and all the manipulations and techniques arise on this foundation.

The partition problem is in no wise a serious one if only one refrains from dragging in psychic factors underived from the original interbehavioral data. Certainly the fact, that when an observer is interacting with original data a perceptual factor is introduced, brings in no psychic elements nor any basis for an ultimate differentiation between the data of any science, physical or psychological. Within the psychological field we have a continuum which borders on biological interbehavior, in which the organism, as one of the interacting objects, becomes partially or completely transformed unless it changes its position from one of immediate contiguity with a burning object. The simplest perceptual action may be described as differentiating or identifying an object. This signifies essentially that the organism and object now interbehave differently because of prior mutual contact (289, ch. 9). As interacting objects, however, the organism and the perceived thing maintain their individual identity and stability. In specific instances when the interbehavior is not merely discriminating or identifying, some further action may be taken as the criterion of differentiation. Neither ineffectiveness of perceiving nor any form of illusion or hallucination suggests the dispensability of the original object or its behavior in the field. Perhaps the cases in which identification is followed by other action may more properly be described as a knowing response than when sheer identification completes the field.

No fact of perception justifies the notion that a physical

object or the physical world is created or inferred. Such a problem never arises from any sort of scientific observation. It is entirely based upon a confusion of objects in the original interaction or crude datum with constructed objects constituting parts of the scientific description concerning the original interaction. We suggest that an adequate epistemology should take account of the whole range of facts, including what happens in elementary-discrimination responses as well as the situation in which conceptual structures are built on the basis of investigation and system building.

Chapter 13

PSYCHOPHYSIOLOGY

Physiopsychology and Psychophysiology

HAVING used the term *physiopsychology* for the sensory province of traditional P.P. we now group the materials of the motor or actional province under the heading *psychophysiology*. This admittedly-arbitrary use of terms conforms closely with the conventional way physiologists treat their crude data.

Whereas sensory and motor phenomena are both presumed to involve psychological and physiological correlations they are differently stressed. In sensory phenomena the emphasis is upon the *biological* structures operating to mediate or produce psychological processes. Psychological events are presumed to be biologically rooted. In the psychophysiological domain, by contrast, the emphasis is placed on the *psychological* process. The task of the physiological psychologist, then, is to formulate physiological descriptions and interpretations of those processes. Since in both provinces the traditional postulates demand the correlation of mental and physiological factors, the distinction is really a pragmatic one.

This difference between the physiopsychological and psychophysiological type of correlation has been recognized since Wundt's day. What has made it stand out is the more essentially experimental character of psychophysiology. When laboratory workers make measurements of physiological processes while psychological responses are being performed, they enjoy a greater control over the experimental situation as compared with the restricted case of sensory discrimination. Accordingly, the earliest physiological psychologists must have observed the difference between (1) setting up a correspondence between organic and psycho-

191

logical action and (2) asserting what tissues and organs do in producing mentality.

Still, this distinction has made no difference in P.P. constructions, since the investigations were intended experimentally to discover correlations between (1) psychic processes constituting part of the philosophical stock in trade, and (2) the organic materials of the physiologists.

Today the putative parallelism between psychic and physiological factors is to a great extent avoided by most psychologists, though physiologists still concern themselves with the problem. Both, however, prefer to write in terms of correlations of biological and psychological events. Nevertheless, the essential ideological continuity existing between earlier and present workers is easily detected. Although current psychologists for the most part do not discuss mind-body problems, there is no break in thought between those who sought "to record the bodily changes which accompany the passage of an affection through consciousness" (597, p. 243) and those who record muscle potentials when thinking goes on.

We have already pointed out (chs. 7, 8, and elsewhere) that the physiological or neural functions, regarded by the earliest psychological experimenters as necessary substrata for the psychic, were autistically created. From the time of Wundt to the present the only evidence of such functions has been derived from the analogical facts of (a) anatomical organization, (b) neuropathology, and (c) animal extirpation experiments. The basic analogy is exploited by using the term *function* to cover (1) behavior interference through mutilation and (2) assumed unique biological action for specific perceptual differential responses and other behavior.

In the present chapter we are concerned with attempts made in the experimental laboratory to correlate biological activities and conditions with psychological processes, both when they are and are not overtly described as psychic. We want to consider especially the efforts in this direction since (1) radio engineering has provided technological instruments for refined biological measurements, and (2) biologists and biochemists have developed increased information concerning physiological activities. For convenience of exposition we subdivide the experiments treated in this chapter into psychomotor, psychovisceral, and psychoelectrical correlations.

PSYCHOMOTOR CORRELATION

Early in the evolution of P.P., psychologists developed the experimental method of expression for the study of affective processes. This method paralleled the impression method in which the subject reported his affective introspections. The expressive method was used to record the subject's bodily states as "expressions" of certain mental states called feelings. In addition to records of pulse rate and blood volume, muscular expressions have been registered by means of the automatograph. Underlying this work, of course, was the theory of psychophysiological parallelism. Although it was soon recognized that "we have gained little from the method except a number of divergent results" (597, p. 249), the same general theory underlies the recent use of electrical recording devices for ascertaining the presence of bodily processes while psychological action is going on.

Psychologists have been keenly alert to the development of cathode tubes, amplifiers, and other electronic instruments, and have increasingly employed them. Having thus achieved facility in making refined measurements of muscle action they have performed a large number of experiments classifiable as psychomotor correlations. Some of these experiments have been reported under the heading of the motor theory of consciousness, whereas others have been regarded as general studies of the correlation between psychological and motor or muscular events. In the former the experimenters imply, at least, that they are interested in the correlation of psychic and organic processes, while in the latter they either attempt to bypass the implication or simply ignore the question.

Motor Theory of Consciousness. In 1930 Jacobson (260-

265) published a number of papers concerning muscle potentials obtained from subjects who were asked to imagine movements such as bending the arm, to image visually certain objects and acts, and to think about abstract things. This experimenter assumed that the muscles from which action currents are obtained were particularly concerned with the imagined actions. The general tenor of Jacobson's interpretations is that mental actions are correlated with actual organic processes. More specifically he believes he has provided evidence that the physiology of mental activity is not confined to closed circuits within the brain but also include muscular action.

Another series of experiments implying the same general trend of interpretative results was performed by Max (408, 409) who recorded action potentials from subjects in different conditions such as waking and sleeping, and while engaged in various activities—for example, dreaming, performing kinaesthetic imagery, and thinking. Publishing his results as experimental studies of the motor theory of consciousness, this writer like Jacobson appears to think in terms of a correlation of mental states or processes and muscle action.

Correlation of Psychological and Muscular Action. The primary differentiation between the above writers and those to follow is that at least some of the latter overtly wish to avoid the consciousness interpretation. For example, Davis (111, p. 5) adopts a peripheral theory which does not introduce consciousness as a middle term. Thus he regards his work as similar to a motor theory of learning or memory. In the paper cited, his results and those of others are regarded as showing a fundamental positive relation between psychological and muscular processes.

Immediately the question arises whether any attempt to correlate muscular movements or tensions with psychological actions such as sets in reaction-time situations can avoid the mind-body construction. One might, of course, correlate a part (muscle tension) with a whole (psychological response), but to insist that muscle process is present is to suggest that the psychological process is something other than the action of an organism.

A possible justification for such an argument lies in the frequent assertion that the organic processes with which psychological processes are correlated are exclusively neural. For example, while studying the foreperiod of the reaction-time experiment, Hathaway (202) failed to obtain any action currents from certain muscles, and concluded that the organic accompaniment of the psychological process is entirely cerebral. Hathaway's failure to elicit muscle-action potentials is traceable to the insensitivity of his apparatus (113, p. 7), but the absence of muscle records does not preclude an interpretation of psychologico-organic correlation.

Another example of alleged psychological action without peripheral or musculo-organic correlation is offered by Mowrer and others (446-448). The action in question is expectancy or anticipatory set which is presumed to be exclusively mediated by central or neural mechanisms. Finding reaction time to be longer when a subject is shifted to an unanticipated stimulus, the writers concluded that since the motor actions are the same it was the cerebrally-localized stimulus expectancy which accounted for the time difference. The two impossible assumptions of this conclusion stand out starkly. First, it is assumed that in some kinds of behavior the organism can act in parts, and secondly that cerebral or, in general, neural action can operate without muscle action.

Probably all psychomotor correlations are subject to the criticism of separating out factors from unitary events. The separation of neural and muscular action or both of these from the remainder of what is a single response throws sharply into relief the following polar constructions concerning psychological events. (a) All psychological events constitute unitary responses of organisms in interrelation with stimulus situations. (b) Psychological events may consist of autonomous responses separated from stimuli or even fragmentary phases of a response. All such analytic constructions as in (b) certainly stem from a mind-body source.

A series of psychomotor studies constituting an extension of the conception of simple psychological and muscle-action correlations is concerned with particular muscle patterns presumed to correlate with uniquely differentiated psychological activities. Those writers, who, like Jacobson (266) incline sharply toward the correspondence of consciousness with muscle action, look for particular muscles or muscle groups as the locus of the correlation. By contrast, the proponents of the general-psychological and motor-correspondence theory allow for a spread and patterning of the motor factors. Thus Freeman (150-153) finds that while at first there is a "spread of neuromuscular activity," the motor effect tends to confine itself to particular local muscles. On the other hand, Davis (112, 114, 115), Shaw (544), and Daniel (108) are convinced that there are fairly widespread muscle actions while performing various activities (imagining, multiplying numbers, learning nonsense syllables, tracing mazes), though the muscle action is patterned with maximal and minimal points.

The psychomotor situation is clear. We need only compare the protocols with their related hypotheses and interpretative constructions. With respect to the motor theory of consciousness, does it not seem strange that experiments are required to show that while a subject is imagining or thinking he is also performing muscular work? Is it permissible to suppose that when an organism acts no muscular action is involved? Despite the obvious dualistic thinking behind such experiments, they actually constitute the testing of techniques to record muscular action rather than methods of showing the correlation of mental and physiological processes.

Similarly, investigators who attempt to correlate psychological and physiological processes operate under a dualistic formula though they ignore or deny the fact. So far as the protocols go we have, of course, only data concerning muscle action under various behavioral conditions. When the measurements are efficacious one achieves precise data concerning muscle action in addition to demonstrating that muscle action always constitutes a part of all responses or response patterns.

But to interpret the findings as showing psychological and muscular correlations is reminiscent of dualistic thinking. To avoid this a forthright acknowledgement of the following is necessary: (a) that one is simply exploring isolated movements or patterns of action as features of a total interbehavioral field, and (b) that the responses and response patterns constitute loci or matrices of response functions which are phases of larger events which always also include stimulus functions.

PSYCHOVISCERAL CORRELATION

Bard (24) begins his discussion of the neuro-humoral basis of emotional reactions with the sentence: "For centuries bodily change has been the criterion of emotions." This statement indicates the historical fact that from the earliest differentiation of spirit and flesh or mind and body a more intimate correlation has been assumed between "emotion" and the organic than between bodily processes and other psychic states. Hence the idiomatic phrase "expression of emotion."

The very nature of affective behavior has forced upon psychologists the obvious fact that the organism's activity should be in the forefront of psychological description. Though the organic factors have been interpreted in dualistic terms, writers dealing with affective behavior have found it necessary to take account of visceral as well as nonvisceral organic actions. Thus Titchener (597, p. 479 f.) in his discussion of the James-Lange theory of emotions points out that its emphasis of the organic and visceral has been anticipated in modern times by Malebranche, Descartes, Spinoza, Lotze, and others, and in the ancient period by Aristotle.

Quite in keeping with the scientific circumstance that newly-ascertained data are assimilated to prevailing theoretical constructions, the increased knowledge of the anatomy and physiology of the autonomic nervous system and the endocrine glands was aligned with the general physiological tradition of correlating pulse rate, heart changes, and blood volume with feelings and emotions.

Obviously, organisms act differently under different conditions. All their organs and functions change when the circumstances under which they exist vary from moment to moment. A number of such deviations have become established fact. For instance, the literature on complex exciting behavior contains standard enumerations of visceral and vascular changes. Cannon and his numerous collaborators (79) have specified that in emotional situations the direct secretion of adrenin into the blood stream results in: (1) modification of blood distribution; from the abdominal viscera it is driven to heart, lungs, central nervous system and limbs. (2) Blood pressure becomes varied. (3) The spleen is influenced to release red corpuscles into the blood stream. (4) Blood is coagulated at a more rapid rate. (5) The liver releases glycogen into the blood stream. (6) Smooth muscles and the bronchioles are relaxed.

The process of assimilating the data concerning the autonomic factors of the nervous system and the functioning of the endocrine glands to traditional theory can be conveniently traced in recent writings on emotions. The psychophysiological problem centers about the priority of the visceral happening or the psychic process.

Recall that according to James:

The bodily changes follow directly the perception of the exciting fact, and that our feeling (= psychic state) of the same changes as they occur *is* the emotion (267, II, p. 449).

The full flavor of the psychic and physiological relationships involved, as well as the generalization of the theory to cover both crude and subtle emotions, is clearly revealed in the following passage.

An object falls on a sense-organ, affects a cortical part, and is perceived; or else the latter, excited inwardly, gives rise to an idea of the same object. Quick as a flash, the reflex currents pass down through their preordained channels, alter the condition of muscle, skin, and viscus; and these alterations, perceived, like the original object, in as many portions of the cortex, combine with it in consciousness and transform it from an object-simply-apprehended into an object-emotionally-felt (267, II, p. 473-4).

Challenging this statement of the relationship between the psychic and physiological processes, Sherrington proceeded to bring experimental evidence against it. Working with dogs, he transected the spinal cord in the lower cervical region, thus cutting off from the brain "all nexus with the thoracic abdominal and pelvic viscera, except that existing through certain cranial nerves." Yet, Sherrington reports:

If reliance be placed on the signs that are usually taken to signify pleasure, anger, disgust, then these animals showed them as unmistakably after as prior to the transection of the cervical spinal cord (549).

Again, Cannon and his coworkers removed the entire sympathetic division of the autonomic system from cats who had been kept in a healthy state for many months, and with "no effect upon the emotional response of the parts which remained capable of reacting" (79, p. 301). Cannon reports (1927) that in the sympathectomized cats:

All superficial signs of rage were manifested in the presence of a barking dog—hissing, growling, retraction of the ears, showing of the teeth, lifting of the paw to strike—except erection of the hairs (78).

The physiologists concluded, then, that the psychic state of emotion does not follow visceral changes but is indeed independent of them. Cannon offers five arguments against James's theory:

(1) Total separation of the viscera from the central nervous system does not alter emotional behavior; (2) the same visceral changes occur in very different emotional states and in non-emotional states; (3) the viscera are relatively insensitive structures; (4) visceral changes are too slow to be a source of emotional feelings; and (5) artificial induction of the visceral changes typical of strong emotions does not produce them (79, ch. 18).

In the words of Bard:

Every relevant fact points away from the periphery directly

toward the brain as the site of the processes which determine whether or not a stimulus shall give rise to emotional feeling (24, p. 305).

What strange uses experimentation can be put to! Nothing less than to establish the nature and locus of psychic states. Constructions about these psychic states are presumably made because no possible differentiation can be discovered between emotions on the basis of visceral patterns or the independence of emotions from the viscera. And what about the nature of emotion! It is hardly true that experimental work has necessitated the interpretation that emotions are psychic states correlated with either the visceral or other physiological processes (531, p. 214 f.). The conception of emotional expression or the correlation of the psychic and the organic is a tribute to the psychophysiological tradition and nothing more.

Cannon (78), Dana (105), and Bard and coworkers (23-25) have developed a psychophysiological theory which they regard as in line with the experimental evidences that still make the psychical primarily dependent upon the brain. This is the well-known diencephalic theory, that emotion results from the action and reaction of the cerebral cortex and the diencephalon. The latter it is believed contains the neural pattern responsible for emotional behavior, while at the same time it exerts the kind of influence upon the cerebral cortex which is necessary for emotional *consciousness*. Admittedly these workers have garnered many facts which throw light on the operation of the thalamus and point to changes in behavior resulting from its pathology. But is it possible to make out a case for localizing emotions primarily or secondarily in the thalamus? Lashley (350) and others (404) have incisively criticized this localization interpretation.

Those who are able to set aside the psychophysiological tradition which correlates psychic and visceral processes are free to adopt a completely different interpretation of the available data concerning emotions. First as to expression. Even dualists have shown that expression is not really a feature of the organism's responses, but a description of the observer (86). Such an observer need not at all regard these expressions, or what the organism does, as correlates of psychic states, but rather as features of a complex pattern of action performed under specific behavioral conditions. Secondly, to take account of the activity of the organism, whether in an intact or mutilated condition, provides sufficient material for differentiation of responses. Whether the action is anger or fear or some other kind is a function of the total situation as well as of the interbehavioral history of the organism in such situations. The difficulties we have mentioned concerning the indifference of the visceral pattern with respect to emotional behavior are all cleared up when we do not begin in the first place with a correlation hypothesis but instead with an interbehavioral situation.

According to the interbehavioral hypothesis the visceral, muscular, and in general, organic events, are participating factors in a complex field. Beginning our study of the organism in its diverse particular interbehaviors with objects under specific setting conditions, we describe the various organic activities as component factors in the organism's response. On this basis we can readily account for the likenesses between such organic events in different situations and for their differences in similar fields. Emotions do not become indifferently psychic states (fear, pain, hunger, etc.,) correlated with similar bodily conditions and actions.

Again, to take account of actual interbehavioral events precludes overlooking various organic patterns in emotional, genuine affective, and other forms of responses (289, 292). In each type of activity we expect a different set of reaction systems depending upon the type of stimulus and response functions as well as the immediate setting and individual's general reactional biography. To study organic factors in complex responses helps to differentiate between the orderly activities of feeling and the disruptive behavior of emotions (289, 292), or between shock and startle, on the one hand, and authentic emotions, on the other. Discarding the basic postulate of psychovisceral coordination allows a clear view of the contrast between the feelings found in ordinary interbehavior with stimulus objects and the behavior called cold emotions induced by the administration of adrenalin (81, 335, 397).

Those who seek expressions of emotions in the form of general bodily and facial gestures overlook two important items. First, they lump together feelings, emotions, pain, and other types of interbehavior. Secondly, they pay no attention to cultural factors, and thus simply assume that there are or must be organic signs or symptoms of psychic states. But even those objective psychologists who would banish consciousness or the psychic from their descriptions make use of the nervous system as an explanatory principle. What little correlation is discovered between various feeling responses and gestural-action patterns can certainly be accounted for by the same type of cultural factors that account for the wide distribution of similar speech forms.

PSYCHOELECTRICAL CORRELATION

The Psychogalvanic Reflex. When Féré (138) and Tarchanoff (591) first called the attention of psychologists to the electrical conductivity, which Veraguth (606) named the psychogalvanic reflex (PGR), they naturally oriented it to the psychophysiological laboratory. As an indicator of physiological activities, which at the same time was precise and clear-cut, the PGR appeared promising for psychophysical correlations. Since it soon became evident that the PGR was associable with action in the autonomic nervous system, the way seemed clear to use it for measuring bodily action correlated with emotions.

From the standpoint of conventional P.P., the usual story unfolded—early enthusiasm with many investigations begun and more or less completely carried out, followed by discoordination of results and interpretations. Though PGR was thought to promise most for emotional situations, opposed evidence accumulated rapidly. Prideaux (502, 503) found that the PGR was certainly not proportional to the amount of excitation, while Jones (282) and Landis (334) obtained inverse correlations. The inverse correlation was not corroborated, however, by other workers, for example Seward and Seward (543).

Psychologists who do not atomize the individual nor attempt to find correlations between the action of organic parts and specific psychological performances would never have expected PGR and emotional correspondences. Some investigators, however, found unmistakable PGR effects during intellectual work (502, 540), though the writers mentioned and others associate electrical-resistance changes with variations in difficulty, stress, and comfort of whatever type of reactions performed.

Is it an extreme conclusion that PGR like many other physiological effects constitute merely indicators of general action and change of action, and therefore as data are concerned with responses more or less neutral with respect to the stimulus conditions so significant for genuine units of psychological responses? Since skin resistance with its sympathetic involvement participates in many situations it is quite plausible that we learn from the PGR only some details of organic operations and not anything essentially psychological.

On the other hand, PGR investigations are very important in clearing the way for the study of specific characteristics of psychological events. Granted that whatever physiological indicators are common to many types of psychological action show nothing more than that psychological actions are performed by organisms, can we remain content with them? What psychological enterprise is advanced by tolerating such a simple level of data? Only on such a level, however, may we regard PGR data as correlational; therefore merely in the sense that they make us realize the need for more adequate constructions do they constitute important features of psychological investigation.

Electroencephalography. Interest in psychoelectrical correlations has quite generally shifted from PGR to electroencephalographic (EEG) studies. As an item of psychological history, the facts of origin and assimilation of EEG follow closely the PGR and other developments in psychology. It is only a minor variation in general pattern that psychologists stressed mental processes in the PGR, such that deviations in electrical resistance became their indicators, while the emphasis in EEG studies was placed on brain effects.

So recent are EEG developments that investigators are still feverishly searching for correlations. Because of the traditional association of psychological processes with brain processes the attempt is being made to associate electrical activity with intelligence, emotional behavior, personality traits, mental abnormalities, etc. The various excellent summaries of EEG findings (268, 269, 322, 372) effectively indicate how little promise there is in this direction. No sooner is a claim made for a particular type of correlation than it is negated. The following are typical examples. In 1938 Gottlober (186) correlated a high alpha wave type of EEG pattern with extravertive traits. When Henry and Knott (218) made a similar study they did not confirm his findings. Again Lindsley (371) failed to get significant relationships of EEG patterns with intelligence, dominance, and emotional-stability ratings, though such correlations had been reported.

Similar attempts have been made to correlate behavioral pathologies with particular EEG patterns. For example, Lemere (363) reported a correlation of "good" alpha waves with the cyclothymic mentality type, and "poor" alpha waves with schizoid, while others (538) have attempted to correlate psychoanalytically-derived instinctive and emotional trends with an alpha index. In view of the dubious existence of these traits and factors as general correlational items and the fairly arbitrary classification of EEG patterns, one can but be skeptical of correlation results between mental make-up and EEG rhythms.

It is already becoming clear that EEG events will have their greatest significance in studies concerned with biological events,[1] while psychoelectrical correlations will meet with the same criticisms as the PGR and other psychophysiological correlations. An important indication of the nonpsychological character of brain rhythms is that they occur during states of relative rest and in the absence of special stimulation.

To date, probably the most significant results of EEG studies concern the possibility of detecting and localizing brain lesions. Though such results, like many other distinctly biopathological findings, possess value for psychology, the connections are special, if not remote. Certainly such studies promise nothing for any traditional P.P. theory.

[1] Important here are Darrow's studies (108a, 108b) showing the interrelation of EEG with autonomic functions and vasomotor changes in the brain.

Chapter 14

PSYCHONEUROLOGY

THE self-elucidating term *psychoneurology* is employed to designate that branch of P.P. which attempts to explain psychological interactions by internal principles residing in the organism's neural tissues. The psychoneurological formula, "The brain is the organ of mind" implies that an organism is a self-mover or at least contains within itself cognitive, conative, and affective powers which account for its mode af action. When the formula is applied to abnormal situations it is assumed that the internal powers are somehow interfered with. In our discussion we shall use the term *cerebrology* to refer to neural constructions applied to general normal psychological processes, and the term *psychoneuropathology* when the formula is employed in dealing with abnormal behavior.

CEREBROLOGY

We have already referred (ch. 8) to the large number of brain explanations of sensory, ideational, conditioning and learning behavior by means of engrams, traces, general brain organization, and other purely arbitrary constructions. And in our historical résumé (ch. 7) we suggested that the inordinate emphasis of neurons and neural tissue arises from the traditional connection of the brain with the soul or consciousness. Even though psychologists no longer wish to have commerce with epiphenomena, they still cling to the spiritual seat as the source of internal powers that regulate and determine the organism's action patterns. This explains why the problem of centers and function localizations constitutes so basic a feature of cerebrology.

For a perfect example of cerebrological constructions we fortunately need go no farther back than James. In his discussion of the production of movement he points out that the final result of the purely inward processes and products must be some form of bodily activity. This resulting activity is:

. . . due to the escape of the central excitement through out-going nerves. The whole neural organism, it will be remembered, is physiologically considered, but a machine for converting stim-uli into reactions; and the intellectual part of our life is knit up with but the middle or "central" portion of the machine's opera-tions (267, II, p. 372).

What James means by intellectual is, of course, psychic. Recall that in his theory of emotions the basic point is that even if the emotional mental state does not precede move-ment there are perceptual mental states that always do. It is apparent, then, that cerebral action is emphasized because of the psychophysiological tradition. A similar theory of psy-chic process going over into external action is found in Wundt's (650) description of volition. For him, volition con-sists of an external act following an emotional state which constitutes its preparation.

The only factual basis for cerebrology therefore lies in the facts of neural or general anatomical organization. The anatomist's ability to work out pathways or lines of inter-connection between sense organs and brain terminals, coupled with the psychoneural tradition, has led to every variety of localization and correlation construction. Not a single item in these investigations shows more than that neural mechanisms operate to integrate and coordinate the organism. Also, neurophysiologists have piled up evidences of the unitary and total operation of the organism in both normal and mutilated animals. Analyses of postural tonus by Sherrington (549), Magnus (389, 390), and many others have demonstrated the coordination of the organism's actions with the conjoint effects of motor, proprioceptive, cutaneous, vestibular, and visual conditions.

The classic cerebrological construction of specialized powers of neural tissues—mediating consciousness, storing up skills, or controlling the actions of muscles and glands—is plainly anthropomorphic and magical, as the following quotation indicates:

Nerve structure is far more important than elaborate motile organs in developing skill. The presence of muscles is essential to movement; but the coordination and fine adjustment of movements is controlled by the central nervous system. A study of handwriting will demonstrate this. First write your name in the ordinary way; then write it in very small letters, using only finger-movements; then keep your fingers rigid and use only the wrist; finally write your name in large letters on the blackboard, using only arm movements. Although the muscles involved are different in each case, there is found to be a general similarity between the several results; the individuality of a man's handwriting is due to characteristics of the impulses from the brain centers, not to the constitution of the muscles (613, p. 379).

What warrant is there for separating the action of nerve impulses from muscles, and endowing the former with guiding and determining powers? Clearly, the neural functions are made to do what the psychic processes were invented for. Complex behavior is reduced to functions performed by, or related to, brain processes. Interestingly enough, when James puzzled over this relationship he rejected the notion "that each cell stands for an idea or part of an idea" (267, I, p. 81). Nevertheless, he did not hesitate to make general connections between brain processes and consciousness, a tradition which continues to the present day. We quote a lucid statement of James concerning brain processes basic to mental processes.

Too much anatomy has been found to order for theoretic purposes, even by the anatomists; and popular-science notions of cells and fibres are almost wholly wide of the truth. Let us therefore relegate the subject of the *intimate* workings of the brain to the physiology of the future (267, I, pp. 81-2).

How powerful cerebrology is and how ineffective were James's warnings, and before him Lewes's (367), against imaginary physiology may be gathered from the present-day urge to manufacture physiology for psychological purposes, even when the science of physiology provides no raw materials (501).

Despite the obvious fact that the development of knowledge concerning the workings of the nervous system precludes neurological explanations of psychological events, such explanations persist unabated. This is as true for behavioristic as well as mentalistic psychology. Though, as we shall see in Chapter 15, extirpation and other studies reveal no definite neural patterns basic to psychological action, there is no cessation in the construction of traces, engrams, and complicated but indefinite patterns and complexes of patterns. In Chapter 10 we saw that psychologists go so far in this direction that they even assert a coalescence of neurology and psychology (353, 369).

The persistence of cerebrological theories is excellently illustrated by Lashley's writings. This author has effectively demonstrated the fallacy of localized traces or engrams subserving specific "functions." He has pointed out the unusual occurrence of generalization—that is, the ability of organisms to react to the larger or brighter of two objects when it has become trained in the transposition experiment to respond to the present smaller or less bright object as the relatively brighter or larger object (354, p. 302). He has also indicated that this ability does not involve transcortical association or control by "higher" intellectual centers. Furthermore, he has affirmed that the principle involved in the transposition experiment:

. . . is that the reaction is determined by relations subsisting within the stimulus complex and not by association of a reaction with any definite group of receptor cells (354, p. 304).

And finally he asserts that a second stimulation by an object need not and practically never does involve the original combination of sensory cells.

In the end, however, Lashley cleaves to a cerebrological explanation. When he speaks of certain proportions or relations among the elements of a stimulus pattern (354, p. 305) he refers to an organization of neurons in the cerebrum. What clearer exhibition is needed of a prejudice for neural explanations not warranted by any necessities of the scientific situation! In the meantime the remainder of the organism is not only neglected, but the coordinating functions of the neural tissues are enlarged upon way beyond the facts.

Significantly enough, it is Lashley himself who has shown in how many different ways an organism's responses may be carried out. For example, writing with the right hand, left hand, and teeth displays noticeable similarities in product. Also rats suffering motor incoordination from cerebellar lesions traverse a previously-learned maze by means of movements very different from those involved in the original learning (357). Cerebrological constructions are therefore made superfluous by taking into account interbehavioral interrelations of the total organism (intact or mutilated) with stimulus objects and surrounding conditions.

Lashley undoubtedly confronts the dilemma of carrying far enough the implication of experimental findings, and the danger it holds of crossing over to wrong theory. He is apparently afraid that to abandon the search for the neurological basis of behavior might land him in the vitalistic camp. This fear is as groundless as it is dangerous to psychological theory. A field explanation constructed in conformity with the original events is objective and scientifically satisfactory.

Cerebrologists cling as rigidly to their neural explanations as their predecessors to the mental, and appear to set aside or overlook the actual conditions of behavior. Lashley (351) quotes Borovski (50) who showed that gulls which retrieve eggs from some distance will not do so except under particular conditions. Though they retrieve objects other than eggs —for example, small pebbles, potatoes, and billiard balls, despite texture, weight, and specific heat, but only if they have a round or oval form—they will not retrieve cubes or angular stones. He quotes his own observation on terns, which reject eggs if their forms are distorted by having mud or wax stuck on them.

The stimulus, Lashley says, must be adequate. It may be

defined as "a round object of certain limited size and texture" (351, p. 455). He also quotes Stone (583) as defining the stimulus to sexual excitement in the male rat as an object of a certain size which exhibits a definite jerking movement.[1] He goes further to indicate that the setting of the behavior is also important. The mother rat reacts differently to her infants in and out of the nest. The same thing is observed in the behavior of the sooty tern with respect to a chick when the nest does or does not form the setting. Lashley asserts significantly:

Psychological theories based upon the relations of stimulus and response remain sheer nonsense so long as the stimulus is defined only as whatever the experimenter puts in front of the animal (351, p. 455).[2]

But he is not content until he invokes some internal factors in the organism on the basis of perceptual organization.

Lashley likewise has demonstrated another important condition for learning—namely, the selectivity of set, or otherwise put, the effect of its interbehavioral history. Rats were trained to discriminate between two circles of unequal size. Then a triangle was substituted for the larger circle which was preferred for its size. When the triangle was reduced in size to the same surface area as the smaller circle the rats failed to show a preference. Later when the rats were presented with a larger and smaller circle they reacted to the larger, as also when a large circle and smaller triangle were presented. These results are similar to those obtained with human subjects on the basis of such conditions as directed attention and specific selected instructions (p. 73). To attempt to explain these events by neural mechanisms is to run directly into imaginary physiological functions.

Psychoneuropathology

Pathological behavior has always been a rallying point

[1] Why not interpret these data in terms of stimulus-response functions. Cf. ch. 10.
[2] Cf. also (355).

for physiological psychologists. Variations of behavior based upon malformations and injuries have historically been regarded as demonstrating the dependence of psychological events upon biological conditions. This dependence, of course, has been differently construed by the proponents of varying psychological viewpoints. It is still the prevailing view, however, that psychological deficiencies can be accounted for by untoward conditions localized in the body. Concerning the functional psychoses, Cameron points out:

> Notwithstanding the disadvantages for scientific investigation that it entails, a purely metaphysical mind-body dualism is still the most widely accepted working hypothesis among research workers in this field (75, p. 454).

Again, the vicious circle. On the one hand, pathological events are presumed to support traditional psychophysiological theory, whereas, on the other, the alleged supporting facts are really constructions based on the accepted doctrine.

On the whole, of course, the cerebral part of the body is made the locus of psychopathology, though there is an increasing emphasis upon biochemical and other nonneural organic factors. In both cases we face the question whether psychological abnormalities constitute psychic disturbances mediated by or parallel to biological conditions. But even when psychological deficiencies are more objectively interpreted one may question the propriety of making organic difficulties the cause of complex behavior events (325, 507). In the present chapter we consider the problem only as it applies to neural structures and functions. Elsewhere (p. 316) we discuss nonneural localization of psychopathology.

Biopathology and Psychopathology. If classical psychoneural ideas have predominated in the field of psychopathology we can not in justice overlook the fact that data complexity constitutes an extenuating circumstance. Whenever we deal with any disordered condition of an individual we must expect to find a large number of intricately-integrated factors.

First as to the data themselves. Do we have before us a biopathology or a psychopathology? In the former we are concerned with some disorder, maladjustment or deterioration of the organism. The basic criterion, of course, is the loss or dysfunction of an anatomical part or its action; or the trouble may involve the total organism. In psychopathology, we are dealing with a disorder or irregularity of interbehavior. Whether or not some biological condition is a factor in the situation is to be determined by an examination of that situation.

Next we are interested in the interrelation of data. Very often particular instances of biopathology and psychopathology are complicated with each other. Even what is regarded as the most certain psychopathology, for example some definite hysterical behavior, need not be uncontaminated with biopathology. When the two types of pathology are found in the behavior situation of the same individual we may ask which is primary, either from the standpoint of date of occurrence or cure.

At all times assuredly we are concerned with constructional questions. Are psychopathologies to be regarded as mental disease or as behavior characterized as undesirable, unadaptable, or simply inconvenient and perhaps unconventional?

Organic and Functional Troubles. The fact that psychoneural conceptions have been based upon malformation and destruction of neural tissue appears to stress priority of neural deficiencies. On the other hand, it may well be that the emphasis on neural abnormality is simply a consequence of the well-intrenched psychocerebral tradition. Both of these views are set in the general dualistic matrix of modern scientific culture. What we are interested in, therefore, is the consideration of the general construction of organic and functional behavior abnormality.

When neuropathologists assert that this distinction is an improper one and argue that the term *functional* is a misnomer and clinical slang (91) because all behavior abnormalities must be rooted in organic difficulty, they simply aim at the target of a detached psychic. This is a commendable view, but it eventuates in nothing better than the continuation of the dualistic types of construction. For example, Cobb (91) regards it as axiomatic that function cannot exist without an organ which is functioning, and then goes on to adopt Pavlov's (479) idea that psychology consists of functions of highly integrated neural processes. Aside from continuing the psychic tradition those who hold this view and base the so-called functional disorders—schizophrenia, manic-depression, hysteria, etc.—on unknown lesions transform the biological nervous system into a seat for psychic processes or at least make it responsible for undesirable behavior. They overlook that their original data consist of persons in trouble, and so no question ever arises of not having a definite object with which to deal. The argument for a neural organ to harbor the mental function we have already noted is simply a consequence of the traditional dualistic presupposition.

Two consequences of the search for neural seats of function may be mentioned. First, all the work that gives negative results is set aside. The attitude is taken that it is so much the worse for the investigations and the facts produced. The second and more significant consequence is that any investigation leading to the actual factors which might be discovered in the origin and continuation of behavior troubles is discouraged.

We turn now to a brief examination of some abnormal behavior situations in order to throw light on some of the issues involved.

Defective Development. The literature devoted to those abnormalities traditionally labeled amentias presents clear-cut data showing that individuals suffering from organic deficiencies such as malformations and destructions of cortical tissue are unable to perform psychologically as do organically-normal individuals. But the data are not described or interpreted in a manner indicating an objective appreciation of the purely biological nature of the brain and the behavioral character of psychological performance. Instead, the axiom "that the brain is the organ of the mind" is regarded as universally admitted (91, p. 550; 140, p. 424). Accordingly innumerable correlations of brain defect and behavior deficiency are brought to the front. After postulating the dependence of mind upon brain it is easy to demonstrate such alleged correlations in various clinical cases such as hydrocephalic, microcephalic, amaurotic, and cystic idiots and imbeciles. The question, however, is: Are not these correlations simply interpretative consequences of prior assumptions?

What the data actually show is a lack of development of psychological behavior, and that the individuals are precluded from such development because they are not biologically complete or sound enough to enter into the necessary situations which result in psychological evolution. Is it not unequivocally apparent that the development of behavior equipment requires the prior development by organisms of the biological structures and functions which participate in such behavior?

In the study of amentia, or individuals lacking behavior equipment, one must decide whether a participative or correlation construction is more desirable. The former, of course, avoids all assumptions of function localization, and adheres closely to actual behavior conditions. When malformation or destruction is relatively complete the individual is unable to develop any but the simplest responses, whereas partial malformations and destructions do not prevent him from developing a certain amount and a certain type of behavior. For the partial biological deficiency, substitute forms of action may be evolved. For example, malformation or injury of visual projection terminals hinders the individual from developing visual reactions as performed by other persons, but he can interact with the auditory qualities of the stimulus object.

Look at the aments whose primary difficulties are not

cerebral at all. What becomes of the correlation and localization principles in such instances! Or the cretins whose biological deficiencies may be traced primarily to glandular and hormonal disturbances. Then there are the deprivational cases—individuals who are not prevented from developing behavior equipment because of biological deficiency, but because they are hindered in coming into contact with stimulus objects allowing for psychological development. Kaspar Hauser is an instance (601).

Behavioral Deterioration. Deterioration of behavior may, of course, be closely paralleled with brain lesions. The classic illustration is obviously the progressive deterioration of the cerebrum in dementia paralytica. Moreover, in such cases one observes the invasion of the central nervous system by the syphilitic microorganisms *spirochaeta pallida.*

As long as we remain on the broad level of crude data the general correlation of cerebral and behavioral deterioration is unobjectionable, especially if we regard this correlation as rooted in the principle of the deterioration of participating organic parts, a deterioration which interferes with the individual's manner of behavior. Difficulties arise, however, as soon as specialized interpretations are made concerning the causal effects of brain deterioration. The next unfortunate step is to assume that particular mental symptoms, such as delusions, are directly caused by cerebral deterioration.

After all, is there any way of differentiating between cerebral or neural and nonneural deterioration as correlates of behavior deterioration? For example, behavior deterioration parallels closely the deterioration of the vascular system, as in arteriosclerosis. Also the psychiatrist must admit that very similar forms of psychological deterioration can not be correlated at all with organic lesions except by argument and intention. Such facts are easily handled on the participation principle; since any of the field factors in a satisfactory behavior event are necessary, it follows that any imperfection in one or more of the factors modifies the total event. In

short, wére psychological behavior not compromised with the
dualistic interpretation there would be no question concerning the correlation of the biological and the mental.

Disintegration of Behavior. Such types of behavior as
manic-depressive and epileptic maladjustments are exceedingly important for P.P. studies. Especially in the former,
neurological interpretations prevail despite the complete lack
of adequate evidence. Even though writers like Wertham and
Wertham (629) have seriously criticized the attempts to
correlate cerebral lesions with psychopathological phenomena, and despite the numerous objections of neurologists
and psychiatrists to localization of mental disease, the correlation conception remains the standard one.

More recently, we admit, exclusive preoccupation with
neural seats of pathological behavior has given way somewhat to other organic bases such as metabolic changes. Unfortunately the same dualistic principle is retained. The
more the pity, since the metabolic processes afford so fine
an opportunity to think in terms of participating factors in
unsatisfactory behavior situations.

Epileptic behavior besides being a fertile source of traditional P.P. interpretations also reveals the origin and significance of psychoneuropathological theories. A recent authoritative volume on the subject carries the localization item in
its title (485). On the whole the literature on epilepsy constitutes a record of many attempts to discover a physiological
or organic basis. Current writings on epilepsy are still prominently influenced by Hughlings Jackson and his theory of
the uninhibited irradiated discharge of impulses; thus it is
important to note that the rooting of epileptic behavior in
cerebral action is by Jackson's own testimony derived from
the P.P. doctrines of Herbert Spencer.

Epileptic behavior has undoubtedly appeared so favorable
to psychoneuropathological explanation because of the use
of the term *epilepsy* or *epilepsies* for a tremendous number
of both biopathological or psychopathological conditions.
Writers have adhered rather closely to the definition of

seizure, a fact which has favored a paucity of differentiation between the diverse kinds of behavior involved. Even when such differentiation is forced upon writers they still indulge in generalized interpretative constructions. Epilepsy is regarded as excessive neuronal discharge in the central nervous system. This construction, based on local brain pathology, has been generalized to cover all recurrent interruptions or disintegrations of behavior. Cases in which localization in the brain can not be assumed are disregarded. Nor are idiopathic or cryptogenic and symptomatic epilepsy distinguished, much less the range and variation of explosive behavior which includes *petit mal* cases and others departing widely from the generalized description of convulsion. Naturally enough, medical writers fail completely to consider behavioral seizures of the tantrum and strong affective and emotional forms not brought into the clinic or hospital.

The development of electroencephalogram techniques has led to a tremendous emphasis upon cerebral conditions in epileptic behavior. EEG findings are believed to reinforce the cerebral basis of all seizures. Actually, the attempts vigorously to correlate epileptic and organic activities offer indeterminate results. On the other hand, whatever positive findings there are can all be fitted into the formula of specific participating factors.

Traumatic Behavior. To study the literature on traumatic behavior yields more information concerning prevailing philosophical conceptions and culturoideological trends than how brain injuries influence behavior. It is not only rare but almost impossible to discover a writer who describes his findings without a superfluity of presuppositions. For medical clinicians the brain is unquestionably a seat of mental faculties. What they offer in consequence is a mass of spurious correlations—unfounded associations of brain injuries and psychological losses. Such dislocation of factors in complex situations goes much further than one might expect because of the lack of control yielded by laboratory studies.

Likewise, psychopathologists do not swerve far from the conventional construction that psychological events are basically functions correlated with, if not localized in, specific brain parts. But they must at least be credited with considerable vacillation when facts are revealed which upset the equilibrium of their conventional beliefs.

For our purposes it is sufficient to confine ourselves primarily to the aphasic type of traumatic data. Such data are not only abundant but also closer to psychological problems and more definite in description. Anyone interested in the influence of cultural ideas upon the theory of speech localization should study the history of aphasic concepts. When Broca established his speech center, presumably on the basis of an aphasic condition plus an autoptical finding, he was merely demonstrating a focalistic theory of brain functioning as against the totalistic theory of Flourens (146) and those of his predecessors and successors. Recall that both the focalists and totalists deal with mental functions or faculties on the one hand and something which is not language or speech on the other.

a. *Localization and Faculties.* All localizations of function in the brain imply dualistic psychology of the faculty variety. The two constructions of mental faculties and brain functions are homozygotic twins. This is equally true when the faculties consist of specific ideas or mental states as when they are said to be complex patterns of figure and ground (182, p. 84).

b. *Language and Speech.* The writings of Hughlings Jackson undoubtedly constitute a landmark in the study of the characteristics of language as a problem in aphasia. For one thing, he questioned whether articulation could be separated from speech. In his own words:

> The ataxy of articulation is a quasi-mental defect—an inability to combine muscular movements in a particular mental act (252, II, p. 223).

Also he thought of speech as propositioning instead of simple word utterance. Despite the Spencerian dualistic psychology which he espoused he certainly helped to advance the problem of the brain's operation in normal speech and its place in traumatic situations. Considering the time of his writings he deserves credit for showing how difficult it is to localize the "faculty of language."

> To locate the damage which destroys speech and to locate speech are two different things (252, II, p. 130).

Head, building on Jackson and clinging to the conventional notion of expression of thought, analyses speech into four functions, verbal, syntactical, nominal, and semantic. Departing from the notion of a single faculty, Head embraces the four already mentioned, and follows Jackson in distinguishing between localization and part-causing. He concludes:

> If the lesion falls over the lower portion of the central convolutions and the parts beneath them, the patient has difficulty in finding verbal forms in which to express his thoughts. Injury to the temporal lobe, on the other hand, leads to disordered rhythm and want of grammatical structure; speech tends to become true jargon. A lesion lying between the post-central fissure and the occipital lobule disturbs the appreciation of meaning, either verbal or general. Should the destruction occupy the neighbourhood of the angular gyrus, it is mainly the nominal value of words which suffers. If on the other hand it lies in the region of the supra-marginal gyrus, the patient finds difficulty in recognizing the ultimate significance of logical conceptions evolved by himself, or placed before him orally, in print or in pictures (205, p. 478).

Though Weisenburg and McBride (620) see clearly the difficulties and ineptitudes in the traditional localization of speech faculties through correlation of defects and lesions, they finally yield to such blandishments because of their own acceptance of the historical postulates of dualism and brain functions. They divide language functions into: (1) expressive, *i.e.*, motor acts, (2) receptive, *i.e.*, sensory action, (3) mixed expressive-receptive acts, and (4) amnesic conditions. Half-hearted localizations for these disturbances they arrange as follows:

(1) mostly in anterior zone.
(2) primarily in the posterior area.
(3) both of the former.
(4) undetermined (620, p. 473).

The localization of various arbitrary characteristics of speech is another item in aphasic discussions. Those who find neural parts responsible for the loss of semantic, verbal, and other functions build up a complete system—functions on the language side, versus injuries on the part of the brain. The development of such correlations seems uncomfortably close to the phrenological localization of destructiveness, wit, and benevolence.

c. *Conflicting Data and Lack of Correlation.* As early as 1868 Jackson reported a case of disease in Broca's area without defect of speech (252, II, p. 234). Since then obvious evidence has appeared that traumas can not be regarded as causes. In addition we have plenty of proof that speech difficulties and impairments can be studied on the basis of the individual's disturbance in traumatic situations. In this way we can take adequate account of shocks of various sorts. Certainly we can dispense with the simplicistic ideas of faculty and hypothetical brain localizations. On this basis, too, we can assimilate such theories as Marie's, that aphasia is a difficulty of intelligence, and Goldstein's doctrine of a trauma as a catastrophic event.

CHANGING IDEAS IN PSYCHONEUROPATHOLOGY

Although we find medical writers still glorifying the historical conception of mental functions and their localization, materials are available for a better interpretation of the data. Penfield and Erickson write:

It is now possible to recognize a localization of a portion of the nerve chain activity which underlies the more complicated mental processes of memory and dreaming, as well as certain autonomic activities (485, p. 32).

Their own findings, however, contradict the implied construction. Similarly, the observations of Fritsch and Hitzig
did not bear fruit as items in the proper understanding of
the biological organization and operation of the brain in
behavior. Instead by means of a semantic misinterpretation
those observations became the basis of psychocerebral correlations because of the use of the term *function* for physiological and psychological activity. The opportunity for
interpreting brain operation in normal and abnormal conditions as a participating factor in responses is constantly
missed. The attitude is maintained that the brain is a sacred
and inviolable organ rather than one anatomical and physiological member of the organismic household.

Obviously, mutilation of the brain or any other complex
organ must result in behavioral impairment and deficiency.
But the availability of facts has little effect. The Werthams
write:

Reichardt was one of the first to state definitively that, in psychoses, the brain stem played as important a role as the cortex.
He came to this conclusion through investigations of the vegetative disorders in dementia paralytica and other psychoses. But
the dogma that the cortex is the exclusive seat of psychic life
was, as far as anatomical investigations go, little influenced by
these conclusions (629, p. 365).

As to the cerebral localization of psychoses, the same
authors write:

. . . all attempts to find in the brain some region or regions
specific for psychoses have flatly failed. The problem of localization for psychoses is neither solved, nor is there any good pros-
pect of its solution. Indeed, it is possible that no problem, state-
able in such simple terms, even exists (629, p. 367).

Still, the Werthams, with all their insistence that the brain
is an organ of the body like any other and not something
unique, maintain that the doctrine of functional localization
in the central nervous system is well founded (629, p. 3).

Studies of brain injuries in war should certainly have led

to a full appreciation concerning lack of functional localization and to the reduction of the idea that thinking, speaking,
remembering, as well as other complex psychological activities, are simplified functions somehow correlated with the
operation of brain parts. These ideas, of course, could likewise be derived from observation of sporadic injuries occurring in civil life.

Among recent writers, Goldstein (181, 182) has stressed the
organismic view that the organism is a unique total entity and
that injuries produce total or catastrophic effects. But even
he finally resorts to generalized localizations of factors (183).
When, we ask, will the traditional notion of psychological
events as functions of organs or even of the organism be dissipated? Certainly this point must be urged against those who
really understand by function some psychic process. When
psychological events are described as the actual interbehavior
observed, this functional construction will disappear of itself,
or at least appear in its proper light.

So far as speech in particular is concerned, almost any kind
of disturbance of the individual is likely to affect speech behavior much more strikingly than any other apparent kind
of action. It is a common observation that speechlessness or
speech inhibition occurs even in simple startle or surprise
situations. Speech is so sensitive an indicator of an individual's condition that stuttering is frequently present in even
mildly-exciting circumstances. A similar condition is observable in the case of temporary amnesia, when moderate
disturbances and disintegration obtain. It is such amnesic
conditions which are made functions of aphasic malbehavior.

Chapter 15

EXPERIMENTAL PSYCHONEUROLOGY

IN the present chapter we examine extirpation experiments designed to investigate the neural mechanisms of learning, intelligence, discrimination, and other psychological activities. Since we can not hope to summarize the large mass of accumulated materials, we plan only to refer to some typical samples of experimental problems and results. Our aim is to reveal the postulates and hypotheses involved and the types of interpretation made.

Background of Experimental Psychoneurology

Because of the importance of experimental psychoneurology for P.P. theory it is interesting to glance briefly at the background and sources of this work. Investigators have striven either to prove or disprove traditional neural theory. Experimental psychoneurology, therefore, originated not from problems directly suggested by events investigated, but rather from events heavily encrusted with psychological and biological theory.

(a) *Localization of Mind.* Animal-extirpation experiments imply the historical postulate concerning the organs related to or responsible for mentation. Psychoneurological experiments may be traced back to the efforts of Flourens (146), Goltz (184, 185), Lewes (367), Pflüger (492), and others to determine what parts of the nervous system are centers of consciousness. At least there is a continuity between the present studies and earlier ones designed to test the claim that the spinal cord and other neuroaxial organs carry on such functions as were unhesitatingly attributed to the cerebrum.

(b) *Neural Mechanisms of Behavior.* With the rise of behaviorism a new impetus was given to ablation experiments. Psychologists were either no longer interested in purely psychic problems or they had become engrossed with the facts of conditioning and learning. Behavior in itself took on immense importance. The problem was to discover basic neural mechanisms. Lashley (343, pp. 14, 158) informs us, he began the study of cerebral functions with a definite bias toward the interpretation of learning as the concatenation of conditioned reflex arcs in the cortex. This bias, of course, was unsubtantiated, since his extirpation experiments led him to conclude that habits have a unitary character and involve large masses of nervous tissue rather than restricted conduction paths. This change of view, however, does not weaken the cerebral bias. Lashley still believes that it is precisely brain mechanisms which determine the individual's effectiveness in performing certain actions (343, p. 12). Actually this bias simmers down to the indisputable fact that "the nervous system is of unquestioned importance for the adaptive responses of the adult organism (347, p. 457). That this really is a bias is clear when we consider: (1) that other parts of the organism are not equally stressed and (2) that mutilation is not prominently featured as one of many other conditions in a learning situation.

Survey Plan

Depending upon the postulates adopted, one may choose either of two general plans for surveying extirpation studies. If the postulates of function and structure are chosen one looks upon extirpation investigations as yielding evidence of function loss when structures are ablated. If a field postulate is chosen, in other words if one does not regard psychological behavior as simply actions of organisms or their parts, extirpation data are sampled in order to discover the effects of mutilations. Mutilations on this basis are investigative factors in larger behavior-field situations which vary with changes in the organism's condition. For convenience of exposition we follow the conventional structure-function mode of presenting extirpation data, but at all times we endeavor to suggest the objections to such a procedure.

Visual Discrimination

The experimental investigation of the cerebral functions established in the middle of the 19th century was originated by biologists and especially physiologists. At that time it was as inevitable as it was proper to work on the structure-function plan. We can not but admire the zeal and devotion of such workers as Panizza (474), Hitzig (236), Shäfer (539), Munk (452, 453), Henschen (219, 220), Wilbrand (631), Luciani (385), Ferrier (139), and others with respect to whether visual functions are localizable in the occipital lobes, and above all in the striate area.

Today, however, should we not profit by our temporal advantage to achieve insight into the trials and errors of the early workers, and thus discontinue following their line of thought! Should we not expect an investigator to make a clean distinction between (1) the hypothesis that vision constitutes brain operation and (2) the fact that a mutilated organism can not perform visual behavior in the same manner as an intact one?

The accumulating data concerning visual behavior in mutilated animals may be conveniently grouped under the headings: (1) light-dark (2) comparative brightness (3) pattern and (4) movement discrimination. As a base line for surveying these data we choose the implications for an interbehavioral interpretation.

(1) *Light-Dark Discrimination.* Comparatively early experimental results have shown that the formation of light positive discrimination habits in rats is not retarded by the destruction of even as much as 60 per cent of the cortex including the striate area. Animals that formed the habit prior to operation upon the striate area lost it, although the retention of the habit learned by mutilated rats was not significantly inferior to that of normal animals (343, p. 121). What seemed most surprising was that mutilated animals were somewhat superior to normal ones in originally learning the light-going habit.

Krechevsky (326) vigorously questioned this lack of effectiveness of operated animals and offered evidence to explain the results. His suggestion was that any cortical lesion serves to reverse a rat's normal tendency of preferring the dark to the light path of a discrimination box. More recently, however, Abelmann and Morgan (1) have reported that the removal of the visual cortices in rats results in a markedly increased aversion from light. Apparently then if one regards dark preference as a satisfactory adaptation, mutilated animals show an improvement in behavior. Incidentally Krechevsky himself pointed out that the differences shown by normal and operated rats in learning light-dark habits tend to decrease when electric-shock punishment is used.

In a study published in 1934, Lashley and Frank (356) found that although the extirpation of the striate cortex in rats disturbs light-dark discrimination, these operated animals are able to relearn the behavior in the same number of trials as unoperated rats. Hilgard and Marquis report that the removal of visual cortex in dogs and monkeys studied by the conditioning method produced almost no change in the lid closure reaction to light.

The rate of acquisition and extinction of the response did not differ in the operated animals from the normal. The form of the response was unaltered, although its latency was slightly increased (232, p. 316).

The increase in latency mentioned is certainly a minimum of behavior change after such serious mutilation. An interesting comment upon these results is offered by Morgan (444, p. 507), who asserts that the area is used normally but it is not necessary that it should be so used. This remark is intended to favor functions and their localization.

(2) *Comparative-Brightness Discrimination.* Although the discrimination of the brightness differences between two lights is regarded as a more difficult reaction than light-dark discrimination, similar results are obtained in extirpation experiments on a large variety of animals.

Lashley, working with rats (343), Marquis (398) and Marquis and Hilgard (400) with dogs, Smith (565, 566) with cats, and Klüver (317, 318) and Marquis and Hilgard (232, 401) with monkeys have found that the ablation of the striate cortex does not abolish brightness-discrimination behavior. Such experimental results, however, do not discourage neurological interpretations. Those inclined toward general and special functions and their localizations argue that subcortical centers, for example the superior colliculi, take them over (173, 174, 222; 444, p. 508).

Referring to Lashley's rats, which after operation failed to perform brightness-discrimination reactions, but relearned them in about the same number of trials as normal animals, Morgan (444, p. 214) remarks that only habits are lost but not capacities. How revealed is the fragility of neurological constructions! They are built upon internal powers rather than upon actual neuronal operations!

A similar adherence to neurological dogma is evident in the following:

We may therefore conclude that learning a simple visual habit normally depends upon changes in specific visual structures (the striate areas of the cortex which are related to the lateral geniculate nuclei), but that such learning may take place in the absence of such structures (394, p. 321).

This statement refers to what Lashley (348, p. 61) calls the paradoxical result that the visual habit is somehow dependent upon the striate cortex when it is learned by the normal animal, and yet is formed just as readily when the striate cortex is absent.

(3) *Pattern Discrimination.* On the assumption that mutilation affects complex actions more than simple ones and that the more complex the organism the more serious any mutilation proves to be, pattern vision is thought to be more gravely disturbed than light-dark or comparative-brightness discrimination. Investigators agree that when the striate cortex is destroyed mammalian animals become permanently unable

to perform pattern discrimination reactions (232, p. 317; 346, 352, 444, p. 215; 567).

That the mutilation is to be stressed rather than cerebral localization is evident from a report by Kirk (308). Experimenting with rats he found that so relatively complex a reaction as discriminating between an upright and an inverted F was disturbed both when striate and unstriate tissue was ablated. In fact, the continuance of the discrimination reaction was more affected by nonstriate destruction.

Most certainly the exploration of more conditions operating in extirpation experiments than are now available will yield data favoring the general mutilation assumption rather than the specifying localization hypothesis. For example, Smith (565, 567) reports that striate-cortex operated cats when tested under lower illumination could discriminate between patterns of vertical and horizontal bars.

(4) *Movement Discrimination.* Although operated animals display a loss of effectiveness in discriminatory movements (307a; 444, p. 509) they do not fail to learn such acts. On the other hand, Smith (565) found that extirpation of the visual cortex in cats and other animals resulted in an improvement of their reflex eye movement in response to moving striations.

AUDITORY DISCRIMINATION

As Fulton (160, p. 337) points out, the history of the temporal lobes has been less dramatic than that of the occipital lobe. Because of its copious anatomical connection with other parts of the cortex Flechsig (145) concluded that it must be an important association center. As early as 1878 Heschl (228) traced auditory fiber radiations to the superior convolutions of the temporal lobes.

Imbued with the positive notion of centers and seats for functions Ferrier (139, 140) vigorously proclaimed the superior temporal convolution to be the exclusive seat of audi-tory functions. The bilateral ablation of this area in monkeys and other animals he was certain resulted in deafness. This finding was disputed by Brown and Schäfer (59), Munk (452,

453), and Larionow (341). It is interesting that the latter writer, as well as Kalischer (283) and more recently Henschen (219), localizes musical functions in the temporal lobes.

Quite aside from the venerable conception of function localization, recent data concerning the destruction of the so-called auditory cortex warn against close correlations as a basis for any theory. Wiley (632) and Pennington (486) have shown that rats can reacquire auditory habits after bilateral ablation of the temporal lobes. The latter author asserts (487, 488), however, that sound localization is obviated by the destruction of the projection regions. Jacobsen and Elder (256) report that the symmetrical bilateral ablation of the temporal lobes left a trained baboon essentially normal even in the delayed reaction test. They did find a slight upper-gradient visual defect. The animal was certainly not deaf, in fact reacted to the significance of spoken command sounds though it was somewhat deficient in localizing their sources. Fulton (160, p. 342) refers to an unpublished study by Wendt on monkeys and baboons in which slight impairment of auditory activity was found after subtotal ablation of the auditory cortex.

As happens so frequently, ablation experiments demonstrate more than are called for by localization or correlation hypotheses. Klüver and Bucy (320, 321) report that monkeys which undergo severe bilateral temporal-lobe ablation suffer psychic blindness. That is, they no longer react to things they formerly did. They cease to fear snakes, and pick up inedible objects and convey them to the mouth before rejecting them as unsuitable. These data are comparable to those brought forward by Herrick (225) concerning the rhinencephalon problem. The olfactory cortex, he asserts, not only mediates specific associations but also serves as a nonspecific activation for all cortical activities.[1]

---

[1] For statements concerning generalized neural functions see Herrick (226) and Lashley (344). Klüver and Bucy (321) report, however, that the bilateral ablation of the temporal lobes does not impair the ability to "generalize" in responding to visual stimuli.

Even though psychologists have followed the ideological pattern set by the older biologists who confused anatomical organization with seats for faculties, the results achieved by psychologists quite definitely fail to support such an ideology. In view of such results experimental psychoneurologists could well proceed on the basis of specific total actions performed under different field conditions.

SOMAESTHETIC DISCRIMINATION

Strangely enough, in their experimental ablation work students of the nervous system are surprised that neural-tissue mutilations result in impairment of behavior. Needless to say, this is the localization bias in reverse—in other words, a minimization of the obvious importance of the brain.

Interested in investigating the localization or representation of functions in the parietal lobes, Ruch (529) separately ablated the precentral, postcentral, and posterior parietal areas in monkeys. Little interference with the performance of weight discrimination occurred. Initial disturbance was overcome three or more weeks after both unilateral and bilateral lesions. Similar results were obtained in the case of tactile discrimination (roughness).

In the chimpanzee, separate postcentral gyrus and posterior parietal-lobe ablation probably results in a little more serious interference with discrimination of weight, roughness, and geometric form. After removing the posterior parietal lobule of a chimpanzee it regained discrimination between a cone and a pyramid but not between a pyramid and a wedge. The method used was palpation in the dark. A significant result, however, is that even when chimpanzees are completely lobectomized parietally:

. . . weight discriminatory capacity, roughness discrimination, and stereognostic capacity are permanently impaired, although not completely abolished (160, p. 359).

Consider the significance from an interpretative standpoint of the conclusion reached by Ruch, Fulton, and German

(530) concerning four human patients with parietal lesions. Of these, two were surgical cases, one with an anterior, and the other with a posterior lesion. An extended series of weight discrimination and roughness tests yielded evidence of decreased performance in all. While the physiologist finds it interesting that intraparietal zonal localization appears ruled out, we must also note that the loss was not as great in these four cases as in completely parietal-lobectomized chimpanzees. The importance of the findings lies precisely in the correlation of extent of injury and behavior loss rather than in any zonal localization.

MAZE BEHAVIOR

Extirpation studies employing maze running occupy a large place in the literature. The reasons are simple. Mazes by their ease of modification and their suitability for work with rats have long proved to be adaptable to investigations of relatively complex behavior. Also, since Watson's (617) studies on the factors of maze learning, the mutilation procedure has become traditional. With Lashley's investigations on the neural basis of learning the brain became a locus of mutilation.

The results of these investigations have become notorious. Although from the standpoint of correlating general mutilations with reduced effectiveness of action, the results are in line with expectation, they are usually treated from the angle of function and faculty localization and consequently are as disturbing as they are striking. So much so in fact as to lead to frenetic modifications of the laws of brain action.

Since Lashley first systematically explored the domain of maze behavior and has generally set the pace for these investigations, we can do no better than quote his summary of results.

1. The capacity to form maze habits is reduced by destruction of cerebral tissue.
2. The reduction is roughly proportional to the amount of destruction.

3. The same retardation in learning is produced by equal amounts of destruction in any of the cyto-architectural fields. Hence the capacity to learn the maze is dependent upon the amount of functional cortical tissue and not upon its anatomical specialization.

4. Additional evidence is presented to show that the interr 1ption of association or projection paths produces little disturbance of behavior, so long as cortical areas supplied by them remain in some functional connection with the rest of the nervous system.

5. The more complex the problem to be learned, the greater the retardation produced by any given extent of lesion.

6. The capacity to form simple habits of sensory discrimination is not significantly reduced by cerebral lesions, even when the entire sensory field is destroyed.

7. This immunity is probably due to the relative simplicity of such habits.

8. The capacity to retain is reduced, as is the capacity to learn.

9. The maze habit, formed before cerebral insult, is disturbed by lesions in any part of the cortex. The amount of reduction in efficiency of performance is proportional to the extent of injury and is independent of locus.

10. Reduction in ability to learn the maze is accompanied by many other disturbances of behavior, which cannot be stated quantitatively but which give a picture of general inadequacy in adaptative behavior.

11. No difference in behavior in maze situations could be detected after lesions in different cerebral areas, and the retardation in learning is not referable to any sensory defects.

12. A review of the literature on cerebral function in other mammals, including man, indicates that, in spite of the greater specialization of cerebral areas in the higher forms, the problems of cerebral function are not greatly different from those raised by experiments with the rat (343, p. 175 f.).

In the general framework of the investigations and the findings the emphasis is all on the part played by the brain. What appeared so striking was that careful quantitative studies should yield results so at variance with established thought concerning brain functions, especially the cortex. Although Lashley formulates his general results in brain terms, he does take account of the general deterioration of the operated animals. This is indicated by item 10 of the summary.

Maze-running results with cortical lesions are well established, as indicated by the work of Cameron (74), Loucks (381), Buytendijk (69, 70), Maier (393), and others. For us, the interest lies in the accent given to their interpretations. For example, Maier and Schneirla are careful to point out:

> . . . that no animal, even with 80 percent of its cortex destroyed, failed to learn at least to some extent (394, p. 326).

And still no question about the cortex interpretation is raised!

Similarly, Morgan (444, p. 499), who is decidedly under the domination not only of brain theory but also localization doctrine, is definitely puzzled by the fact that a smaller lesion is required to interfere with performances already established than in the case of those to be acquired. He is undoubtedly mindful of the tradition that (for the most part) brain interpretations are most serviceable as a basis for retention.

That noncerebral interpretations are possible for maze behavior is indicated in such recent findings as those of Erickson (133) and Honzik (238). The former presents data showing that in addition to the difficulty of the mazes the extirpation results correlate also with the success and failure of normal animals to learn mazes. With approximately 19 per cent cortical ablation, retardation of performances varied inversely with average learning performance. Morgan's reference to these findings is interesting:

> Thus the more intelligent rats seemed able to do without the given amount of cortex more easily than the duller ones (444, p. 499).

In a revised form of Watson's end-organ ablation Honzik has reported results of accumulative effects of injuries on maze behavior. In a descending series blind, anosmic, and deaf animals suffer greater inefficiency than blind, anosmic subjects; and these, greater effects than blind-deaf, and still greater than simply blind animals. There is doubtless some basis in these findings for the correlation of general mutilations with decrease in effectiveness of action.

PROBLEM-SOLVING BEHAVIOR

Descriptions of ablation effects in various problem-solving experiments take on a highly conventional pattern. The simpler the problem the greater the lesion required to disturb performance with respect to it. Investigations with rats yield such data as the comparisons that the solution of the relatively simple double-platform box used by Lashley (343) can be performed with cortical lesions up to 60 per cent, whereas a 30 per cent lesion interferes with the solution of latch-box problems. The solution of latch-box problems requires: (1) pushing a lever, (2) tearing a strip of paper, (3) pulling a handle, (4) pulling a chain, (5) depressing a rod, and (6) stepping on a platform (348).

As compared with discrimination and maze behavior the descriptive pattern of ablation effects varies somewhat. While the learning of such problems is independent of injury locus, the retention of latch-box behavior is connected with the frontal part of the cortex (343, 348) if the lesions are sufficiently extensive. But rats with destroyed frontal areas learn to open the boxes with a normal number of trials and still retain the behavior with further unlocalized destruction.

Results apparently out of line with the various problem-box experiments have been reported by Krechevsky (327) who devised a type of *Umweg* situation. Working with 76 rats he found that whereas normal animals adopted *Umweg* solutions in order to facilitate reaching the food boxes in the apparatus, relatively minor cortical lesions disturbed this behavior. An average of less than 20 per cent ablation is sufficient to interefere with the animal's performance of what the author believes is a more basic behavior pattern than in other studies. Extremely interesting, however, is the finding that no correlation exists between size and locus of lesions and the behavior disturbance.

Conditioning

Experimenters in the psychoneurological field face a number of questions concerning generalization from one type of animal to another or from one kind of performance situation to another. If one assumes that dogs, for example, are more complex animals than rats, or that conditioning is a more complex performance event than maze running, one may then question the pertinence of rat ablation experiments as bases for psychoneurological theory.

We have already seen (p. 132f.) that conditioning occurs in dogs and cats with absence of the entire cortex. Shall we then conclude that these investigations are sufficient to set aside the psychocerebral dogma? Difficulties arise, of course, if one adopts the view that the varying conditions of different animals and tasks must be kept distinct. As a matter of unique biological organization there is justification for the speculation that cortical ablations in rats disturb them more than they do dogs. But what if such tissue destructions have little psychological effect on conventionally-accepted higher animals? Experimental decortication data on primates are scanty. Granting that even in the dog, and certainly in the higher mammals, conditioned responses in completely decorticated subjects can only be obtained with intensive stimuli and prolonged training (232, p. 316), there are still many facts accumulating concerning cortical excisions in man (ch. 16) that makes adherence to the cerebral dogma a bold venture indeed.

In view of the acceptable doctrine of comparative neurology that in the ascending series of animals there is increasing encephalization, it is astonishing how many neurologists and physiological psychologists adopt the inverse theory that when the cortex is removed subcortical structures take over the displaced functions. True enough, when decorticated animals perform particular actions, whether or not conditioned, their subcortical tissues are present and participate in the coordinative behavior, but the function and localization constructions are supported not by the facts but only by an ideological system.

DELAYED REACTION

Because of their acknowledged complexity and difficulty, and because of animal type used, the important experiments on primates reported by Jacobsen (253, 254, 258), Malmo (395), and Finan (141-143) are especially interesting. These reports yield significant information concerning the effects of experimental presuppositions upon consequent interpretations concerning cortical functions.

Jacobsen trained monkeys to go for their food (which they saw placed under cups) after an interval during which they were prevented from doing so by a door interposed between them and the cups in a suitable apparatus. After extirpating various parts of the cortex he found that the excision of the. prefrontal areas rendered the animals unable to perform the delayed reaction. In a number of careful experiments performed in collaboration with others (257, 259) the conclusion was reached that only the prefrontal lobes were concerned with the performance. Lesions of the motor and premotor areas showed a slight improvement in performance (257).

Although the performance abolished was relative in the sense that the unoperated animal can solve the problem after a minute or two in the case of the monkey, or as long as five minutes for the chimpanzees, and whereas the operated animals can only do so by maintaining a posture directed toward the proper cup, the interpretation involved a definite area and the specific function of memory or anticipation of the future. The results obtained led Moniz and other surgeons to apply the findings to the surgical treatment of human pathologies (160, p. 425; 154, p. 11).

By a simple variation of the experimental procedure, Malmo (395) working with monkeys obtained decidedly different results. The change consisted in extinguishing the lights during the delay period. While under normal illumination Malmo's results were similar to Jacobsen's, when the lights are extinguished prefrontal animals are quite capable of performing delayed reactions. In fact, they do so with a high degree of accuracy (160, p. 424). Accordingly it could not be the prefrontally-localized function which enables animals to remember. Apparently the absence of distractions by other visual stimuli is one of the necessary conditions.

Fulton-Jacobsen obviously veer away from the memory-localization theory.

The situations in which frontal area deficit is most clearly demonstrated are those in which external stimulus control of behavior is at a minimum (160, p. 424).

Such situations include any performance in which a time interval separates the precurrent and consummatory phases of an action. The authors admit that this deficit is not absolute in the light of Finan's (141) experiments with the shuttle box and temporal maze problems, in which the animals are required to respond differentially to the passage of a fixed period of time. Finan's operated animals were able to solve temporal maze problems.

This shift of opinion concerning the functions of the frontal lobes must be emphasized. Whereas at one time the delayed-reaction ablation experiments were presumed to reveal memory-trace functions, now they are regarded as the seat of the ability "to keep a set in the face of distracting circumstances" (444, p. 556). Seats and functions at all costs! Anything but mutilations as participation factors in behavior situations!

Later work on delayed reaction becomes still more threatening to localization theory. In his 1939 study (141, p. 219) Finan reported that the cortical injuries which did not abolish the shuttle box and maze habits permanently impaired the delayed-response performance. Further investigation, however, yielded different results. Monkeys with ablated frontal lobes were able to perform delayed action when behavior conditions were modified (142, 143). Finan trained two animals by a reward method in the pre-delay period. Simultaneous bilateral frontal lobectomy completely abolished the behavior. But:

> Successful response was reinstated however by actually rewarding the subjects on the pre-delay trial for running to the presented drawer. Results obtained under this altered condition proved comparable in terms of accuracy and length of delay to those yielded by the same animals under preoperative conditions (142, p. 496).

REASONING

The topic of reasoning in the literature of experimental psychology is rarely treated. Maier (391-393), however, has reported some ablation results on rats. Defining reasoning as a behavior situation in which an animal becomes serially familiar with two separate parts of a problem, both of which must then be performed, he attempted to find the critical amount of anterior and posterior cortex necessary to destroy the performance of such behavior. His results showed that the critical mass for the anterior part of the cortex is 18 per cent. In general, lesions up to 10 per cent have little effect on the behavior, whereas the critical amounts mentioned result in a sudden falling off in reasoning ability; lesions greater than 25 per cent abolish it altogether. Maier emphasizes that aside from the quantitative difference in potentiality of the anterior and posterior parts of the cortex, there is no definite function localization. Mass rather than locus determines what will be the effect of a lesion.

Morgan (444, p. 553), as an extreme localizer, focuses on the fact that even a 10 per cent lesion anywhere in the cortex has some effect, and concludes that this generalized effect may be accounted for because reasoning involves several aspects of experience and response and thus concerns a considerable part of the cortex.

SUMMARY OF ABLATION EXPERIMENTS

The analysis of the literature on experimental psychoneurology informs us quite as much about the experimenters as about the data they investigate. This fact is deplorable only on the premise that complex human behavior is less interesting than the comparatively simpler activities of laboratory animals. Above all, we learn how tenaciously investigators cling to their presuppositions no matter how powerfully the winds of data blow. Even when they shift their position with respect to working hypotheses they stand firm with respect to general cultural trends.

The only clear-cut result of extirpation experiments is that mutilations are correlated with (a) simple difference, (b) deficiency, or (c) reduced effectiveness of action. Despite this evidence the view prevails that the brain is the basis or seat of psychological performances. True enough, some workers are emancipated from the doctrine of strict localizations. But all are apparently loath to give up the brain as the seat of psychological behavior. At best, the doctrine prevails that physiology or biology is the essence or basis of psychology.

The thought pattern of extirpation workers is obvious. Actions are grouped and generalized as functions regardless of whether they are psychological or biological. Any realization that psychological events consist of specific interactions with stimulus objects is totally lacking.

Obviously, ablation investigations like all others must be selective and contrived. But is the primary objective to obtain light on the nature and operation of psychological events or to substantiate the presupposition of an organ of behavior if not of mind? Why should the fact that ablations affect total vision or hearing be singled out as evidence of a particular area localization? Such strict localization involves anatomical projection—that is, the participation of specific organic tissue in psychologically indifferent behavior. We still have the alternative, however, of thinking in terms of the specific interbehavior of organisms with particular stimulus objects.

CEREBRAL FUNCTIONS AND FACULTIES

Despite the general opposition of psychologists to faculty concepts, most of them, including behaviorists and especially physiological psychologists, are still influenced by them. How else account for the persistent search for localizations and mediations of functions, when obviously there is a sharp rift between the correlation of functions and structures and the effects of injuries upon behavior performance. To attempt to locate the cerebral correlate of *speech*, for example, means that the term *speech* refers to a faculty. To attempt to locate *learning* signifies that learning is some sort of power usually called ability. Such conceptions stand in sharp contrast to the fact that speaking or learning constitutes complex inter-behavior specifically developed in particular behavior fields.

It is a simple matter to avoid the errors of functions and faculties. We need only keep alive to behavioral events. Such events can in no sense be limited to acts performed by organisms irrespective of interactions with objects. We have previously discussed (ch. 8) alternative constructions concerning *functions* and the differences between correlating: (1) tissue losses with lack of functions and (2) mutilations with behavior modification. Now we are interested in emphasizing brain mutilation as a condition of psychological performance.

Cerebral Action and Behavioral Conditions. Freedom from neural and especially cerebral dogmas allows for the consideration of brain action, whether of normal or mutilated tissues, as conditions of behavior. On this basis it is easy to assimilate the findings that interference with action is proportionate to mutilation whenever organic structures immediately participate in action. What this fact of participation signifies may be illustrated by equivalent movement behavior (343, pp. 159-160). For example, paralyzing the left arm while training the right in complicated manipulative movement does not prevent the recovered arm that was not used in the training to perform the action. The point is that the organism achieved the adaptation and could perform it either as a right- or left-arm behavior pattern or configuration. Lashley interprets these facts as follows:

It may indeed be stated as a general principle of behavior that psychological functions are of such a character that they must be independent of the particular nerve cells excited and be determined by the patterns or relations between points of excitation (353, p. 464).[1]

Revealed here is the neural bias, though the organismic view is approximated.

Taking the animal into consideration does not minimize the importance of any part. On the contrary, it serves more effectively to analyze the pattern of factors. As a rule we expect greater mutilations to constitute factors of more severely modified behavior conditions; for example, bilateral mutilation produces greater behavior interference than comparable unilateral destruction or injury. In addition, other factors whether or not organic must be taken into account.

Emphasis of interference conditions is exemplified in the study of the relative effects of peripheral and central or cerebral, or general neural factors. It was an historical error to regard such peripheral mutilations as Watson and others carried out in searching for maze-running factors in animals (617) as pointing to central neural mechanisms. Light upon this problem is available in Finley's study of equivalent losses in accuracy of responses after central and peripheral mutilations.

Under conditions described, interference with the central reception. of visual areas results in no greater loss of accuracy for rats running an elevated maze than does the enucleation of their eyes or the elimination of visual stimuli, and (that) the effect of central interference differs in no detectable way from that of peripheral (144, p. 235).

Lashley-Tsang (604) disagree. Naturally, the conclusion that:

Lesions involving approximately the same surface area of the

[1] See also (343, p. 158).

rat's cortex, but affecting more than one functional area or brain center may produce very much greater losses of accuracy in maze running than lesions limited to a single functional area (144, p. 235)

simply emphasizes the principle of greater interference with more varied integrating and coordinating tissues. Such results parallel Honzig's (238) findings of the relative effects of various peripheral mutilations and their combinations.

An interesting implication for condition study is found in Krechevsky's (326) attempt to account for Lashley's findings (a) that brightness discrimination is unaffected by rats lacking as much as 60 per cent of the cortex including the striate area, and (b) that mutilated animals are superior in their performance. His point is that a dark-positive problem is an altogether different kind of problem for an operated animal. He declares:

To assume that one and the same learning problem can be used to test the same function in both normal and mutilated animals is apparently unjustified in the light of the present data (326, p. 433).

It is highly probable that psychoneurologists have not accorded sufficient importance to such factors as attention, insight, and initiative, as Lashley (348, p. 38), Krechevsky (326, p. 47), and others (76a) point out. Though brain-biased writers take such factors lightly they are important for the student of actual animal behavior.

SPINAL CONDITIONING

Experiments designed to discover whether animals with transected spinal cords could be conditioned illuminate the problem of mutilation as a behavior condition. Working with spinal rats and recording muscle-action potentials, Prosser and Hunter (504) reported that the responses to clicks and electric shock were extinguished by 65 or more repetitions and reinstated by nonstimulation intervals of 15-20 minutes. Similar extinction and disinhibition occurred when the leg and tail were shocked or pinched. The authors did not regard their results as primarily showing conditioning because of the constant latency of the reactions.

Culler and Schurrager (99, 100, 557) transected the cord in dogs at points between the cervical and third lumbar spinal roots, and exposed the semitendinosus muscle. Using as conditioning stimuli mechanical and electrical stimulation of the tail, and unconditioned stimulation of the left hind-paw, the exposed semitendinosus muscle at first contracts or twitches only when the paw is shocked and later does so when the tail only is stimulated. These results are based on complete conditioning records of 57 dogs out of a total number of 219 experimented upon, though actually conditioned responses were elicited and extinguished in 98. The investigations lead to the belief that conditioned responses are different from spinal reflexes on the basis of two criteria: (a) extinction with repeated unreinforced stimulation and (b) lack of summation with continued conditioned stimulation.

Furthermore, these writers propose a definite neural explanation for their results.

Instead of the generalized functions commonly invoked to explain learning in the intact or thalamic animal, specific synaptic states are suggested as the responsible mechanisms for conditioning and extinction in the spinal preparation (557, p. 158).

The work of Culler and Shurrager poses a number of questions. For may we conclude that spinal preparations are able to perform complicated psychological action or even a type of physiological action resembling the former? We are reminded here of Mathew's comparison of the autocatalytic behavior of linseed oil with memory, and of various mechanical and electrochemical models of learning and conditioning.[1] We might well argue that Shurrager and Culler's results have demonstrated what complex actions mutilated organisms can do, without letting the name *conditioned re-*

[1] A list of these is given in Boring (49, p. 184n.).

sponse cover the muscle-twitch action of a spinal preparation as well as the conditioned type of actual learning behavior.

That the Culler-Shurrager animals were probably not exhibiting more than some complex form of physiological action is indicated by the reports of Kellogg and his students (302, 303) on spinal conditioning. The present investigation was made on four dogs in a considerably modified experiment. (1) Kellogg administered electric shock to the left rear foot for the conditioned stimulus, whereas for the unconditioned stimulus an electric shock was delivered to the right rear foot. (2) The animals were completely conditioned before transection to the point of 100 per cent flexion in 20 consecutive trials, and were kept alive for about three weeks after operation instead of being sacrificed on the same day. (3) The movement of the entire limb was recorded while the animals were held in an upright position, and not inverted with drill rods piercing the femurs as in the Culler-Shurrager studies.

Kellogg regards his results, which in some respects are similar to those of the earlier studies, as yielding not definite conditioning but some sort of change in reflex action, for example a surgically-segregated portion of a startle pattern. For one thing, he has observed similar action in intact-animal conditioning experiments. Again, both legs flexed on shock application to the left leg. The response was small in amplitude and of short latency, with no increase in the former with training. And finally the experiment indicated, besides the flexion movement, an antagonistic crossed extension movement in the unshocked leg.

Discounting the apparent implication in the Kellogg report that to obtain evidence for spinal conditioning, behavior similar to that of normal animals should be available, we agree that both studies indicate the differences between authentic psychological action and complex physiological performances. But most important, neither investigation implies that normal conditioning, whether or not identified with learning, consists of some sort of cortical organization, whereas spinal animals can only perform reflex action.

We suggest, therefore, that authentic psychological conditioning involves such a correspondence of response and stimulus functions that a stimulus function can be made to inhere in a second or third stimulus object in addition to the original one. In the two investigations before us the actions are primarily organic, irrespective of stimulus objects. The electric shocks allow little scope for stimulus functions which could correspond to response functions of any elaborate sort. This fact is suggested by Prosser and Hunter (504) and Kellogg (302, 303) when they describe the responses as startle reactions.

BRAIN-ACTION THEORIES AND BEHAVIORAL CONDITIONS

A prominent paradox of experimental psychoneurology concerns the fact that although brain investigations clearly imply that injuries constitute a condition of action, such injuries are assimilated to theories of brain localization and determination.

Mass Action. On the whole, extirpation experiments show that amount of mutilation is proportionate to efficiency of action. Under the influence of brain tradition this fact is formulated in a construction which implies that efficiency of behavior is proportionate to amount of functional tissue remaining. The emphasis, then, is on brain power rather than on the excision of structures participating in the response factor of the interbehavioral field.

Such construction bypasses several facts: (1) The mutilation constitutes the truncation of an organism and not of specific sources of power. (2) The mutilation of other than brain tissues likewise results in behavioral deficiencies. (3) Any modification in psychological-field components corresponds to changes in the total field event.

Lashley who formulated this mass-action theory (343) has given it up on the basis of later visual researches in favor of an all-or-nothing principle (349, p. 74). The postoperative loss of the brightness-discrimination habit he regards as occurring only after complete destruction of the visual mechanism and not proportional to the amount of tissue destroyed irrespective of locus within the visual areas.

Equipotentiality. On the basis of extensive extirpation experiments, primarily upon maze-learning behavior, Lashley proposed his theory of equipotentiality, described as follows:

> . . . the apparent capacity of any intact part of a functional area to carry out, with or without reduction in efficiency, the functions which are lost by destruction of the whole. This capacity varies from one area to another and with the character of the functions involved. It probably holds only for the association areas and for functions more complex than simple sensitivity or motor coordination (343, p. 25).

Clearly the assumptions that the various parts of the brain sustain particular functions and that there are psychological association areas are in no manner required by the experiments. They call simply for a construction based on correlations of mutilation and behavior interference. The idea of psychological functional areas goes counter to many of the data turned up in the experiments and to the established biological principles concerning the nervous system.

But how powerful is the neural bias! Even those who oppose the equipotentiality theory do so only on the basis of more definitely localized seats of function than Lashley allows for maze or other learning. For example, Hunter (243, 244) holds that extirpation studies show that behavior deficiencies are proportional to the number of specialized seats of functions disturbed. Maze learning, he asserts, involves a multiplicity of stimuli, only a portion of which may control the behavior in reduced form. Curiously enough, Hunter accuses Lashley of adhering to a doctrine of a central neural engram. This, Lashley denies, of course, but he does claim that in certain kinds of behavior:

> . . . the projection areas have in addition to their specific sensory or motor functions, a nonspecific (perhaps facilitative) function in which they are equipotential (345, p. 13; see also 604).

Need we look further for demonstration of the unfortunate interference of neural dogma with the interpretative phase of psychoneurology!

Vicarious Function. The adherents of psychological brain functions resort to the remarkable principle of vicarious functioning to explain the perplexing fact that behavioral deficits and incapacities can be recovered. When brain regions are injured or destroyed, such that the mediating structure for a function no longer exists, some obliging area which previously lacked the function conveniently takes it over. The doctrine of vicarious functioning became established long ago, yet there has never been any evidence that it represents any event or even that there can be such an event.

Inded, this construction constitutes an exemplary instance of a term confused with an event. It is probably not taking too great an advantage of a *lapsus calami* to quote Morgan's remarks on the subject:

> The theory of vicarious functioning was proposed nearly a hundred years ago in the first experiments of Fritsch and Hitzig, and so many instances of it have been uncovered since that there can be little doubt of it (444, p. 538).

What have been uncovered are many reiterations of the theory. What there is no doubt of, is interrupted performance through mutilation and succeeding effective retraining. But why not interpret these facts as evidence against the original brain doctrine? Not to do so is to pile up a series of errors. Activities are made into functions; functions are localized, yet not localized since other parts can determine and perform them. As Lashley (343, p. 126) points out, attempts to discover the loci of such vicariously-functioning structures for maze learning have been fruitless in almost all cases. Actually there has never been any evidence for localization, either in the part that has lost the function or the part taking over. By such willful attribution of function-locus one can argue for any power of any part of the nervous system.

The justification of vicarious functioning is based on what

takes place in the case of vision. Here a large system of anatomical structures is involved, so that the loss of some part, say the striate cortex, makes necessary that another part of the system, the superior colliculi, take over. Now if one reinterprets this fact to signify that mutilated organisms can learn to perform discrimination behavior, the interpretation is not objectionable. It is probably in this form that Lashley assents to the doctrine in the case of brightness discrimination. But such participating structures are not available in maze or other sorts of learning. One can only extend the structures left after mutilation to include the organism as a whole minus simply the destroyed parts, neural or otherwise.

Diaschisis. The amazing organizational balance of biological organisms demands a restored equilibrium even after serious organ destruction. It is probably an allowable speculation that this restitution and rehabilitation constitute adjustments of balance continuous with normal metabolic processes. On such a basis we may accord considerable importance to the diaschisis concept. Naturally we reject this construction in the form given it by von Monakow (436) who provided the term. He believes that there are temporary, specific functional losses by other cortical portions than those directly affected by destruction; he also posits specific primary correlations of functions and cerebral tissues. A great portion of what is regarded as specific function restitution may be accounted for by recovery from shock and equilibrium disturbance.

NEURAL CONSTRUCTIONS AND DATA INCONSISTENCIES

While reviewing the work on cerebral functions in the dog, monkey, and other forms Lashley (343) refers to contradictions and controversies relative to both data and constructions. This dilemma we have dwelt upon frequently in our discussions of the historical-dogma basis of postulation and hypothesis in the investigative situation. Such inconsistencies, of course, may be accounted for at least in part by the complexity of the data, but the influence of preconceptions is

too transparent to be denied. The result is a body of interpretative artifacts arising from the predisposed clash between reports of behavioral events and requirements of
theory. The situation may be illustrated by referring only to
the literature concerning the frontal and temporal lobes.

General Activity. Morgan (444, pp. 391 ff.) reviews the in-
harmonious findings of Richter (518, 519), Jacobsen (255),
Beach (28, 29), Kennard (306, 307), and others with respect to the relation of the frontal lobes and general activity,
but he is puzzled that the findings are so erratic. Doubtless
a mitigation of the emphasis on inhibiting and facilitating
brain functions would remove some of the difficulty.

Special Functions. A similar conflict of reports concerns
the more specialized functions of the cerebral areas. To the
same regions of the brain are ascribed different functions,
whereas different lobes are believed to harbor the same
functions. For instance some writers localize emotions in the
frontal lobes; others regard the frontal part of the brain
as the seat of intelligence.

An interesting reversal of view centers around the temporal
lobes. Conventionally these areas of the brain are connected
with projection functions associated with auditory, gustatory,
and olfactory discrimination. Klüver and Bucy (320, 321),
however, find their temporal-lobe ablations in monkeys correlated with (1) emotional and temperamental changes, (2)
peculiar oral forms of behavior, (3) transformed sexual
behavior, as well as (4) a large number of visual-behavior
modifications (agnosia). Because of the striking novelty of
visual-behavior findings, Fulton (160, p. 343) suggests that
the lesions may have been so extensive as to involve what is
generally acknowledged to be a terminal for optic projection fibers. Klüver and Bucy admit that the temporal lobectomy did involve "a small ventral part of the corticotectal
system passing from the peristriate area (field 19 of Brod-
mann) to the superior colliculus" (62, p. 2). But as they point
out: "traumatic lesions of the occipital lobes in macaques do

not give rise to agnosic 'symptoms' " of the same type (318; 320, p. 52). Klüver and Bucy support their findings by referring to Brown and Schäfer (59) who had secured similar results in rhesus monkeys, but who were not impressed by the observation (62, p. 3).

NEGATIVE AND POSITIVE ASPECTS OF EXPERIMENTAL PSYCHONEUROLOGY

What a survey of experimental psychoneurology eventually yields in the way of scientific information depends naturally upon the interest of the surveyor. Psychologists have traditionally sought the neural basis of psychological behavior. From this standpoint it is probably safe to conclude that the survey is in large measure negative. In other words, the nervous system does not play the part in psychological behavior which tradition ascribes to it. On the whole, psychoneurological investigations do not inform us concerning the organic factors operative in psychological action, but rather that what was once regarded as the controlling conditions and their seat is not verified.

But since negative findings in science should not be discounted, the great value of the numerous experiments in psychoneurology consists in upsetting a cultural theory. In other words, it is just as important to eliminate bad hypotheses as to establish good ones. Again, these experiments are valuable from the standpoint of general scientific techniques. The accumulation of experimental procedures serves to further science even if such techniques must wait to be employed in investigations different from those in which they were first developed. And finally, the experimental findings of physiological psychologists have thrown tremendous light upon the physiology of the nervous system. Not only are such results important for the biological departments neighboring on psychology; they may be profitably used in building up a system comprising both psychological and biological events.

CHAPTER 16

CLINICAL PSYCHOSURGERY

BRAIN SURGERY AND PHYSIOLOGICAL PSYCHOLOGY

THE enormous progress recently made in the field of human-brain surgery promises to be of the utmost importance for P.P. The rapid extension of medical knowledge concerning the brain, and the daring operational skill employed to mitigate pathological conditions will undoubtedly add to our understanding of the interrelationship of biological and psychological events.

Our present advantageous position with respect to human-brain knowledge may probably be primarily ascribed to war experience and technological advances. At any rate they have provided many brain-lesion cases which can be precisely investigated. No longer are psychologists and physicians limited in their studies to accidental brain injuries, vascular pathologies, developmental anomalies, and various neoplastic and degenerative tissue changes. Today surgeons can explore and ablate specific regions with fairly precise techniques.

So far, however, clinical psychosurgery has been held in check by traditional brain theories. An interesting observation is how long the historical connection of the brain with mind or soul has been a hindrance to the surgeon's freedom of action, and, thus, to the development of new knowledge concerning that organ. Still we may expect that the plethora of material made available in the last few decades will force psychologists and neurologists to modify if not completely erase traditional theories concerning brain functions. Facts are piling up which are entirely incongruous with those theories. Psychologists especially should cease their search for correlations between localized brain tissues and "higher" mental functions.

In order to discover the implications for P.P. we sample

in this chapter the findings of clinical manipulations of human-brain tissues as compared with experimental ablations in nonhuman organisms. Though at this point we are primarily interested in the newer precise results of brain surgery in connection with biological and psychological pathologies, we shall also refer to findings dating earlier than current psychosurgery.

The Development of Clinical Psychosurgery

The accumulation of psychological evidence concerning brain functions through medical and surgical cases constitutes a fascinating chapter in the history of P.P. No apology is required for interrelating this material with P.P. since obviously there is a definite continuity in thought and practice concerning the brain. The leitmotif of connecting mental and cerebral events runs through experimental work on animals, the gathering of data on traumas and brain disease, on down to the studies of operated patients. For this reason a history of clinical psychosurgery may justifiably include case reports from all sorts of sources, since case studies constitute developmental phases of a single system. In our brief survey of the data we consider some cases recorded prior to the recent upsurge of brain surgery.

I. Early Medical Period

We are now familiar with the fact that the earliest technical reports concerning the relationship between brain and mental conditions are firmly based on the conception that the brain is the seat of the mind. Accordingly, as we have seen, the early pathologists attempted to locate the seats or centers of mental functions by looking for correlations between brain pathology and mental diseases or disturbances (p. 212).

But even at that time, cases were reported which conflicted with that conception. There are records of serious brain injuries without the prescribed mental losses. These disharmonies of theory and fact have led to various arguments instead of an examination of the theory.

(a) *General Psychological Changes.* An outstanding example of such a case disturbing to the traditional theory is that of Phineas Gage (154, p. 43 ff.). Though this individual certainly sustained extensive cerebral damage, neither the older nor recent references enlarge upon his remarkable recovery and efficiency, but instead emphasize changes in his psychological makeup. For example, Freeman and Watts (154, p. 43) refer to this case as an illustration of mental symptoms following injury to the frontal lobes. That a man should be able to carry on such extensive and complicated activities, including an attempt to establish a line of coaches in a foreign country, are facts overlooked in favor of general behavioral changes. That some of the changes appear to have been in the direction of more venturesome and even executive experience pale in the face of the theory of brain powers (309, p. 87).

Another striking illustration is Andral's case referred to by Bastian:

A man who died in his twenty-eighth year, had a fall when three years old, after which he continued paralyzed on the left side. The right hemisphere of the brain was found to be so completely atrophied that a great part of the "pia mater" on this right side formed a cyst, in which not a trace of cerebral matter remained. This membrane constituted the upper wall of a large cavity, the floor of which alone was formed by the Thalamus, the Corpus Striatum and all the parts on a level with these two bodies. No nervous matter existed, therefore, above the level of the great ganglia on the right side—and yet Andral says: "Cet individu avait reçu de l'education et en avait profité; il avait une bonne memorie; sa parole etait libre et facile, son intelligence etait celle du commun des hommes" (27, p. 493 f.).

Bastian comments:

. . . it is a remarkable fact that there has been not only a preservation of such an amount of Intellectual Power, as to have given the appearance, at all events, of no loss in this direction, but that the special modes of Sensibility (such as Sight and Hearing) have not been abolished on either side . . . (27, p. 494).

In the interest of a philosophical conception opposed to the integration of mental and cerebral facts Chevalier cites the following two cases.

A workman in the St. Jacques factory at Montlucon, whilst engaged in making crowbars with the rammer, was struck by one of the wedges used to give the bar the right curve. It flew off at a tangent and came back with an unforeseen ricochet, striking him with terrific force behind his protecting shield. Part of his skull was shattered and a large quantity of cerebral matter carried away with it. Under the influence of the shock the man lost all consciousness, power of movement, and memory, and remained in a state of coma for many weeks. He had to be fed artificially all that time and for some weeks after. Then by degrees he recovered the use of his limbs; he began to walk, though round and round at first; he learned to feed himself and to talk once more; finally he made a complete recovery (90, p. 187).

A soldier, a native of Le Brethon in Allier, who had been brought to the Montlucon ambulance station, had had part of his skull at the base of the left parietal carried away by a shell. The brain was ruptured; it mortified, and about one-fifth of its substance was removed. The man lived thus for rather more than two months, almost without suffering and without showing diminution of his cerebral or motor faculties, any disturbance of judgment or reasoning powers, any change of memory. He talked in a normal way and wrote séveral times to his family; then he was suddenly overcome by coma and died within forty-eight hours (90, p. 188).

(b) *Special Functions.* The reports of mental or psychological changes following or accompanying cerebral lesions are, of course, prepared by physicians. Even when the intention is to describe special and precise losses the stress is still upon gross faculties and general behavior conditions. Those who summarize the literature collect numerous statements concerning intellectual deterioration, distractibility of attention, changes in affectivity, such as euphoria and depression, character and personality alteration, impairment of abstract thinking, and the like. Such summaries are subject to the exigencies that reporters may have handled different kinds of cases—say, traumas instead of tumors. Or they may differ in the sort of psychological (original descriptive) categories they employ. In this case they may use the same categories for different behavior or different categories for the same behavior changes. As a consequence some writers report all the changes mentioned among others, whereas others offer only selected items in varying arrays or sometimes only one.

Now it is obvious that anyone interested in the correlation of organic lesions with psychological changes may find evidence in any patient, though such evidence is hardly of psychological significance. This point is well exemplified by the following comprehensive summary of psychological changes reported as owing to frontal-lobe tumors and traumas. Klebanoff (309) has culled these materials from 20 articles on traumas and 19 on tumors. Only one author has a report on each.

Psychological Changes Reported	Trauma	Tumor
General Intellectual Deterioration	9	8
Euphoria–Hyperactivity	8	15
Personality Alteration	7	14
Loss of Initiative	7	8
Depression-Retardation	6	10
Memory Loss	6	5
Attention Defect	5	4
Impairment of Abstraction	5	

For trauma the authors range from Fritsch and Hitzig in 1870 (159) to Ruffin in 1939 (532). Tumor reports begin with Jastrowitz in 1888 (270) and run to Duus in 1939 (131).

Such a summary appears to indicate that tumors result in different psychological troubles from traumas, though it is the affected lobes which are presumed to correlate with the changes. Moreover, it is difficult to say whether the variations in the reports as to what is affected are more or less impressive than the underlying phrenological conception. Certainly there is no precise determination concerning what changes actually take place nor what brain spot is the primary locus of what faculty and mental process. On one point there is general agreement among neurologists—namely, that complex psychological processes are more closely connected with the frontal and temporal lobes as against the parietal and occipital.

In view of the casual observations underlying the reports, and the indifference as to exact brain region or psychological process affected, may not these findings simply indicate general behavior changes in pathological individuals? Could the brain tradition be set aside, would not comparable noncerebral injuries result in similar general behavioral deficits? In other words, would not seriously-injured persons of any sort display restlessness, inattention, and other marked changes? As to the comparatively larger number of reports showing hyperactivity and depression with tumors as compared with traumas, might not such a condition be expected merely on the basis of the generally-different conditions of the patients?

Despite accumulating evidence that the brain along with other parts of the nervous system constitutes a biological organ operating as a general coordinating mechanism, neurologists have clung to the idea that the frontal lobes constitute centers and bases for psychological action and especially the so-called higher mental processes.

II. CURRENT SURGICAL PERIOD

The current surgical period may be introduced by the report of Dandy concerning the lack of untoward psychological results with the removal of the entire right hemisphere. Since this report is a crucial turning point in the history of brain surgery we quote his conclusions (106).

(1) Complete extirpation of both frontal lobes resulted in no detected disturbances in mentality.

(2) Ligation of the left anterior cerebral artery resulted in the complete and permanent loss of consciousness. Ligation of the right anterior cerebral artery did not produce this effect.

(3) Mid-line severance of the entire body of the corpus callosum resulted in no appreciable disturbance of function.

(4) Removal of the entire right hemisphere above the basal

ganglia resulted in no detected disturbance of mentality.

Dandy's radical and revolutionary surgery failed to free him from the cultural incubus of mind and its cerebral seat. Three years later he was still perplexed because extirpation of vast areas of brain tissue affected mental functions so little.

It is difficult to believe that some functions of the mind are not stored or at least not activated there (107).

Finally (107a), he became convinced that bilateral ligation of the cerebral arteries did not destroy consciousness, which he decided was centered in the anterior part of the corpus striatum.

Once the avalanche of brain surgery began, an increasing number of reports appeared to support Dandy's type of findings. We may refer to Ackerly (2), O'Brien (468, 469), Gardiner (167), Hebb (207, 208), Hebb and Penfield (209), Brickner (54, 55), Alford (8), Rowe (528), Penfield and Evans (483, 484), Worchel and Lyerly (645), Rylander (533), Freeman and Watts (154), Porteus and Kepner (500) among others who report operations on various parts of the brain with lack of traditionally-accepted results. Extensive summaries are provided by Brickner (54), Rylander (533), and Freeman and Watts (154).

REFINING THE SURGICAL DATA

As the surgical material expanded it was inevitable that closer approximations concerning extent and locus of brain injury were necessary. Also, neurologists and especially psychologists demanded that information concerning psychological changes be made more precise. The point was soon reached at which tests and measures became assiduously employed. But as we shall see, since the attempt to secure quantitative findings was based on the old function and localization postulates the same confusions and misinterpretations flourished.

The extent to which phrenological conceptions dominate neurosurgeons may be illustrated by a remark of Bailey in his monograph on *Intracranial Tumors* dated 1933.

I hesitate before amputating a frontal lobe. This procedure is always followed by more or less great alteration in character and defects in judgment. In a washerwoman these results may be of little concern, but when the patient is a professional business man, who must make decisions affecting many people, these results may be disastrous (17, p. 433).[1]

On the other hand, the facts becoming available in the rapid accumulation of cases persistently militate against such preconceptions. The following samples of available materials demonstrate the increasing efforts to obtain precise information concerning the psychological effects of brain mutilation.

Psychiatric Inventory. In 1932 O'Brien (468) and in 1933 Gardiner (167) reported a case of total right-hemisphere ablation with what they regarded as no disturbing psychological effects except occasionally some slight apathy.

In 1934 Penfield and Evans (483) presented seven cases of cerebral lobectomy: four frontal, one temporal, and two occipital. They concluded that though cerebral lobectomy involves loss of large amounts of brain substance, little disturbance of function is detected. They lay special emphasis on (a) one case in which the right frontal lobe was removed to within one cm. of the motor gyrus and (b) another left frontal lobectomy carried back to one or two cm. of the precentral gyrus. In the former, a woman of 43 returned to "her duties as wife and the mother of six children with greatly increased efficiency" (483, p. 375). In the case of (b) some aphasia developed which cleared up in three weeks, leaving no speech difficulty whatever. The patient was dissatisfied with his trouble in doing mental arithmetic and playing bridge, though he said he could think better, act more quickly, and was less irritable than before the operation. The authors assert he had lost some of his initiative.

About the same time, Zollinger (659) published a case of complete left-hemisphere removal in a right-handed woman.

---

[1] This statement is preceded by the remark: "to the neurologist each cell and fiber is sacred" (17, p. 429).

For nearly three months prior to operation she developed progressive speech deficiencies until her vocabulary became practically depleted. Almost immediately after the operation her speech behavior began to improve and continued until she died 17 days later. That serious brain destruction in the middle third of the left hemisphere need not result in aphasia is corroborated by several hemiplegic cases published by Alford (8), and by temporal lobectomy cases presented by Fox and German (148) and by Nielsen and Raney (466).

Psychological Tests. The search for precise determinations of brain-injury effects inevitably leads to the employment of general psychological tests. In consequence the literature burgeons with reports concerning the results derived from Binet and similar tests under all sorts of conditions. Patients with large and small brain losses have been tested after operation for removal of various lobes, of one or both hemispheres, and of either one or the other complete hemisphere.

Samples of such reports are: (a) right-temporal lobe excision, Hebb (207) Nielsen and Raney (466); (b) left temporal, Fox and German (148, 172), Nielsen and Raney (466); (c) left frontal, Hebb (208); (d) right-frontal, German and Fox (172), Rylander (533), Jefferson (275), Lidz (370); (e) bilateral frontal, Brickner (54, 55), Ackerly (2), Nichols and Hunt (465), Hebb (208a), Hebb and Penfield (209) Porteus and Kepner (500); (f) various unilateral lobes, Halstead (200); and (g) right-cerebral hemisphere, Dandy (107) Rowe (528).

The materials mentioned uniformly yield fairly negative results with such tests. Not only do they fail to show deficiencies and losses with serious cerebral mutilations, but it is even thought that the mentalities of the subjects are improved (154, p. 74; 309, pp. 599, 616). Such negative findings have stimulated the argument that certain specific tests are necessary to discover the characteristic defects one assumes to occur (183, p. 188).

Two elaborate reports on brain destruction are illuminating in this connection. One of these is Brickner's elaborate case study, and the other, Rylander's monograph on 32 different cases. The importance of Brickner's case A lies in the close study given the patient for longer than five years (54) and the follow-up report three years later (55). The operation resulted in the removal of 116 grams of frontal lobe or 9 per cent of the total weight of the brain, 45 grams of the left and 71 grams of the right lobe. Despite the fact that Brickner believes in specific psychological brain functions and their localization, he has been forced to the following conclusions.

(a) The patient's symptoms are numerous. None of them indicates an alteration in the fundamental nature of any mental process, but only the impairment of its completeness. Hence, the changes are fundamentally not qualitative, but quantitative in nature.

(b) Only one function is considered as primarily affected. This is the elaborate association or synthesis into complex structures of the simple engrammic products associated in the more posterior parts of the brain.

(c) The deduction has been drawn that the frontal lobes are not intellectual *centers* in any sense, except, perhaps a quantitative one, and that they play no specialized role in intellectual function.

The handling of the test and observation results and their interpretations is typical. The numerous symptoms quoted, boasting, joking, speech changes, etc., are no different from what one would expect of any person with the background, occupation, and serious illness of the present subject. The synthesis of engrammic products mentioned in (b) is obviously pure construction, as the writer himself indicates in conclusion (c).

Rylander (533) made an elaborate study of his 32 cases after operation for various right and left frontal-lobe excisions. This study is singled out not only because of the number of cases, but also because it was based upon a critical reaction against the lack of thoroughness in other observers. Also, Rylander adopted the method of matching each patient with a control chosen from the healthy population of the same environment, age, occupation, and education.

Although Rylander is obviously dominated by the mental-seat brain dogma, his results indicate that after operation, general mentality, or what he calls the more automatic form of intelligence, remains relatively well preserved (533, p. 297). He is obviously more concerned with proving the localization of mentality, especially intellectual functions, than in revealing the actual results of brain excisions. Thus he bases his interpretations on group averages, despite the actual findings in individual cases. In this connection Hebb (206) has criticized Rylander for not making a real analysis of the anatomical data. Cobb (91) questions Rylander's results because of their incongruity with other findings that unilateral excisions are remarkably free of psychological effects. Above all, Rylander's study shows how closely his results follow the presuppositions adopted and how well properly-chosen techniques help to prove propositions about questionable and even nonexistent mental functions.

Experimental Investigations. As we have previously mentioned (p. 257), the established theory, that the brain, and especially the frontal lobes, is the seat of mentality, resulted in the conviction that more thorough methods would reveal what general psychological tests fail to do. Workers have now attained the stage of what may be regarded as experimental investigation for the discovery of various psychological brain functions. For the most part they assume that the operated individuals undergo personality changes. The next step is to work out tests and techniques to establish this hypothesis.

Goldstein writes:

Certainly one will find changes only if one examines patients with such tests suited to bring the characteristic defect to the fore (183, p. 188).

Again, Halstead (200) asserts that despite the fact that the frontally-injured individual may hold a job, adjust himself to his family and friends, and even his physician may see no change in him, still he may fail in a specific test situation.

Halstead's investigation on 26 brain-operated patients was

carried out in conformity with the canons of experimental psychology. He was interested in discovering basic psychological functions, and so, following a number of workers, he developed a classification-of-objects test (62 objects) modeled on Klüver's (314, 315, 316) "method of equivalent and nonequivalent stimuli." This test he administered to normal and pathological individuals. His results indicate:

> In comparison with the performances of normal individuals, the greatest deviations in the performances of the patients with a cerebral injury occurred in the grouping behavior of individuals with a lesion in one frontal lobe, regardless of whether the primary lesion was on the right or left side of the brain (200, p. 1287).

Rylander (533) studied his cases with a battery including tests for attention, memory, noun vocabulary, picture interpretation, object grouping, proverb interpretation, and others. His results are interpreted as changes in personality, especially in the higher intellectual faculties. These changes, however, do not prevent the patients from leading normal social lives, but in his opinion may be fatal to their doing qualified intellectual work.

The particular feature of the frontal-lobe patients according to Goldstein (183), who developed special sorting tests, is the "impairment of abstract attitudes." An abstract attitude concerns the facility of making and using various categories in organizing objects into groups. This function, believed to be a basis in the abstractive processes of thinking, may also be interfered with by injuries to other lobes (183, p. 200).

Summary of Findings and Interpretations

A summary of the materials in clinical psychosurgery reveals a common ideological attitude, but a heterogeneous mass of details concerning data and interpretation which are incongruous and contradictory.

(1) *General Phrenological Attitude.* The entire literature of clinical psychosurgery is organized under the general dogma of the brain as the seat of the mind. Whether the mind is regarded as a single power or subdivided into special

faculties it is unanimously regarded as localized or correlated with the brain. Also it is almost universally accepted that somehow the frontal lobes are especially interrelated with complex mental processes,[1] as compared with other lobes or areas to which simpler psychological functions or border-line psychobiological functions are relegated.

(2) *Incoordinate Details of Data and Interpretation.* Despite their common ideology writers are at cross purposes in their reports of the effects following brain surgery and their interpretations of the findings.

(a) *Data.* Some of the outstanding differences concern unilateral or bilateral destruction. With respect to speech "functions" there is almost complete agreement concerning unilateral location. With respect to other "functions," many writers report serious intellectual deficits from the destruction of a lobe on one side, whereas others insist that only bilateral lesions have psychological effects.

Whether the lesions are unilateral or bilateral the reports of findings are contradictory concerning the location or correlation of function. Despite the tremendous inclination toward the frontal lobes as the primary seats of the higher mental functions, their destruction is reported to result in various affective changes, such as euphoria and depression. Particular writers disagree whether similar effects result from injury to frontal or other particular lobes. Again, it is reported that many kinds of deficiency, whether intellectual or affective, are correlated with destruction of various non-frontal areas.

Of especial interest in the findings are the various implications concerning the correlation of brain injury with certain specific sorts of functions. For example, there is the suggestion that removal of some area in the frontal lobes resulted in a deficit or loss of ability to play bridge or to perform mental arithmetic (483, p. 374).

[1] An occasional denial is found, however; for example, Hebb (208a) asserts that an uncomplicated, bilateral frontal excision need not be followed by social and intellectual defects.

An important incongruity in the various reports concerns the issue of specific cases vs. group averages. The question arises whether the findings of particular cases are not more important as data than the averaging of results (206). On the whole, the presentation of average results minimizes the overlap; thus apparently different results are obtained from what appear in the presentation of specific cases.

In this connection attention is directed toward the cavalier treatment of the exceptional case. If the materials presented are for the purpose of drawing conclusions concerning psychological effects of brain destruction, the value of even one exceptional case can not be overestimated. Consider aphasic material which has always been regarded as the classical type of localization. Although neurologists have recorded exceptional cases since Hughling Jackson's time, they have not been properly weighed in the face of localization theory. Even in his day Jackson was very emphatic concerning the ability of the speechless to speak, as indicated in the following extract from his article "On Affections of Speech from Disease of the Brain" (251) first published in volume I of *Brain,* in 1878-79.

I have records of still higher degrees of utterance by one speechless patient. A man, for several months under my care in the London Hospital, was absolutely speechless. He never *uttered,* much less spoke, anything but "pooh," "pooh," so far as I or the students knew. But I was told by his friends of three utterances. Once, when he had had enough bread-and-butter, he said "No more." This, however, is only a degree of speech. . . . But I was told that one day the patient said, with difficulty of articulation, "How is Alice (his daughter) getting on?" A third utterance was, I think, as high, if not still higher, in speech. His son wanted to know where his father's tools were. In reply to his son's questions, the patient said, "Master's." Although here is but one word, where in health there would have been a sentence, there is a proposition; it told his son where the tools were as fully as the most elaborately worded and grammatically complete sentence would have done. It was far higher than the most elaborate oaths, and higher even than such utterances as "no more," "good-bye," "very well," etc. Once more I would urge that speciality in speech ("high speech") is not simply an affair of number of words, nor simply of complexity of their arrangement. We have to consider precise adaptation to special and new circumstances: "master's" did not come out upon a common and simple occasion, like "good-bye"; it was definitely uttered to signify a very special relation, moreover a new relation (252, II, p. 180 f.).

(b) *Interpretation.* Conflicts concerning interpretations, as we have implied, fall within the general boundary of brain localization. They concern the question of general or special faculties and their particular hierarchical organization. Is there a general loss of categorial[1] attitude or specific inability to attend to details? Is there a distinction between the functions of a lobe and the functions of an area of a lobe (91, p. 565)? Then there is the difficulty about restitution: whether some other area or lobe takes over the function or whether the original one has simply been shocked into inability to perform its function and then recovers it. A symptomological type of interpretation concerns the conflict between cortical and subcortical areas. When the findings show destruction without loss it is insisted that the proper seat of the functions has not yet been located. Typical here is Alford (8) who, armed with evidence that no part of the cortex is responsible for aphasia, clouding of consciousness, or dementia, found the seat of consciousness to be "a quite small area lying posteriorly near the base of the brain" on the left side.

PSYCHOTHERAPEUTIC BRAIN SURGERY

The recent practice of surgically injuring the frontal lobes as a therapeutic measure for psychological troubles (154) is, after all, a covert recognition that the brain is a biological structure. The readiness to operate upon the brain certainly does not suggest that it is a distinctively different and inviolate organ. That the practitioners operate upon the putative basis of localized functions does not seriously challenge our proposition.

From the literature on psychosurgery it may be gathered

[1] In the literature, usually written categorical. Is this a confusion of terms?

that therapeutic human-brain operations stem in part from animal-experiment sources. In 1890 Burckhardt (63), a Swiss psychiatrist impressed by Goltz's animal extirpation experiments, undertook the removal of small portions of intact brain as a means of curing mental disorders. In four consecutive operations on one greatly-disturbed patient he removed 5 grams from the left postcentral region, 2.5 grams from the left temporal, 5.5 grams from the left parietal, and 5 grams from the left frontal. The results were reported as an improvement though not a cure of dementia, but the general comportment of the patient was changed for the better.

Altogether, Burckhardt operated on four patients, but his work was not followed up. Freeman and Watts (154, p. 9) find two major difficulties with Burckhardt's pioneer work. First, his patients were too seriously pathological for good results, and secondly they point to his ignorance concerning the emotional mechanisms and their localization within the central nervous system. Though these writers note the surprisingly small aphasia that resulted from Burckhardt's operations they regard it as dangerous to tamper with the dominant hemisphere, and especially the language area. In general, they believe that psychosurgery must be bilaterally performed, since the two frontal lobes operate as a unit (154, p. 11).

Aside from the isolated attempts by Puusepp (508) in 1910 to transect association fibers between the frontal and parietal lobes as a therapeutic measure, and the case of Ody (470) and Morel (439) in Geneva, the present wave of psychosurgery begins with the work of the Portuguese neurologist, Egas Moniz (437, 438). Moniz is said to have been influenced by reports on the function of the frontal lobes presented at a Neurological Congress held in London in 1935 (154, p. 11; 160, p. 425). That same year Moniz began to perform prefrontal-lobotomy operations and was soon followed by Freeman and Watts in 1936.

The bilateral frontal-lobotomy operation has been performed in various ways; for example, cutting a sphere or core, or cutting the white matter in the plane of the coronal suture. The aim is to divide the band of fibers connecting the thalamus and the prefrontal region. The theory here is that the partial separation of the frontal lobes removes the emotional nucleus from the psychosis (154, p. vii).

Working in the venerable tradition of the brain seat of the mind, psychosurgeons argue vigorously that the brain and especially the frontal lobe is the proper organ to operate upon for mental disturbance. Freeman and Watts refer to the fact that various visceral organs and the endocrines have been inadvisedly operated upon for this purpose. They say *amen* to DaCosta's criticism that he has never seen the slightest improvement in the mental condition of patients whose viscera have been operated upon, and add: "If the trouble is in the head, why work on the belly" (154, p. 7)?

The illustrative lobotomy cases (154, 386, 588) yield a bewildering variety of results. Some individuals do not long survive the operation. Of those who do, some are said to improve in behavior, while others are pronounced unchanged; still others are changed for the worse. On the whole, the operation is a hazardous one both as to biological and psychological consequences, even though affording possible relief from disturbing behavior. When a patient is claimed to have been relieved of pathological symptoms, undoubtedly the same remedy might have been obtained by any sort of severe shock. Psychiatrists who closely follow psychosurgical work facetiously remark that similar results have been observed when a patient falls off a horse. Perhaps the suggestion sometimes made that the primary effect of brain extirpation in laboratory animals is an extreme shock to the organism may well have its application in psychosurgery situations. Certainly this suggestion merits some consideration when the issue of damage versus localization is under consideration.

The psychologist naturally is especially interested in the underlying theory concerning the nature of mental events and their relation to the biological organism and its behavior. Since Freeman and Watts are the most outspoken lobotomists let us briefly consider their views. For them the frontal part of the brain is the seat of foresight or futurity.

Just as the post-Rolandic cortex is concerned with the past, the pre-Rolandic cortex is concerned with the future. Aside from certain small areas that mediate voluntary control over muscular movements and the regulation of visceral functions, the rest of the frontal cortex is, according to our hypothesis, concerned with the projection of the whole individual into the future (154, p. 302 f.).

The significance of this foresight is explained in the following:

The prefrontal lobes enable us to form an image of ourselves and to project that image into the future, visualizing it in all its relationships not only with the external world but also with the internal bodily mechanisms. By virtue of this cerebral equipment we are made aware of our duties and obligations to ourselves and to others, of the figure we cut in the eyes of other people and of the quality of the work we do (154, p. 314 f.).

Perhaps it is only a curious coincidence that for Freeman and Watts the topographically back part of the brain is concerned with the temporally back part of action or the past, whereas the complementary front part is allegedly involved with temporally forward action—the life to come.[1] Was it an oversight to localize intelligence in the post-Rolandic region (154, p. 302)? Or is intelligence not concerned with the future?

Whether lobotomy is good or bad medical practice, and notwithstanding the peculiarities of the theories underlying the practice, psychosurgery is an item in a possible change of view concerning the "sacredness" of the brain. Recently a prominent neurosurgeon asserted that objections made by psychiatrists to therapeutic brain operations amount to "indignation resting on the subconscious conviction that the removal of the brain robs a man of his soul" (18). It is highly significant then to find the psychosurgeon declaring:

[1] A similar correlation was made by the Scholastic Albertus Magnus (387).

. . . in the past it has been considered that if a person does not think clearly and correctly it is because he doesn't have "brains enough." It is our intention to show that under certain circumstances an individual can think more clearly and more productively with less brain in actual operation (154, p. 74).

Nielsen and Rainey (466, p. 1.) conclude on the basis of 5 cases that a person without any left temporal lobe is in general far superior to one with a slightly damaged lobe still in situ. Similarily striking benefits are reported as following frontal lobectomy by Stookey, Scarff, and Teitelbaum (585).

PSYCHOLOGICAL EFFECTS OF BRAIN SURGERY

The developments in brain surgery probably mark as great a potential achievement in P.P. as in medical practice. An outstanding gain is that despite theoretical attitudes the brain is more and more becoming regarded as the biological organ that it is. Evidence for this view has long existed in numerous records of accidental destruction of large parts of cerebral tissues (p. 254f.), but brain dogmatism operated to relegate such evidence to the limbo of the sporadic and bizarre. Today, the development of brain surgery along with the multiplication of war-casualty cases forces this evidence into prominence. No longer can the brain be considered a special entity, biologically different from any other.

An even more pointed result of the impact of brain surgery on psychological problems is the change in ideas concerning particular brain functions. Though physiological psychologists have never acknowledged more than a general correlation between mental processes and neurological structures and functions, their views have in principle differed little from neurologists who precisely or vaguely localized thoughts (526), musical power and calculation (221), will and moral power (60, 233, 526), human need, longing and hope (55a), whether in general centers or as functions of definite cells (77, 219, 220, 310, 311). Through clinical experience, however, such ideas are giving way despite the inertia generated by psychological fashions of thought.

CHAPTER 17

PSYCHOCHEMISTRY

PSYCHOCHEMISTRY AS A SUBDOMAIN OF PHYSIOLOGICAL PSYCHOLOGY

SINCE the organisms operating in psychological fields constitute complex chemical mechanisms it follows that chemical reactions are involved in all their behavior. Some of these reactions are confined, of course, to purely *biological* or metabolic events. They operate exclusively to maintain organisms as integrated units of their respective species and as adjustive mechanisms interacting with their environments. Other chemical events are undoubtedly definite factors in authentic *psychological* behavior, for example, when they constitute (a) stimulus objects directly interacted with, or (b) setting factors, such as the various constituents of the surrounding atmosphere and endogenous toxins.

Psychochemistry as the study of the relationship between psychological and chemical events thus constitutes a cross-reference investigative domain connected with both general psychology and P.P. The connection between psychochemistry and general psychology is easily discernible when chemicals comprise the stimuli and settings in psychological fields. Certainly the gross facts of interbehavior with chemically-constituted objects are readily available. Psychochemistry is most intimately related with P.P. when chemical factors are localized in the organism and its behavior. Our problem in this chapter then is to examine what and how physiologico-chemical or biophysical events must be included in our descriptions of psychological fields.

Because organisms are unceasingly in action both on psychological and chemical levels, there must be innumerable points of intersection of the two kinds of events. A first step in describing these points of contact is satisfactorily to isolate

271

biological and psychological events (p. 133). When we do so we may well find that the organism's endogenic and exogenic chemistry may be only indirectly if at all concerned with essential psychological events—that is, interaction of stimulus and response functions (p. 135). In other words, the chemistry of the organism may be neutral with respect to its psychological behavior. On the other hand, chemical conditions seriously affecting organismic action as biological participants in psychological fields may comprise important though peripheral factors in psychological situations.

Chemical events that are exclusively biological we need not expect to be significantly interconnected with psychological happenings at all. Throughout the history of P.P. almost every type of biochemical fact has been unverifiably alleged to exert immediate influences on psychological events. Undoubtedly there is discernible here the old dualistic pattern of thought. Chemical substances have been treated as the supports or determiners for psychic states, or else the old driving powers of the psyche have been vested in chemical substances. The result has been that chemical events even of the purely biological sort have been accorded an inordinately large place in psychological descriptions. It is evident then that psychochemical problems are of the utmost importance for P.P. Since all psychological happenings comprise biological events we must allow for the possibility that even remote chemical reactions of organisms play some part in larger psychological fields.

Psychochemistry as a subdomain of P.P. is therefore not only a source of numerous facts but also a basis for various theories. For example, it affords the possibility of shifting the center of gravity from the nervous system to general organochemical events as items in psychological description. The study of the organism's chemistry allows a modification of interest in neural mechanisms and the localization of psychological functions. Should psychologists persist in forcibly connecting biochemistry with the nervous system as a locus of psychological functions they would plainly create psychoneural situations independently of their observation of psychological events. When such arbitrary constructions are clearly focalized, however, we can steer safely around them.

IDEOLOGICAL BACKGROUND OF PSYCHOCHEMISTRY

The theoretical problems involved in psychochemistry center around the general nature of psychological events. Traditionally, of course, the interest in chemical facts was pursued against a psychophysical background. The question was asked how psychic processes are influenced by chemical conditions and changes in the organisms. James includes a short section on "Phosphorous and Thought" in his *Principles* (267, I, p. 101 f.). In it he takes issue with the views current since the German materialistic period of the 1860's, when it was declared that "Ohne phosphor kein Gedanke." James questions the propriety of selecting out phorphorous from the numerous brain chemicals as a cause or basis for psychic processes. Why not say, he asks, "Ohne Wasser kein Gedanke," or "Ohne Kochsalz kein Gedanke." He even takes pains to deny the facts centering around a statement attributed to Aggasiz to the effect that fishermen are more intelligent than farmers because they imbibe more phosphorous-containing fish. What James really controverts is the idea that the stream of thought which accompanies brain secretions can in any sense be compared with such material secretions.

Psychologists, if not psychiatrists or neurologists, may no doubt resent tracing back their ideas of what correlates with chemical action to historical psychophysics. But if the cat is gone the grin remains. Psychologists certainly indulge in such correlations when they regard psychological events as constituting general "processes," "characteristics," and gross "conditions." Such a correlation is made when a chemical factor—say, an anesthetic—is presumed to deprive the individual of his state of awareness or when a drug is regarded as producing psychological disorientation or delirium.

Similar correlations and even causal conceptions are exhibited by behavioristic psychologists who abjure mentalistic doctrines. For example, when it is reported that hormones determine organisms to exhibit drives toward some sort of psychological action, such as sex behavior.

The hypothesis that psychological events constitute interactions of organisms and stimulus objects enables us to achieve an effective solution of psychochemical problems. Not only can we avoid the construction of chemical causes of mental and organic action, but we can properly interrelate chemical and psychological components in specific interbehavioral fields.

BIOCHEMICAL EVENTS AND PSYCHOLOGICAL FIELDS

To describe all types of psychological and chemical reactions is an insuperable undertaking. We can only consider selected samples. Even this task requires a schema if we hope to achieve anything at all. The following proposed

SCHEMA FOR PSYCHOCHEMISTRY

Focal
Factors

I. *Essential Psychological Data*

1. Response-stimulus functions,
   symbolized as f ($r \leftrightarrow s$).
2. Response-stimulus behavior,
   symbolized as ($R \leftrightarrow S$).
3. Organism-object, as interacting things,
   symbolized as ($O \leftrightarrow O$).
4. Setting or environing factors,
   symbolized as (Set).
5. Individual life-condition adjustments,
   symbolized as ($I \leftrightarrow LC$).

Peripheral
Factors

II. *Prepsychological (Biological) Data*

1. Chemistry and species evolution
2. Chemistry and ontogenetic evolution

III. *Parapsychological (Biological) Data*

1. Preservative and favoring chemical effects
2. Hindering and obviating chemical effects

schema is based on an analysis of interbehavioral fields. It is designed to differentiate between the relatively more focal and peripheral factors, in order that we can more precisely locate the interrelation of psychological and chemical data.

As this schema shows, the intimate response-stimulus functions constitute the central or focal factors in actual psychological fields. The next closest factors to the nucleus consist of: (a) the organism and its responses (behavior) as the outer shell or matrix of the response functions and (b) the stimulus object and its stimulating action as the corresponding matrix of the stimulus functions. The stimulus object may be regarded as a physico-chemical entity even when it is an organism. Next in order come the setting factors which environ the organisms and objects. And finally we make place for general adjustments to life conditions. The most peripheral factors consist of such essentially biological conditions as organismic evolution and personal hygiene.

Obviously psychological and chemical relations vary on the basis of whether they intersect focal or peripheral factors in psychological fields. In fact, we may point to a general rule that psychological and chemical relations are closer and more direct the farther out they are on the periphery of our schema. Of course, chemical factors are more abundant and more effective in prepsychological and parapsychological domains. In the psychological domain proper, chemical factors affect psychological events only through their primary connection with the organism and objects in psychological situations. Again, in the immediate settings of psychological interbehavior we find less chemical influence than in the factors of the individual and his life conditions. For example, while estrogenic hormones may effectively operate as interbehavioral setting factors in a human female's reactions in a sex situation, the sheer presence of hormones can not be compared in significance with other field factors, such as personality traits, habits, social taboos, etc., involved in adjustment to her particular life conditions.

I

ESSENTIAL PSYCHOLOGICAL DATA

1. *Stimulus-Response Function and Chemistry*

Although basic stimulus and response functions are in general far removed from chemical events, they are not ever completely free from chemical influences. Such influences are naturally exerted upon them through the organism and object matrices. The degree of that influence depends upon how deeply stimulus and response functions are set in their matrices. Here it will be well to distinguish between simple and complex psychological events, for example, universal reflex action and individualistic linguistic interbehavior.[1]

In universal interbehavior, such as pain reflexes and the very elementary differential reactions, the stimulus-response functions are uniquely and deeply imbedded in their respective organism-object matrices. Here we may agree that chemical factors exert appreciable effects. But in most complex psychological interbehavior the chemical factors are neutral and hence negligble. What features of the variant ways in which French and English speakers "say the same thing" can be attributed to actual chemical reactions?

At most we may attempt chemically to account for such features of complex behavior as intensity and vehemence of performance by invoking brain, liver and adrenal-gland mechanisms of the sort suggested by Crile (95-97) for varying energy output.

2. *Response-Stimulus Action and Chemistry*

Response-stimulus chemistry concerns the chemical events observable in what organisms and objects do in psychological fields. These actions of organisms and their stimulus objects as the matrices of response-stimulus functions operate as invariable participants in total psychological fields. We treat

[1] For the definition of and differentiation between universal and individual interbehavior, see Kantor (289, 291, 292).

separately the relation of the psychological and chemical events as they are primarily intersected at the point of response and stimulus.

A. Response Chemistry

(a) *Neurochemistry.* These chemical factors are highly specialized inasmuch as they concern a particular system of the organism instead of the total organism. We should expect neurochemical events, then, to constitute a general and extremely remote factor in any total interbehavioral field.

Physiologists are approaching definite agreement that neural conduction and synaptic transmission involve chemical mediation as well as electrical changes (101, 102, 137a, 160, 162, 374). Acetylcholine is acknowledged to be a primary factor in neural conduction and combined with adrenalin it directly operates to facilitate effector-organ action, while atropine, ergotoxine, nicotine, and curare inhibit the effect of neural transmission on effector organs.

For the psychologist, these newer developments in nerve physiology are more or less neutral when ordinary normal behavior is in question. They simply throw light on the coordinating functions of the nervous system and indicate some of the mechanisms of the organism's general operation. When, however, we confront the various pathological conditions interfering with the secretion of acetylcholine and adrenalin, we may expect an interference with psychological events through conditions localizable in the organism's neural physiology.

Incidentally the increasing evidence that there is no qualitative difference between conduction along fibers and across synaptic junctions may well be taken to signalize how inept it is to employ neural synaptic events as explanatory mechanisms for psychological facts—for example, learning.

(b) *Musculochemistry.* As typical participating factors muscle actions bring into the psychological picture a large and complicated set of chemical components. We need only mention the complex contraction reactions involving, among other factors, glycogen ($C_6H_{10}O_5$), glucose ($C_6H_{12}O_6$), the production of lactic acid ($C_3H_6O_3$), and the decomposition of creatine phosphoric acid (phosphogen). Then there are the various enzymes functioning in the acceleration of energy and general metabolic processes when muscles operate in the organism's behavior.

Now while every precise description of the response pattern and certainly every reaction system (297) may specify what chemical changes occur, it is problematic what relevancy this enumeration has for the description of the actual psychological field. If the physiologist experiences "a sense of regret that we do not really know how a muscle works" (633, p. 93), the psychologist may well be content merely to take cognizance of its chemistry and energy-transformation properties without prejudice to his behavioral studies.

(c) *Viscerochemistry*. Because of its prominence in emotional and affective situations psychologists of every persuasion have long been interested in the chemical hormone variously called adrenin, adrenaline, or epinephrin. This substance excellently represents the viscerochemical components of response factors. As an internal secretion of the adrenal glands, adrenalin not only occupies a prominent place in the animal economy but is also important as a factor in larger psychological events.

Obviously the kind of relation a psychologist assumes to exist between viscerochemical substances and psychological behavior depends upon his general constructional attitude. But whether writers hold that emotions and feelings constitute psychic processes accompanying chemical events or particular kinds of behavior patterns they do no more than point to the influence of adrenalin on the blood chemistry and on the vascular and visceral-organ behavior. The exciting and inhibiting action of chemical substances thus plays its part only as a factor in large behavior situations and does not constitute specific affective response patterns to particular stimulations.

Those who accept the hypothesis that emotional behavior consists primarily of the disorganization of specific stimulus-response coordinations (289, 292) suggest that interferences with orderly psychological interbehavior must closely correspond with viscerochemical activity. In ordinary affective behavior in which viscerochemical activity undoubtedly does play a significant part, it certainly does no more than contribute such participating factors as increased organismic tone and vigor to the total interbehavioral field.

B. Stimulus Chemistry

Aside from investigations in the field of the so-called chemical senses psychologists have displayed little interest in the chemistry of stimulus objects. Although the small amount of work in this field as summed up in the writings of von Skramlik (564), Crozier (98) and Henning (216, 217) was done against the dualistic background, it has nevertheless brought into prominence the place of objects in psychological situations. Even the transparent dichotomization of the chemical and sense properties of things has not detracted too much from the significance of the interaction between organisms and chemical substances.

The dichotomization mentioned undoubtedly receives some support from the ambiguous use of the term *stimulus*. Mentalistic psychologists in general regard a stimulus as that which arouses sensations through the intermediation of physiological processes. Woodworth excellently illustrates this view in his discussion of the stimulus of smell.

On the assumption that smell, like taste, is a "chemical sense," one is at first inclined to relegate the question of the olfactory stimulus to the chemist, handing over to him our psychological information on the system of smell sensations and asking him to indicate the chemical processes that could serve as stimuli for the several odor qualities. The chemist, however, might prefer to turn over his knowledge to the psychologist. The physiologist also would have to be considered and might well be the central figure in an inter-science committee on the question of the smell

stimulus, on the question, that is, how different chemical substances, by exciting different receptor processes, give rise to the
different odor sensations.

The distinction between stimulus and object is important here.
We have been speaking as if vanilla and turpentine and lemon oil
and tar were stimuli; which is like naming Turkey red and Paris
green and Prussian blue as typical visual stimuli. The visual
stimulus is light, not a pigment. The fact that pigments of quite
different chemical composition can be used for securing red light
is a puzzle for physics and chemistry, not psychology. But in the
case of smell the exact nature of the stimulus is obscure, and
instead of naming the stimulus we are forced for the present to
speak of the odorous substance which is the source of the stimulus
(640, p. 492; see also 48, pp. 449, 457; and 436a).

What this quotation justly points out is that variations in
response indicate a difference between the stimulus function
and the stimulus object. But as a mentalist Woodworth
merely transforms the qualities of things into physiologically-
created psychic entities. The stimulus becomes something
which requires a source.

Though it is true that the effect of the chemical nature
of objects influencing stimulus functions is greater in the
case of universal interbehavior, that fact subtracts nothing
from the importance of the chemical factors. One may safely
predict that with the increasing naturalization of psychology
greater emphasis will be placed upon the nature of objects
as chemical substances. Aside from expanding information
concerning the influence of the chemistry of objects upon
elementary discrimination and reflex behavior, there is considerable promise in the studies on the organism's reactions
to the chemistry of objects in more complex situations.
Signalized here are the data on normal food preferences
and the behavior of abnormal animals toward certain types
of food objects. We need only mention the preference of
fat by animals lacking a pancreas (520), the choice of calcium lactate over sodium phosphate in nephrectomized and
parathyroidectomized animals (634), and the increased intake of sodium chloride by adrenalectomized rats (517).

3. *Organism-Object.Chemistry*

Chemical facts relating to the second and more peripheral matrix of the essential psychological nucleus are concerned primarily with the maintenance and growth of the
organism and the continued existence of objects and organisms in a proper condition for interaction in psychological
fields.

A. Chemistry of the Organism

(a) *Chemistry of Growth.* Chemicals affecting or regulating
growth may perhaps best be illustrated by means of the
hormones of the various glands.

Epiphysis. Whether or not the pineal body is a truly
secretory organ or gland is not yet established. Grollman
(194) and Hathaway (203, pp. 107, 204) conclude that the
pineal has no known endocrine function. There is evidence,
however, that when it is pathologically disturbed there are
untoward effects on the individual (194, 239). Sufficient basis
exists then for assuming that behavioral changes result from
changes in this organ. This assumption is strengthened by the
suggestion that the epiphysis provides a hormone regulating
bodily development and the onset of puberty (239, p. 260).

Hypophysis. The psychological importance of the pituitary
arises not only from its many and complex secretions which
affect various metabolic functions, but also from its interrelation with other important secretory organs, especially
the thyroid and gonads. Psychologists, however, differ in
their estimate of this importance. There are those who believe
that the pituitary and other endocrine glands are definitely
responsible for particular mental powers or behavior traits,
whereas others deny any such direct influence. In both cases,
however, the view is not entertained that psychological
events are specific behavior fields, and so must perforce
include gland action, whether normal or diseased, as a
factor. Even though such differences in view may concern
only emphasis and expository style they must still be taken
seriously when P.P. theory is in question.

Thyroxin. Probably because of the striking facts of cretinism associated with insufficient secretion of thyroxin, psychologists have generally correlated the chemical and psychological facts involving the secretion of the thyroid gland more closely than in the case of other organs. Hathaway (203, p. 20) refers to the theory, which he rejects, that mild hyperthyroidism is responsible for a facilitation of mental action. Shock summarizes the evidence for and against the hypothesis connecting intellectual capacity and thyroid function as follows:

> Within the range of normal variation no relation between thyroid function and intellectual capacity has been clearly demonstrated (554, p. 606).

If, however, the thyroid gland is such an important organ in the organismic economy it is difficult to believe that it could play an insignificant part in behavioral events. We need only eliminate ideas of faculties and functions that correspond to biological processes and which are determined by hormones.

Other Chemical Substances. Among other growth hormones stressed as indirect regulators of psychological behavior a prominent place must be given to the secretions of the parathyroids controlling calcium and phosphorus metabolism. Hoskins quotes McCollum:

> No one with blood containing slightly too low a calcium content and markedly low phosphorus content has a wholesome attitude toward life. The accompanying irritability, lack of agreeableness, and lack of serenity must be an important consideration in determining the attitude . . . toward home, school, and associates (239, pp. 114, 115).

Actually in a comprehensive coverage of the organism as a matrix of psychological responses every type of chemical reaction must be taken into account. So far as internal secretions are concerned the products of the gonads and the Islands of Langerhans should not be neglected.

(b) *Maintenance Chemistry.* From the standpoint of bioecology differentiations between the products, functions, and structures of separate organisms are all arbitrary. This is also true of the division between: (1) growth and maintenance and (2) internal and external secretion. The secretions of the liver and other organs may be envisaged either as internally or externally secretory. Certainly from the standpoint of psychological matrices it is inadvisable to mark off sharply one type of biological fact from another. All of them we must look upon as playing their respective parts in total interbehavioral fields.

General Biochemistry. It is encouraging that physiological psychologists have recently been showing an increased interest in the general biochemistry of the organism. This interest indicates a trend away from the mind-body correlation and toward influences of organic factors in total psychological-behavior pictures. It is still true, unfortunately, that the literature is slanted so that biophysical conditions are presumed to have effects primarily on the central nervous system (21, 22, 407). Nevertheless the interest in organic equilibrium or homeostasis, as Cannon calls it, marks a better attitude in the field. For our present purposes we divide off the facts of general biochemistry into: (1) organic equilibrium and (2) general metabolism.

(1) *Organic Equilibrium.* Under this heading we consider two sample factors affecting changes in behavior.

Sugar. As in the case of oxygen a disturbance in carbohydrate metabolism produces milder insufficiencies in the more complicated reactions, whereas greater deprivations are correlated with disturbances of the cruder reactions. In cases of the most extreme upsets of behavior, involving serious disturbance of organic equilibrium, the most widespread interference with behavior occurs.

Acid-Base Blood Balance. Because of the delicacy of the hydrogen ion concentration of the blood, physiological psychologists have been interested in observing correlations between this sort of disequilibrium and psychological changes. While such correlations from an *a priori* standpoint should be easily demonstrated, the present data are not clear cut. It is plain that the acidity or akalinity of the blood are correlated with particular conditions of wellbeing. On the whole, correlations are better established when general and not specific effects are sought than when specific correlations' are attempted. Also, conclusions are better authenticated when the acid-alkaline balance is considered as a part of the general biological condition of the individual.

(2) *General Metabolism.* Psychologists frequently extrapolate from the findings that general psychological abnormality is associated with severe metabolic disturbance —for example, cretinism and dullness—to the correlation of particular normal behavior with metabolic conditions. Accordingly, many workers have sought to relate metabolic conditions with various psychological traits and action—for instance basal metabolism with intelligence (test scores) (120, 234, 235, 527, 555), speed of reaction (339, 576), scholastic achievement (168, 472, 478), and behavior problems and maladjustment (366, 435, 636). On the whole, though the psychological factors treated are general traits and processes the results are negative. Accordingly, they substantiate the irrelation of specific psychological performances to particular metabolic factors.

B.   Object (Environment) Chemistry

(a) *General Metabolic Objects.* Since the organism is an essential factor in the psychological field it is only to be expected that the metabolic conditions of the individual should be important in his behavior. Metabolic conditions of two sorts may be considered.

1. *Nutritional Factors.* Probably the most notable general observation concerns the influence of malnutrition on effective psychological performance. Similar results are reported on the effects of insufficient diet, as well as excessive food intake.

On the whole, it is well to regard such correlations as general. To adopt the view that certain kinds of foods have specific psychological effects is unwarranted. What the facts may indicate is that disturbances of general wellbeing may have deleterious effects upon psychological performance. Similarly we must guard against overlooking the enormous complexity of the facts, so that tremendous individual differences involving all sorts of personal habits are overlooked. Moreover, as Shock (554) has pointed out, there are numerous social factors complicating metabolic situations.

2. *Vitamins.* An expansive literature testifies to the great interest in the assumed effect of specific vitamins on particular psychological activities. Shock sums up these results in the statement:

> At the present time no evidence available indicates a causal relationship between any specific vitamin and specific mental symptoms (554, p. 600).[1]

Vitamin chemists, perhaps more than psychologists, appear willing to endorse such statements as that vitamin feeding is in some sense capable of fostering intelligence or morality (634a). Once more we point out that if vitamin intake is beneficial to the organism it is owing to an improvement in general metabolic functioning.

(b) *Object-Organism Medium.* Atmospheric substances including various gaseous chemicals may be regarded as biological media. They surround organisms and their environing objects and intervene between them during their interaction. Here as in other psychochemical situations the question to be answered is what is the relation of the $0 \leftrightarrow 0$ medium to specific psychological events?

Anoxia. The reduction of oxygen content in inspired air is reported to produce a regular progression of psychological changes. McFarland (411-414) asserts that small oxygen losses result in impairment of critical ability, mental confusion, and emotional outbursts. At the same time the individual becomes euphoric. Increased oxygen deprivation

---

[1] Confirmatory evidence is reported in a recent study (194a) showing irrelation between intellectual deterioration and B-complex deprivation.

affects speed and accuracy of computation and attention. Severe losses indicate disturbances of motor and sensory performance. Loss of consciousness is reported to occur (364; 554, p. 586) when the blood issuing from the brain is less than 24 percent saturated with oxygen.

One of the most recent reports of the effect of anoxia on behavior (605) indicates that such performances are not equally affected. Also because individuals vary considerably in their performances conclusive findings have to be made on group data. The same individuals suffer differently on different trials. On the whole, one must conclude that we are not dealing here with absolute physiological effects on specific psychological performances;[1] rather, physiological conditions are among the factors operating in larger psychological situations.

Carbon Monoxide and Dioxide. The effects of CO and CO_2 on performance may be regarded as influencing primarily the organism participating in psychological behavior. The case of CO is clear. The prevention of oxygen from combining with hemoglobin generally reduces the organism to a toxic ineffectiveness of contact with things. In some cases of CO poisoning confusion and disorientation (551) and catatonic behavior (284, 516) have been reported.

For the psychologist the important question is how much CO will so modify the biological operation of the organism as to interfere with its psychological behavior. In small amounts CO intake is so harmless as to be employed as a method of determining total blood volume (89; 161, p. 552).

In recent work performed in connection with aviation research (610) a number of subjects were tested on such performances as body sway, size of red visual field, and critical flicker frequency under anoxia and increased carboxyhemoglobin (COHb) conditions. In the latter case the increase of COHb ranged from 9 to 19 percent.

[1] This is a defensible statement even in view of Shock and Scow (556) that reduced oxygen tension diminished the rat's ability to distinguish between upright and inverted triangles.

There was no statistically significant difference between the mean scores of the tests during anoxia and during anoxia following the administration of CO (610, p. 251).

It is assumed that compensating physiological mechanisms operate to minimize CO effects. The results obtained suggest that organisms possess marked adaptability as mechanisms for performing the grosser psychological actions.

CO_2 effects are more complicated because of the close integration of this gas with O_2 in blood content balance and because of its influence on acid-base blood balance. However, it has been well established that breathing air with a partial pressure of a fraction more than 6 percent of CO_2 for an hour or longer produces a general incapacity for effective work (7). On the other hand, an increase of CO_2 content of inspired air to 5 percent improves psychological performance under low-oxygen tension (171; 554, p. 592). Excessively large increments of CO_2 in inspired air, viz., 20-30 percent, have anaesthetic effects (554, p. 593).

4. Chemical Factors as Behavior Settings

It is not surprising that the farther out we go from the center of the essential psychological interbehavioral field the less definite are the boundaries between chemical substances constituting stimulus objects, contact media, and setting factors. Nevertheless, we shall not go far astray if we characterize the chemical events of this division as typically ecological. This we do on the basis that the chemical events on the R↔S level operate mainly in influencing whether or not stimulus and response functions are developed altogether, whereas on the O↔O level such events modify stimulus-response functions on a criterion of normality or abnormality. The chemical events on the set level influence stimulus-response functions in three ways. First, they play a part in influencing whether any of the stimulus-response functions that have been developed will operate at a given moment. Next they influence which of the many f(s↔r)'s that have been developed will be performed. And finally, they influence the speed and intensity with which such f(s↔r)'s are performed.

The ancient maxim *Mens Sana in Corpore Sano* receives a definite interpretation in the modern consideration of the relations of chemistry and psychology. Organisms capable of performing psychological activities or performing them adequately not only must be chemically balanced in their structural and functional aspects but also be surrounded by tolerable or optimal chemical media. Furthermore, there are such important factors as internal and external tolerances, adaptations, and compensations. But all of these constitute factors in specific contacts of organisms with stimulus objects.

It is hardly an objection to this differentiation of the modes of chemical influence that the criteria are not mutually exclusive or that they somehow merge. On the whole, however, set chemical substances consist of endogenous or exogenous drugs, which not only greatly modify psychological actions but also generally hinder or facilitate the performances of psychological behavior. This they may do by affecting primarily organismic factors (fatigue, toxins), stimulus objects (chemically-induced changes of properties), or the surroundings of both. For convenience we consider only organismic drug effects in normal and abnormal behavior situations.

(1) *Normal Situations.* The effects of particular drugs on psychological performances range from general disorientation and disequilibrium to the effects on particular actions, reaction time, maze running, school performance, etc. Our survey of these studies may well be prefaced by a quotation from Shock:

It is practically impossible to make any adequate generalizations with respect to the effects of drugs on mental performance because of the wide differences of experimental technique, dosages, kinds of animals, and conditions under which experiments were carried out in different studies (553, p. 458).

To this should be added that from the standpoint of the observations of actual individual behavior there are many conflicting conditions. When drugs have well-authenticated effects it is because of definite changes brought about in the individual's biological conditions. In turn, these effects depend upon other biological conditions such as age, immunity, tolerance, and general immediate hygienic circumstances. Like all biological conditions the variability range is very large.

Nor can we overlook the cultural and social conditions that have their definite influence. In a given society it is obvious that the deleterious effects of pipe or cigar smoking is not merely the result of the use of tobacco, but its customary use by the population in general or by males as differentiated from females.

And finally, drug effects are very complexly interrelated with the psychological traits and habits of individuals, that is, when the effects are not so profound as to stop all behavior or so disorganize the individual as to isolate him from his usual contacts with objects. Within these ranges similar amounts of drugs have variant effects on different individuals. The drug therefore is a definite stimulus object for the individual as well as an agent for the production of physiological effects.

To illustrate the type of hypothesis involved in drug investigations we sample some of the literature on a small series of drugs.

Alcohol. Though large amounts of alcohol concentrated in the circulating blood serve to disorganize all of the individual's behavior, such findings throw little light on the effects of alcohol on particular psychological behavior. Attempts to discover correlations between alcohol-affected physiological conditions and particular psychological performances are decidedly inconclusive (403). Some studies (88, 432) show that mild doses of alcohol result in improvement in certain activities. McFarland and Barach (415) report an adverse effect on various performances—choice reaction, color naming, pursuitmeter—when the intake amounts to three fourths of a gram of alcohol per kilo of body weight.

Whatever behavioral effects there may be, they are all owing
to general conditions surrounding interbehavioral events. In
this connection Johnson (280) scores an important point when
he refers to the organism's compensation activities when
partially dissociated.

Benzedrine. Though the reports on benzedrine studies are
somewhat contradictory it is probably safe to conclude that
this drug exerts temporary facilitation effects on the organism.
For example, Sargent and Blackburn (537) found that twenty-
five mental patients having taken 20 mg. showed an increase
of 3.9 points or 8.7 percent in the average score on Cattell's
intelligence test. Gwynn and Yater (197), administering each
day the same amount of the drug to each of 147 medical
students over a period of three days, report that of this group
113 said they felt peppy, 72 exhilarated, 42 more talkative;
61 claimed concentration was increased, while 126 suffered
from insomnia. Davidoff and Reifenstein (110, 515) report
similar findings. These same authors, however, state that
other subjects become dull, inactive, and inaccessible. Mc-
Namara and Miller (418) report that such tasks as multiplying two 3-place numbers were not materially improved,
though the subjects thought they were stimulated by the
drug.

Mescalin. What appear to be specific effects of drugs on
psychological performances are reported in the case of
mescalin, which considerably modifies various perceptual
and image reactions. Klüver (313) and others have described
striking changes in imagery following the administration of
drugs. The evidences should probably be interpreted as
showing general disorganizational processes (195, 196, 581).
Such effects, of course, are not altogether limited to mescalin;
however, through general physiological changes, behavior
is definitely modified by the use of mescalin. But in what
sense is this behavior psychological? Only if we isolate
specific stimulus-response function fields do we concern ourselves with scientifically-analytic psychological behavior.

Upon such specific and definitive events mescalin or any other drug can have only an indirect effect when it modifies the conditions of the organism.

(2) *Pathological Situations.* Here we limit our discussion to the administration of metrazol and insulin.[1]

Insulin. Since Sakel (534-536) introduced insulin treatment there have been many reports both of a highly optimistic and pessimistic sort concerning its effectiveness (396, 552). As usual, the original claims made for this drug as a factor in the remission of pathologies such as schizophrenia have had to be scaled down. The basic difficulty is that psychological facts are treated as general functions, so that at best the evidences indicate that if there is any value in the use of this drug it lies in a general change in the individual's biological condition. Such changes, when they occur, constitute for the most part shock or general dis: turbance. It can not be denied that at least for a time good effects are obtained. This explains why workers describe the results in the form of temporary or permanent remission instead of a cure. Generally speaking, evidence is lacking of any permanent cures.

Metrazol. The story of metrazol administration follows closely that of insulin. When Meduna (420, 421) first introduced this treatment in 1935 there began a period of high expectation and strong claims, then a recession of interest and use (324). It is significant also that the use of this drug is considerably forestalled because of the advent of electric shock (12, p. 1123). The use of metrazol shock treatment overlooks most of the important psychological facts concerning pathological conditions. How can a general shock treatment overcome the process of building up particular ways of acting over long periods of time—ways of acting, moreover, dependent upon specific human conditions in the case of the particular patient!

[1] For a competent coverage of chemical factors in pathological conditions see Cameron (73).

5. Chemistry Involved in Individual Adjustments to Life Conditions

The data here consist of complex adjustments of individuals to their life conditions. Clearly this is a level of crude data which merits consideration only because I↔LC events include specific psychological events among many other kinds.[1] Actually there are so many types of events in I↔LC situations as to defy exact analysis and enumeration. But there are two cogent reasons for dealing with this level. In the first place most of psychochemical literature is really concerned with the effects of chemical processes in general behavioral situations involving adaptations of organisms to their undifferentiated life circumstances. Secondly, psychologists and other workers have concluded that psychochemical studies have shown that the psychological nature of individuals or personalities may be attributed to their chemical organization.

On this level of individuals and their surroundings it can not be said that there are chemical facts which are precisely reflected in psychological events. Rather, the part that chemistry plays is diffuse and indeterminate. Certainly chemistry has a small role in the adjustment of individuals to their surroundings in comparison with societal and cultural factors. To say that because obviously chemical events have much to do with the adaptations of persons to their everyday circumstances we have data on chemical influences on psychological behavior is to confuse unanalyzed with scientifically-analyzed events.

The most flagrant example of such confusion is the view that the chemique of an organism determines its type of mentality. The formula here is that psychological personality is determined by the chemistry of the organism. Not the least of the errors here is to regard personality as some vague

---

[1] It is, of course, also true that specific fields include I↔LC factors as components. For example, many interbehaviors of the unwitting-motive type play a part in reasoning and other complex fields.

entity whether or not considered as inhering in the organism.

Technically the individual or personality as a psychological datum consists of a tremendously large panoply of behavior equipments. These are classifiable as traits, temperaments, abilities, knowledge, reflexes, etc. But the hand of tradition has transformed such interbehavioral field factors into an integral psychic unit influenced by bodily factors, for example, internal secretions. Thus has arisen the tradition of the humors and temperaments, and of glands regulating personality.

Despite the following statement of Hathaway:

After going through the experimental and clinical literature the thoughtful reader will conclude that the effects of personality upon glands are more impressive and easier to illustrate than are the effects of the glands upon personality (203, p. 203)

there is a persistent implication that internal secretions have definite and particular effects on psychological performances. This implication stands opposed both to the facts of psychological behavior and the physiology of glandular function.

II

CHEMISTRY OF PREPSYCHOLOGICAL EVENTS

Prepsychological events constitute primarily nonpsychological developments of organisms which at some future date will participate in psychological fields. Prepsychological events are thus of the greatest importance when we wish to keep before us the continuity of events, since the origin and growth of organisms constitute potent links in the total chain of psychological happenings.

Prepsychological events include both the phylogenetic and ontogenetic evolutions of organisms. Both of these successive evolutions are important in the study of potential participants in psychological fields. But until the organisms are evolved sufficiently to enter such fields they exist far out on the periphery of psychological events. Now aside from certain essential biological traits organisms in the prepsychological stage may be regarded as belonging exclusively to the biochemical domain.

So far as phylogenetic evolution is concerned we are interested in the chemical and physical interactions which eventuate in the morphological and functional character of species. This material concerns the relative stabilization of characteristics through adaptation to particular environing chemical and other conditions. Ontogenetic chemistry consists of innumerable chemical reactions originating in the reproductive processes of the individual's progenitors and continuing as the developmental mechanisms in the organism's growth and differentiation from zygote to adult. Of no mean importance here are the processes which maintain the crucial balance between the common characteristics of the species and the unique qualities of the individual. The psychologist's interest centers about the contribution of both types of characteristics to psychological-interbehavior fields.

(1) *Species Evolution.* How remote are the facts concerning the evolution of organisms from psychological events depends upon the problems that face us. When we confine ourselves to behavior questions involving organisms of a given species we find that their structures and functions constitute only possibilities and limitations. Organisms of one particular species are by virtue of their evolution capable or not capable of entering into an interbehavioral history culminating in certain performances. The critera are established by comparison with other species.

When we make such comparisons species differences become closely integrated with psychological facts. Now the inevitable association of the data and the principles of biology and psychology take on a great importance. Psychological and biological events become tightly knit. Obviously the process of species evolution involves a tremendous quantity of chemical processes of various sorts. It is impossible to doubt this, however meager our knowledge of details. Of one thing we may be sure, and that is that such baffling questions as to whether evolutionary processes operate by the accumulation of minute changes or by sudden variations and mutations promise to be cleared up by an increasing acquaintance with specific chemical processes operating within the organism and between organisms and their surrounding media.

(2) *Ontogenetic Evolution.* The chemistry of the growing embryo casts its shadow on its future psychological behavior. Merely consider that the emergence of a normal or pathological organism is to a great extent a matter of the chemical processes which constitute so large a matrix of differentiating tissues and organs. The essential prerequisite for evolving psychological events is the prior embryological development of organisms. When we try to understand that development as actual and precise happenings we must turn to the chemical interactions basic to them. As Butler (68) indicates: There is a physiological chemistry of the developing embryo, as well as of the adult body, in other words a chemistry of inter- and intra-cellular changes.

It will help to keep clear the relation between embryological chemistry and psychological events if we remember that once such reactions eventuate in a normal organism, we then have only the basis or a potential factor for psychological fields. In other words, we have an organism not with any psychological powers or abstruse potentialities, but merely with the proper biological actuality for further psychological interactions. These further interactions are to constitute a psychological interbehavioral history in which the organism takes on behavior equipment and performs response functions, while the interbehaving objects become stimulus objects and the matrix for stimulus functions (293).

At this point we must take account of the fact that since, after all, the organism is only one of a number of component factors in psychological fields, its various abnormalities and peculiarities are only bars to participation in psychological fields in which the presence or absence of specific structures and functions count. While a bifid spine is a bar to athletics, it need not interefere with the performance of mathematical problems.

(3) *Chemical Factors in Heredity.* The distinction between the chemistry of heredity and that of embryology lies in the source of original substances (gametes) which interoperate with the intrauterine environmental factors. Perhaps the kernel of the whole matter is that whatever embryological processes take place in the development of individuals is conditioned by prior developments of their ancestors. This means essentially that whether a sea-urchin or starfish egg is fertilized by the sperm cells of such organisms or by some chemical like magnesium chloride, a starfish or sea urchin develops. This is the basis for similarities in the continuation of a species. The differences in the individuals developed depend upon what interactions take place in their unique life histories.

The science of genetics in the last few decades has been turning away in some measure from the doctrine of general determination to the study of actual chemical interactions (30, 199, 574a). More and more, genes are becoming regarded as complex molecular substances which duplicate themselves. In various studies on simple organisms, such as neurospora, and on viruses, a sufficient number of facts have been elicited to substantiate the hypothesis of complex chemical interactions in hereditary processes. What has been thought of as simple transmission is now known as definite inter-behavioral actions.

The implication of these new conceptions for psychology is that there are many levels of field interaction. In the evolution of species certain interactions give rise to more or less stable organic substances, which if uninterfered with by radiation or other mutation processes maintain and reproduce themselves. These substances are subject to minor variations on other and subsequent levels. Up to a point these organic developments are purely biological and biochemical, but finally play their part in definite psychological interactions.

The conclusion follows that authentic psychological events develop on a level far beyond the phylogenetic and ontogenetic levels, and while the three are continuous we have no warrant for thinking of psychological events as predetermined and transmitted.

III

PARAPSYCHOLOGICAL CHEMISTRY

Under this caption we consider chemical effects on organisms which are essentially biological and related to our theme primarily because they obviate and interfere with psychological performances. Anesthetic drugs serve as a general illustration of such chemical factors. As associated with psychological fields, parapsychological chemical factors may be described as withdrawing organisms from stimulus objects.

An interesting example of the reverse effect of parapsychological drugs is the interference with hedgehog hibernation by the oral administrations of vitamin D (87). An illustration of the more direct sort is the induction of catatonia in monkeys by administering bulbocapnine, and the counter-effect brought about by cocaine injections (61).

The number of drugs capable of greatly or completely reducing the organism's contacts with stimulus objects and thus keeping it out of effective interbehavioral fields is too large to make even a listing feasible. To mention the great number of barbiturate preparations is sufficiently suggestive of the interrelationship of biochemical and psychological situations.

CHEMISTRY AND PSYCHOLOGY

Summary

As the science of basic reactions of things chemistry constitutes a valuable cooperative science for psychology. While no objective psychologist would disagree with this statement, few psychologists have taken advantage of the opportunity it suggests. For the most part, psychologists have been concerned with the chemistry of organisms, whereas they have almost completely neglected the chemistry of stimulus objects.

There is a clear advantage, however, in taking account of the chemistry of stimulus objects. So far as external stimuli are concerned, cooperation with the chemist obviates the construction of unobservable entities or powers to account for interactions with the qualities of things. Again, keeping close to chemical events means that chemical interactions, occurring in the organism as internal stimuli, will not be transformed into self-moving powers or drives.

Psychological and chemical cooperation, it is clear, proceeds on the basis of correlations of two kinds of objective events. Accordingly, constructions signifying that chemical substances are causes of psychological action are unacceptable. An example is the interpretation that when animals are deprived of certain hormones by castration or other mutilations, direct psychological effects have been produced. Such psychological effects are perforce taken to be powers or abilities resident in biological actions and their variations. What we actually observe are coincident changes in behavior and in the behaving organisms.

Correlation thus consists of the co-presence of chemical and psychological events in a field. Obviously none of these events constitutes traditional psychological or psychophysiological processes. As we have shown, such correlations may be close or remote. In every instance and on every level the exact relationship must be specifically demonstrated in full detail. To do so would obviate the assumptions that complex normal or abnormal behavior can be accounted for by the presence or absence of particular chemical substances such as the porphyrins (319), phenylpyruvic acid (147, 277, 278, 489), and others (73, chs. 15-17).

CHAPTER 18

PSYCHOBIOLOGY

PSYCHOBIOLOGY AND PHYSIOLOGICAL PSYCHOLOGY

PSYCHOBIOLOGY as articulated with psychology was organized with the intention to integrate the mind and body which classical P.P. had rent asunder. Whether psychobiologists trace the influence of bodily constitution on character and temperament or treat patients as holistic units, they regard themselves as correcting in practical pursuits traditional psychophysical errors.

In science Shakespeare's "What's in a name"? frequently receives the terse answer: Nothing. This, however, is not the case with the term *psychobiology,* for it clearly illustrates and applies psychophysical doctrine. Since both psychobiology and classical P.P. are ensconced in a common dualistic tradition, the corrective attempts of the former paradoxically accomplish the opposite of what was intended. All efforts to interrelate mind and body are not only bounded by the psychophysical way of thinking but indeed serve to perpetuate it.

Psychobiological constructions of all varieties can be dispensed with only if we extrude all mind-body implications from psychology. To achieve this, of course, means the radical emendation of our technical constructions. It means to free ourselves from the implication of anatomical science that there are bodies standing over against minds. On the side of technical biology we must observe the sharply-outlined boundary between the data of the dissection table or the histological laboratory, and those of the living and discriminating organism. So far as psychology is concerned, the elimination of both minds and bodies is decidedly helpful in properly evaluating the relations between biological factors and the larger psychological situations in which the former play their inevitable parts.

Psychobiological writers must indeed be credited with the realization that psychological and biological data should be brought closer together. This is a tribute paid to events. Accordingly we proceed to study some representative subdivisions of psychobiology, hoping to clear the way for interrelating psychological and biological events without employing psychic and pseudo organic constructions. At the same time we plan to show the new light this procedure will throw on P.P. problems. Our three examples of psychobiological materials fall under the headings: (a) psychosomatypology, (b) psychoheredity, and (c) somatogenic psychopathology.

Psychosomatypology

The psychosomatypological enterprise is designed to establish dependence of psychological and anatomical types. Psychosomatypologists search for biological or constitutional factors corresponding to psychological characteristics of behavior and biological predispositions to certain types of mental abnormality. Somatypological quests appeared in the earliest days of psychological writing, and burst through the pages of history in forms varying with the climates of opinion current in different periods. It is not illegitimate to trace back all somatypological doctrines to the Hippocratean saga of the four humors. Carrying over the philosophical doctrine of the four elements air, fire, water, and earth with their four properties, heat, cold, dry, and moist, to the domain of biology, the Greek physicians developed the theory of the four cardinal humors, blood, yellow or black bile, and phlegm. When the humors, the hot and moist blood, the cold and moist phlegm, the hot and dry yellow bile, and the cold and dry black bile were properly mixed in sufficient quality and quantity, health prevailed.

In view of the objective character of Greek psychological thinking, it is entirely understandable that the early physicians should have taken into account the biological characteristics of individuals when discussing their psychological traits. Thus arose the correlation of humors and temperaments.

Persons in whom black bile slightly predominated were melancholic; blood was connected with the sanguine temperament, phlegm with the phlegmatic or lymphatic, and yellow bile with the choleric. Though Galen and Averroes are very prominently associated with this doctrine, there have been numerous proponents through every time period, despite minor variations in doctrinal detail.

With the establishment of dualistic or psychophysical ways of thinking the humoral doctrine and the correlation of humors and temperaments flourished. While the psychic interpretation of psychological characteristics persists to our own day, the humors from time to time have become transformed into more acceptable substances, even into internally-secreted hormonic materials. As long as psychologists and physicians remain on the superficial level of every-day observation it is not objectionable to search for similarities in persons' general characteristics and biological traits. Certainly it must be granted that such attempts lead to the investigation of the morphological variations of the human animal.

Although psychological science as much as any other has been set in a matrix of popular thought, it is probably true that the subject of personality types and their relation to morphological characteristics has converged for the most part with common-sense observation and theory. Classification of mind and body has been a popular pastime among literateurs, philosophers, and physicians. Shakespeare not only made use of contrasting personalities (Hamlet, Laertes; Falstaff, Percy) as a technique of playwriting, but also indicated his absorption of popular theories.

> Let me have men about me that are fat,
> Sleek-headed men, and such as sleep o'nights.
> Yond' Cassius has a lean and hungry look;
> He thinks too much; such men are dangerous.

It is even claimed (558, p. 153) that Shakespeare's plays can not be understood without a knowledge of the humoral theories.

We do not propose to enter into the history of psychosomatypology nor to make an inventory of the various systems. It will suffice first to illustrate the impetus given to such studies by French mechanistic and materialistic philosophy and by the species-gradation tradition of Darwinian evolutionism, and then to exhibit a few current examples of psychosomatypological systems.

French Materialism. Following the lead of Descartes' correlation of the mechanistic body and the inextensible soul, numerous writers attempted to refine this relation. Their problem was to show what kind of bodily machine is associated with a specific type of mind. Recall here de la Mettrie (1700-1750) and his *Man a Machine* (428), in which the different states of the soul are shown to be correlated to those of the body, and the diversity between man and other animals proved to arise from the different quality and quantity of their brains. Then there is Condillac (1715-1780) with his statue body determining the character of mental life (92). And finally we mention Bonnet (1720-1793), the mystical Swiss naturalist and philosopher (40, 41), who wrote:

... I perceive that I have ideas only by the intervention of my body, and the more I reflect upon myself, the more I am compelled to recognize the great influence of the machine upon all the operations of my soul (509, p. 333).

Though there exists the anecdote that Gall (1758-1828) developed his cranioscopy and phrenology from a youthful observation that prominent eyes bespoke an efficient memory (43, 387), there is no question that he and his pupil Spurzheim (1776-1832) both simply absorbed the traditional mind-body doctrine elaborated by the French mechanists who merely modified medieval dualistic doctrine. As anatomists Gall and Spurzheim specialized on cranial construction; still they belong to the same cultural tradition which cast up Lavater (1741-1801) (359) and other physiognomists and characterologists interested in other than cranial bodily aspects. This is indicated in their partially-joint treatise (164).

Darwinian Evolutionism. With the establishment of the evolution doctrine and its emphasis on organic variability and the application of descent or transmission conceptions to the mental as well as the organic, psychosomatypologists became interested in the general morphological organization of individuals. Again we can not enter into the many developments here. We should mention, however, Galton's (166) assiduous study of individual variation, both of mental and bodily characteristics, and also the attempt of anthropologists to correlate civilization with the bodily characteristics of races. Most pertinent, of course, is the intense study of the contribution of bodily construction to individual mental characteristics. The Italian movement, indicated by the work of de Giovanni (176), Viola (607), Naccarati (456), Pende (481) and others, is especially prominent. Here the work of the anthropologists in attempting to correlate bodily characteristics with criminality and other traits is important. Notably Lombroso (375-378).

Constitutional Psychopathology. Among physicians it has long been a custom to seek for constitutional factors of disease. Apparently it seems eminently rational to expect the size, bulk, and shape of the anatomical seat of diseases to reveal dispositions and propensities toward pathology (64, 480, 491). There even exists a constitution clinic for the investigation of such predisposing factors (123, 124). An easy transition is made to discover supposed constitutional factors for mental disturbances. The best-known of these psychosomatypological systems is, of course, that of Kretschmer (328). Building upon numerous predecessors, he has adopted a distinction between linearity (leanness) and laterality (stoutness) of physique, which he calls respectively the asthenic or leptosomic and pyknic types. With the latter he correlated cyclothymic forms of pathologies, and with the former, schizophrenic.

We shall not attempt any criticism of Kretschmer's typology and mind-body correlation within the framework of his constructions. That task has been ably executed by a number of writers (312; 476, p. 233). Despite some favorable inclination on the part of those who accept Kretchmer's premises (546, p. 26 f.) it is usually held that his structure totters on the most shifting of conceptual sands. It is the general scientific constructions that we wish to examine.

First, as to the somatotypes he adopts. Obviously his types constitute nothing more than the crudest division of surface differences in body build. The elaborate verbal descriptions of his two main types are nothing but autistic endowments. Even the various attempts to reduce the simple basis of such classifications and typologies by mentioning endocrine secretions and general biochemistry (434. 491) do not help matters much. Stockard (580, p. 299) asserts that only the two linearality and laterality types are necessary to formulate and develop problems of variability in personality and form, no doubt because anatomical study does not yield any principles making for other characteristics. The somatypologists, however, find it necessary to multiply their types.

Kretschmer himself has thought it expedient to separate out an athletic variant from his asthenic type. More significant still is his development of the dysplastic type. Surely this is the type to end all types. A confirmed somatypologist like Sheldon (546-548), however, presumes to profit by this bankruptcy of types by setting up other classifications of body structure, but he gets no further than the utter mixtures which Kretschmer attains by his dysplastic class and the innumerable combinations of the main types.

The body correlates turn out to be, then, nothing but the common-sense factors of thin and thick, though other terms are made but not used as correlational items. Similarly, the mental or character correlates. Kretschmer adopts the popular differentiation of psychopathology into two classes, the schizophrenic and the cyclothenic or manic-depressive. What about excited and slowed up schizophrenics? Aside from the impossibility of keeping these apart, why only two? And are there even these two? Clearly the whole system constitutes an artificial construction. In what sense is there any psychopathology of this sort? Instead of such palpable mind and body entities we had better consider maladjustments and inefficiencies of specific action.

The student of P.P. will not miss the implied connection between psychosomatypology and the various forms of phrenology, physiognomy, and characterology. All these varieties of *die Körperform als Spiegel der Seele* (37) certainly belong more to folklore than science, despite the precision of any measurement of the anatomical characteristics. Not to be overlooked either are the motivations and applications centering in the doctrines of individual and racial worth and destiny.

Dimensionality Variation. An interesting exhibition in psychosomatypology is represented by Sheldon's (546-548) efforts. Well aware of the impossibility of differentiating biological types and despite his assertion that he rejects such a conception, he nevertheless works out a scheme of bodily types which he persists in connecting with types of mentality. His scheme consists in scaling individuals on the basis of variations in somatic dimensions, and then correlating the result with temperamental differences.

Sheldon begins with three primary variables, endomorphy (predominant digestive viscera), mesomorphy (bone and muscle predominant), and ectomorphy (slight development of both visceral and somatic structures). By elaborate manipulations of photographs he builds up a somatypological system. Individuals are given a rating according to a seven-point scale on each of the three dimensions: 1-1-7 is an extreme ectomorph, 1-7-1 the most extreme mesomorph, and 7-1-1 the most extreme endomorph. Seventy six of such somatotypes have been described (548, p. 530).

To match the body variations three categories of temperament have been set up, viscerotonia, somatotonia, and cerebrotonia. For each of these, 20 temperament traits have been constructed. For example, the viscerotonic temperament includes pleasure in digestion, love of polite ceremony, deep sleep, tolerance, etc. The somatotonic is characterized by love of risk and chance, the unrestrained voice, claustro-phobia, etc. The cerebrotonic is agorophobic, a poor sleeper, solitude loving etc.

Sheldon lays great store by his quantitative measurements of both bodily and mental characteristics and the reliability of their correlation. A glance at his scale of temperament indicates that what he is attempting to scale are acts and not mental correlates. Accordingly his practice seems better than his intention to contribute to psychoanalytic dissection of consciousness and body. For this reason we may condone his admixture of behavior such as sleep, tolerance, and speed of reaction. On any basis his correlation of physique and temperament fails to support any psychobiological theory.

No other conclusion is possible than that none of the various efforts to discover biological characteristics making for type of mentality has achieved a satisfactory result. All attempts to discover correlations between organic constitu-tion and intelligence or temperament consist simply of setting up schemes within the framework of psychophysical theory.

It can not be denied, however, that on the level of crude data it is possible to set up rough correlations of every variety. Take color, stature, sex, or any organic property, and you can correlate it with type of activity and achievement. A promi-nent anthropologist (178) is convinced that male sexuality is correlated with creativeness. His evidence is that there is no woman Rodin, Picasso, Beethoven, Wagner, Molière or Tchekhov. But this sort of correlation is neither based on biological nor anthropological science. It does not take ac-count of analyzed factors of sex (165, 656) or cultural princi-ples.

Two important scientific failings stand out in psycho-somatypological thinking and investigation. In the first place, psychological data are taken to be something other than specific behavior events. Psychobiologists assume that men-tality consists of characteristics or general traits of some sort. In the second place, they overlook the fact that cultural con-ditions have much more to do with the traits of persons than their biological constitutions. Probably one of the best correctives is to consider that biological sex differences are the extremes of biological variation; yet the actual traits and performances of sexually-different individuals can be readily accounted for by their individual behavioral histories against a background of more or less rapidly-changing cultural circumstances.

PSYCHOHEREDITY

Arguments from psychoheredity or mental inheritance must be numbered among the typical means to integrate the mind and the body. We say arguments advisedly, since all the data consist of complex interactions. It may easily be predicted, therefore, that arguments based upon mentalistic and dualistic premises will turn out to be not only inconclusive but contradictory.

It is frequently asserted that, since obviously all problems of psychoheredity concern biological structures, mental traits are indissolubly related to bodily factors. This statement, superficially so appealing, immediately prompts the question as to the nature of these traits. Two postulates are clearly implied: (1) that mental traits are general qualities or characteristics, and (2) that such traits are somehow functions of biological structures or mechanisms. Yet in view of the fact that these functions are presumed to be psychological and not actually biological, the argument turns out to be verbal or sheerly assertive within the framework of classical dualism.

Adding to the difficulties of this integrating endeavor is the thorough implausibility of the view that psychological events as complex interactions can in any manner be regarded as functions of particular structures or of the total organism. The psychoheredity arguments thus far, then, are not very helpful to the integration idea nor to the general subject of P.P.

Next, those who oppose the conception of mental inheritance argue that while it is true that mentality depends upon biological characteristics, these biological characteristics surely are changed by environmental factors and therefore mental traits are not inherited. Thus mind-body integration now becomes the means of establishing a theory of mentality instead of itself being established by heredity theory.

The story does not end here. Whatever mentality, more specifically denominated intelligence or intellect, may be, it is claimed by many to be inherited. What can they do, therefore, but fall back on the relative independence of biological and psychological events. Paterson (476) devotes a volume to the demonstration that intellect, intelligence, and temperament are not dependent upon physique, cranial size, health or bodily condition.

Having indicated that psychoheredity problems do intimately concern the basic constructions of P.P., let us consider the events and constructions of biological heredity and their interrelationship with psychological events.

A. BIOLOGICAL ASPECTS OF PSYCHOHEREDITY

Genes and Characters Indirectly Related. Geneticists in their strict interpretations surely disclaim the belief that organisms transmit morphological, physiological or behavioral characteristics to their offspring. We have already mentioned (296) that they are also veering away from the notion that genic materials constitute direct determiners of biological traits. They are turning rather to the idea of physiological changes arising from definite chemical substances under the influence of enzyme catalysts (574a, 646), etc. The conceptual outcome is the notion that there is a long chain of reactions separating the original genic or heredity material and biological characters or traits.

Geneticists are emphatic, therefore, that heredity processes do not constitute the transmission of skin color or any other morphological traits, but that these traits develop under specific developmental conditions (121, 199, 276). A favorite expression is that genic material furnishes a set of undifferentiated potentialities requiring other factors to eventuate into actual biological characteristics. This means, then, that the relation between genes and observed characters is necessarily distant and indirect. In fact, it is only in the case of serological or immunological properties that any direct connection can be assumed (574a, 646).

Now even if one believes that psychological events consist of characteristics or traits and that they are functions of organic tissues, there still can not be any predetermined psychology supporting mind-body integration. When the more preferred interactional view is adopted the predetermination construction is very wide of the mark.

Genetic Dynamics. In the first stages of heredity one must posit intra and intercellular interactions with a possible emphasis on the cells and a slighter stress of environmental conditions. But when the reproductive or genetic process advances, then the environment factor becomes important. Here the geneticist asserts that the same heredity in different environments may give rise to different characteristics or behavior. Dobzhansky illustrates this point by saying:

Diabetes mellitus is inherited, but injections of insulin remove the manifestations of this physiological disorder (121).

This dependence of heredity on environment is least marked in blood groupings, so that "the A-a^B-a blood group genes produce the same 'character' in all known environments" (121). He goes on to say:

The designation hereditary can not be restricted to traits which show a certain degree of constancy of expression. The degree of constancy is itself inconstant (121).

And also:

Behavior is influenced so much by environmental variables, particularly training, social conditions and accumulated experience, that the genetic variable is frequently masked (121).

An obvious conclusion here is that biological and psychological facts must be kept rigidly distinct.

Range of Heredity Traits. What a variety of things are subsumed under the terms *traits* and *character!* Unfortunately these terms are indifferently employed to refer to such diverse things and events as (1) morphological properties (color, size, smoothness of skin), (2) physiological processes (insufficient blood clotting—hemophilia, disease resistance or immunity), (3) organismic behavior (broodiness of hens), (4) ecological behavior (nest and web making), and (5) genuine psychological interactions—from taste discrimination to musical performance.

Still, the genetics literature is replete with inferences concerning the heredity determination of all sorts of behavior on the basis of evidence from elementary morphological characteristics. Only rarely do geneticists question the propriety of drawing conclusions concerning psychological behavior from data derived from morphological traits (445). Haldane (199, p. 25) doubts the existence of congenital musical ability or moral defect, but only because there is in his opinion as yet no psychology as reliable as chemistry.

Cultural Influences on Biological Traits. At this point it is useful to consider how much the phenotypic individual or biological organism is influenced by environmental or cultural factors. Surely the morphological characteristics of individuals are determined quite as much by their life conditions—that is, ethnic group, socio-economic level, family and other conditions—as by purely biological development.

Marrack (402) cites a classical experiment of Corry Mann who worked with two groups of boys. The first group, given a diet regarded as adequate, showed no definite evidence of malnutrition. The other group, similarly treated but with an added daily pint of milk, grew considerably faster and was much more lively. The same writer refers to a study of McCance which disturbs the conception of the innate inferiority of the human female as the anaemic sex. It appears that while the increased iron intake of the average man does not raise the hemoglobin level of the blood, when women are given a large amount of iron to meet their greater need their hemogloblin level matches that of men. In sum, human biologists can not limit the factors making for biological traits to those they usually regard as purely biological or metabolic.

B. PSYCHOLOGICAL ASPECTS OF PSYCHOHEREDITY

Characteristics or Behavior? If on the relatively lower level of biological heredity we must take account of interactions instead of determining substances how much more is it necessary in the case of psychological events. Whatever our psychological views, our descriptions must be made in terms of activities of organisms in connection with stimulus objects. Accordingly, in the field of psychoheredity we can not deal with mentality as a general faculty, function or power of any sort. Whatever heredity or genetic factors one may posit, they operate at long range and through complex evolutions of organism-object interactions.

The view of Dobzhansky is pertinent at this juncture.

A Negro, or for that matter anybody having a highly pigmented skin, may be diffident or aggressive in a social environment in which his pigmentation subjects him to discrimination and handicaps. This "psychology" may correctly be called inherited, just as the skin color is called inherited, although in some people the skin color is greatly changed by exposure to sunlight. Heredity which causes the skin to be black and behavior self-conscious may result in a quite different behavior in an environment where discrimination is absent (121).

Participation versus Determination. Whatever evidence exists concerning the influence of biological characteristics on psychological activities these biological traits always operate by way of biological participation (pp. 110, 139). This principle holds for the potentialities provided by the biology of species differences, as well as for malformations and other presumably hereditary biological traits within species. All the data available, therefore, for regarding psychological and biological factors as integrated or relatively independent diametrically oppose any psychophysical notion.

Environment and Stimulation. Both geneticists and psychologists discuss psychoheredity problems on the level of organisms and their environment. For example, it is said that individuals have had similar or dissimilar environments. Such a statement illustrates an inadequate approach to psychoheredity problems. Environment is a biological construct referring to the general surroundings of organisms. This construct is even insufficient in ecological situations. For example, in pecking-order studies, one must take account of the differences between the animals in the group. How much more is it necessary in psychological fields to consider not only the difference between environment and actual objects but also between stimulus objects and their stimulus functions.

On this basis we realize how far-fetched are the arguments for a genetic basis of psychological interaction. To overlook the details of complex developments and interbehavioral operations is to make room for various mystical constructions. To break up the complicated interbehavioral field with its inherent historical development and make the organism and its properties the center and determination of the whole complex of components invites all sorts of misconstructions. So despite the disclaimer of geneticists that they do not believe in determining powers they surreptitiously introduce them into their descriptions. To argue that there is some inheritance of musicianship because of hereditary influence on hand evolution is to court intellectual disaster.

Psychoheredity and Tests. Investigations of psychoheredity problems have followed the conventional pattern of standardized assumptions. In the first place, there is the heredity-environment conception, though somewhat modified by the notion that the two factors are not completely indepedent. Next there is the assumption that mentality, such as intelligence and temperament, comprises traits of organisms. And finally, there is the assumption that test techniques and statistical inferences can replace the meticulous study of concrete interbehavioral events. Psychoheredity investigations are well illustrated in the studies of twins and foster children.

Twin Studies. Since Galton (166) initiated the study of twins to demonstrate the relatively greater power of nature over nurture, twin studies have become a prominent feature in psychoheredity. In making comparisons for nature-nurture purposes what seems more plausible than comparing twins with ordinary siblings, and identical twins with fraternal twins! Even better comparisons were sought in the study of older and younger twins and those reared together and apart. Galton, of course, employed the method of "circulars of inquiry" or questionnaires. But whether he found that twins were similar or dissimilar, he concluded that they were naturally what they were in mind as well as in body.

Aside from the use of the questionnaire method, Galton's studies were pitched on a general level of mental and moral qualities. Accordingly, when Thorndike (593) introduced the quantitative or mental-test procedure in twin study it was thought that a great improvement was made in the investigation of mind-body relations. Numerous studies have since been made (10, 426, 463, 590, 641) of twin resemblances, many of which have been interpreted to show that mind as well as body is inherited.

In addition to the study of immediate resemblances between fraternal and identical twins and between biological and mental characteristics, mental tests have also been used to study twins reared together and apart. Several decades ago, Muller (450) made a report on identical twins reared apart. On intelligence tests the twins made close scores, but on so-called personality tests, free association, and motor speed they varied considerably. Since that time many investigations have been reported (10, 463, 641) which show wide variation in intelligence scores. The results may well be said to be inconclusive even when one does not raise the question how effective tests are in supplying data concerning mentality.

Foster-Children Studies. While twin studies have been

regarded as throwing light primarily on heredity factors, the study of children placed in foster homes has emphasized the environment factor. A number of studies have been made (65, 66, 149, 360, 419, 559, 560, 563, 568, 573, 582, 626-628), comparing the results of mental tests on children and their natural and foster parents, as well as the influence of orphanges and other institutions upon mental stature. The obvious preconception of the investigators correlates well with their obtained results. A classical conclusion on the part of hereditarians is that while large improvement in mentality takes place—up to 30 IQ points—the results still show merely that the children progress toward their innate capacities, which they can never surpass. The environmentalists, on the other hand, stress the importance of external factors in the development of the similarly-conceived mentality. In both cases mentality is some quality or entity somehow connected with observed behavior.

Test Behavior and Basic Interactions. While it is universally admitted that test results refer to actions developed in the individual's life time, it is still argued on statistical grounds that these tests reveal innate factors. Such arguments involving the constancy of the I.Q. (594) clearly imply all the assumptions we have listed. This consideration in itself suggests how little the twin-and-foster-child studies can support any traditional psychophysical theory. In addition, such studies are conducted on a sociological instead of a psychological level. In other words, they do not penetrate below the surface of crude-data behavior to the underlying stimulus-response function interactions. To go deeper into such interactions reveals the improbability of the hypothesis that psychological events consist of functions of the biological structures.

Authentic Psychological and Biological Integration. In Chapter 10 we discussed at length the close integration of psychology and biology. We envisaged this relationship not in any way that transforms psychological events into psychic processes or functions of biological acts. We adopted the view rather that psychological events constitute definite interactions or interbehaviors which can be satisfactorily interrelated with biological events.

From a genetic standpoint we can go back to the field stage of the organism at which it does not participate in any psychological events, but only in structure-function or biological happenings. Later when the organism reaches a certain stage in its evolution (p. 295) it begins to participate in field events which depend primarily on its interbehavioral history.

As specific performances, psychological events are independent of an organism's biological traits or the natural properties of stimulus objects. But they can be integrated with biological events not only by taking regard of participating biological factors in the response (p. 139), but also by observing the influence upon psychological performances of the organism's health, and the limitations in interbehavior because of injuries and malformations as well as ecological conditions.

Somatogenic Psychopathology

Psychobiological conceptions of mind-body integration have been fostered by psychiatrists on the basis of both practical and theoretical considerations. Psychiatrists concerned with complex human maladjustments almost inevitably attain the position that they must treat individuals and not symptoms. On this basis it is useless for them to maintain the distinction between mind and body (429-431). Again, a number of writers (181, 230, 231) have adopted a general philosophical notion of holism—emphasis of totals rather than parts.

Whether the integration conception stems from practice or theory it does not correct the psychophysical construction. In the first place, the most confirmed mystic can in no manner implement his views when treating patients. Secondly, what is done on the crude-data level does not necessarily carry over to scientific constructions. Technical psychological problems are not solved by dealing practically with the organism as a whole or by merely studying the individual when he makes satisfactory or unsatisfactory adjustments to economic, social, domestic environmental conditions. We must reach down to the basic data and constructions having to do with the specific psychological events of stimulus and response. On this more fundamental level the psychobiologist still does not get away from mind and mental conceptions, even when he regards mentality as a refined type of symbolic action mediated by subtle integrations of neural action. On a more basic psychological level psychopathological views must be emended to eliminate even suggestions of psychic processes, so that psychological events may be treated as specific inter-behavioral operations. These points are illustrated by the following three treatments of somatogenic pathology.

(1) *Southard's Somatogeny.* In a number of studies South-ard (569-572) has considered the problem that the brain is the exclusive seat of mental disturbances. While he does not depart from the traditional correlation of the mental and the biological and from the idea that brain lesions are responsible for some mental disturbances, he still would not account for all mental pathology by brain lesions alone. Instead he gives due credit to lesions in other organs, which we regard as a step in advance.

Southard has stressed a type of case in which, for example, delusions of being stabbed in the chest could be correlated with lesions in the lungs. Such a disturbance could easily be interpreted on an interactional basis which removes all necessity for psychophysical theory. What is needed is sim-ply to consider the person's life conditions. The actual lung lesion with its painful effects constitutes a stimulus object which suggests at least a basis for the patient's trouble.

(2) *Meyer's Psychobiology (Ergasiology).* The psychobiol-ogy of Adolf Meyer (429-431) has contributed tremendously to the revolution of psychiatry. As a formulation of the sci-ence of man the ergasiological conception possesses the great merit of dealing with the activities of the whole organ-

ism, not merely as a biological mechanism but as a personality organization developed and operating in a distinctive human environment. Thus the attempt to eliminate mind-body dualism in all forms and the stress of the individual's biography in his various contacts with his family and other persons, and with social and economic conditions signify a promising approach to the data and problems of abnormality.

Furthermore, the conception of mental abnormality as disturbance and disharmony of the individual's adjustment to his life conditions brings psychopathology into direct continuity with the facts of normal behavior. Mental pathologies or mental disorders, therefore, constitute "experiments of nature" and not manifestations of hidden etiological factors. Patients are treated on the basis of available and observable happenings in their actual failures to adapt themselves to their life circumstances. Unquestionably, psychiatric prac-tice conducted on this plan proves more effective than when based on local lesions and isolated symptoms.

Nevertheless, the psychobiology of Meyer and his followers (35, 451) comprises but a partial step toward the proper interrelation of biological and psychological events. What on the practice level appears as a satisfactory formulation, on a more basic psychological level leaves us with the old dualism of mind or consciousness and organic actions. After all, the admonitions against dualism and the stress of behavior or the unified activity of the individual do not carry far. Psychobiologists include under behavior not only overt action but also implicit functions, the latter consisting of centrally-active and integrative mental functions (sensations, perceptions, memories, fancies) not directly visible to an observer though open to inquiry and test (451, p. 28).

The construct of integration is a central one for Meyer's psychopathology. Through the operation of the nervous system, and particularly the brain processes, subjective symbolizations are built up by the organism. However much the psychic is shot at verbally, the view of integrating complex psychological events by the organs, or the total organism exclusively, leaves the psychic intact, as in the tradition of the age which originally invented it. To reiterate that mentation is integrated with the action of the organism simply accords with the more recent mind-body formula which disallows disjunction as in older prescriptions.

Specific technical descriptions of psychological events such as perception, reasoning, and emotions are not available in ergasiological literature. Thus comparison with classical dualistic descriptions is not possible.

(3) *Goldstein's Holism.* The writings of Goldstein (181-183) provide a fine orientation toward an objective P.P. His delineation of the catastrophic effect upon the total organism of a brain or other injury is especially valuable. He differentiates between older and more recent conceptions of psychopathology as follows:

> . . . the former regarded the observable symptoms simply as manifestations of changes in different functions or structures, whereas in the new approach many symptoms are seen as expressions of the change which the patient's personality as a whole undergoes as a result of disease, and also as expressions of the struggle of the changed personality to cope with the defect and with demands it can no longer meet (182, p. 69).

Goldstein proceeds then to exhibit a vivid picture of the injured patient as he behaves in various situations. Present him with a simple problem in arithmetic which he is unable to solve and he becomes dazed, anxious; his pulse becomes irregular; he may even become aggressive. Certain means are sometimes adopted by the patient to adjust himself to his changed life conditions. He withdraws from contacts with irritating things or in extreme cases with everything, or becomes excessively orderly so that he increases his control over things.

The holistic viewpoint carries especial significance for the localization problem. The general conception of catastrophic behavior would seem to rule out the idea of symptoms as particular functions based on localized lesions. As Goldstein puts it:

Localization of a performance means to me not an excitation in a certain place, but a dynamic process which occurs in the entire nervous system, even in the whole organism, and which has a definite configuration for each performance (181, p. 260; 182, p. 84).

This writer does not, however, give up symptoms as specific acts or lack of acts correlated with particular areas. In a definite sense, then, the holistic idea is not consistently maintained.

A more serious implication is that the holistic type of psychopathology does not avoid a dualistic involvement. Goldstein persistently posits an association between higher mental functions and the frontal lobes. Such a notion certainly does not carry back to basic construction on a consistently objective plan. This predicament is in system related to Goldstein's stress of the organism as the central feature in a psychological situation, with a deplorable disregard of the essential place of the other items in any psychological field.

It is true, of course, that Goldstein writes as a physician and neurologist and is therefore primarily concerned with injury defects. But even allowing for the different interests of the physician and psychologist we may still question the wisdom of looking upon behavior deficiencies as general functions. The psychologist, of course, must go even further than refraining from this error; he must also treat psychological activities as specific events to be meticulously described with respect to their variations based upon injuries as definite field factors.

Howsoever excellent the holistic approach is on the clinical level, it in no wise avoids psychophysical tradition on the side of technical construction. Goldstein assumes that each mental performance corresponds to a particularly constructed and functioning substratum of the brain (182, p.148). Even the admirable practical procedure of not troubling about the distinction between organic and psychogenic symtoms in treatment (182, pp. 64-66) does not obviate traditional mind-body theory.

CHAPTER 19

PSYCHOSOMATIC MEDICINE

AS the term *Psychosomatic Medicine* (P.M.) implies, this movement is primarily of interest to physicians and not psychologists. Still there are cogent reasons why the student of P.P. should take cognizance of this trend in medical practice.

First and foremost is the fact that P.M. constitutes an open espousal by physicians of the traditional P.P. formula. Because psychosomatic writers deliberately accept historical psychological assumptions they propose the transformation of medical practice into an applied form of P.P. Basic to P.M. is a theory of mind-body or psyche-soma relationship (76, p. 867; 473) which, owing to the problems dealt with —namely, the illness and care of persons—is brought to the surface for easy examination and criticism.

Secondly, P.M. has been primarily developed by psychiatrists, a fact which definitely links it to P.P. Whereas traditional P.P. is concerned with the localized problems of special structures and functions in normal behavior, P.M. is concerned with the "interrelationships between emotional life and bodily processes both normal and pathological." In other words, "psychosomatic medicine concerns itself with the psychological approach into general medicine" (505, p. 5).

If further justification is needed for including psychosomatic medicine in a study of P.P. we may point out that a comprehensive interest in human behavior must extend to such conditions as the health and illness of organisms. Unless one takes an inordinately narrow view of P.P. it may well include (1) problems of psychological and biological hygiene, (2) the biological factors operative in abnormal as well as normal conduct, and (3) the mutual influences of psychological and biological behavior upon each other.

The Background of Psychosomatic Medicine

Before we consider the general ideological basis of P.M. it may be well to orient ourselves with respect to its background in medical practice. To begin with, the recent spread of the movement among physicians marks a new stress of their perennial attitude that basically the physician is not exclusively concerned with isolated portions of organisms, with localized structural and functional loci of disease, but with patients living in complex human situations. From the standpoint of therapeutics the P.M. principle is an old one. Throughout the history of medical practice physicians have perforce treated patients even when they stressed symptoms. Symptomological ways of thinking have always been merely theoretical formulations of what medical practice involves. Basic to the recent partitive view is the overemphasis of some fundamental scientific aspect of medical knowledge—, for example, the anatomical background. The various eras of extreme specialization really affect only particular techniques and methods of treatment. This is as true of the overstress of mental as of anatomical factors.

P.M. is not only an expected but also a valid protest against the extreme anatomical specialization of practitioners. It is not a far-fetched view that the psychosomatic movement is a reaction against the anatomist's historical domination of the medical field. Whatever medical theorists may think, practitioners cannot escape the fact that anatomically-localized disorders constitute only some of the illnesses of individuals. For the rest there are the many "constitutional" and "functional" illnesses as well as those involving environmental or ecological factors in human adaptation. The inevitable developments in preventive medicine, the problems of occupational disease, and maladjustments centering in general living conditions all militate against excessive atomism and anatomism.

In addition, P.M. takes account of various psychological factors in illness situations. Whether an illness is primarily organic or not, it is complicated with such psychological factors as knowledge and insight into one's troubles, anxieties and fears concerning it, intelligence with respect to prophylaxis and treatment, etc., etc. Such psychological factors are inevitable features of the health and illness of organisms living in complex and involved social circumstances. In consequence, the P.M. movement marks an important attempt at periodic professional stock taking.

PSYCHOSOMATIC MEDICINE AND PSYCHOBIOLOGY

The obvious similarities between P.M. and the therapeutic phase of psychobiology call for a brief comparison. The proponents of both movements, of course, stress the unity of the organism rather than symptoms as a basis for treatment. Since psychobiology as a psychiatric viewpoint was developed for the purpose of treating mental disorders it stops short at the principle of mind-body integration. On the other hand, P.M. as a general trend in medical practice makes use of the integration formula to emphasize the influence of the mental on bodily processes. The following quotation illustrates the P.M. procedure.

. . . it is not an overstatement to say that fully fifty percent of the problems of the acute stages of an illness and seventy-five percent of the difficulties of convalescence have their primary origin not in the body, but in the mind of the patient (126, p. 59).

So far do some of the advocates of P.M. go that they make the problem of mental influence on the body the basis for equating P.M. with the whole field of medicine. A telling assertion is that of Weiss and English:

. . . all illness is a problem of disturbance of psyche and soma, hence all medicine is *psychosomatic medicine* (624, p. 41).

THEORETICAL SIGNIFICANCE OF PSYCHOSOMATIC MEDICINE

As a protest against the purely organic viewpoint and the emphasis of particular organs in medical practice, P.M. must be regarded as a progressive step. When a physician (624, p. iii) fails to make a cure by investigating a patient's various organs and tissues by laboratory methods, and then sees how easily another doctor succeeds by revealing a family conflict, he is not to be censured for overstressing other than purely organic conditions. It is, however, an unscientific attitude to go to the one extreme or the other. When the organic factors are set off against psychic emotions, P.M. becomes ideologically perverse in its theoretical constructions. Although the term *psychosomatic medicine* may in fact refer to the active study and treatment of persons in their interactions to specific life conditions, and although the users of the term assert that they are referring to such events (505, p. 4), the movement injects old metaphysical doctrines (229-231) into medical practice and thought. In fact, to a great extent current psychosomatic medicine is one military operation in the imperialistic conquest by psychoanalysis not only of the field of psychiatry but of general medicine, as well as the whole range of human life. The following quotations serve as good illustrations.

Dr. Smith Ely Jelliffe was the pioneer in psychosomatic medicine in this country. Like Groddek abroad, Jelliffe stressed here the psychic in organic diseases. The present interest in psychosomatic medicine is thus due directly to psychoanalysis, and indirectly to those farsighted physicians and surgeons who recognized the importance of psychogenetic factors in organic diseases (58, p. 233).

Psychoanalysis as a theory of personality reaches beyond the realm of medicine into all fields which are concerned with human behavior—the field of anthropology, social sciences, and the problem of education. As a therapy of nervous disorders, it has its definite limitations as all forms of therapy do. Its influence on medical thought in general however can be well defined already (6, p. 11).

Considering the practical interests in the background of P.M. we may grant that physicians are justified in spreading over the wide range of human situations. The problems involved in diagnosing and treating illnesses demand as full a consideration as possible of the life circumstances of patients. Even psychiatrists may be allowed to define their domain as the science of human behavior (406, p. 3). But it is one thing to enlarge one's scope of investigation to take account of an increasing number of factors involved in an undesirable situation, and another to impose upon those factors a type of ideology that is basically erroneous. To do so not only vitiates a good intention but also prejudices whatever value there might be in carrying it out.

And so while it is true that the practice of medicine is certainly enlarged by the psychosomatic conception of all illness as failures of adjustment of the total organism to life conditions, the gains are more than outweighed by the losses incurred through faulty constructions concerning the nature of the psychological factors involved. There is no escape from the principle that to achieve a good end one must employ proper means. While superficially it appears that all sorts of wrong principles may be effective in bringing about cures, for example, faith healing, fundamentally only valid and confirmed principles can have effective and lasting results.

PSYCHOSOMATIC MEDICINE AND PHYSIOLOGICAL PSYCHOLOGY

We have already commented upon the good words used by the proponents of psychosomatic medicine in their propaganda literature. For example, they disavow concern with the metaphysics of mind and body. They also refer to psychology as "total responses of the organism to its environment" (6, p. 14). Fundamentally, however, psychosomaticists and psychoanalysts maintain the mind-body metaphysics. This fact is not only demonstrated in their conception of the "psychogenic organic disorder" (6, p. 16) but in their basic idea of the effect exerted by emotions, emotional tensions, and other psychic phenomena on the organic processes.

(1) *Conception of the Psychic.* What the proponents of P.M. understand by the psychic is made clear by Alexander:

. . . we understand psychic phenomena as nothing but the subjective aspect of certain bodily (brain) processes (6, p. 14).

Similarly, Masserman (406, p. 17) declares that emotions are "subjective" epiphenomena which accompany stressful adaptations and which are expressed (sic) in bodily dysfunctions such as anxiety, pity, enthusiasm, esthetic appreciation, etc. What could be more explicit and more like the traditional psychophysics than the following?

The central nervous system has both the function of the regulation of the internal vegetative processes of the organism and also the regulation of its external affairs, its relations to the environment. The integration of all the external and internal affairs of the organism is the function of a central government represented by the highest centers of the nervous system which in human beings we call the personality. In fact it became obvious that the physiological study of the highest centers of the central nervous system and the psychological study of personality deal with one and the same thing from different points of view. Whereas physiology approaches the functions of the central nervous system in terms of space and time, psychology approaches it in terms of those subjective phenomena which we call psychological and they are *the subjective reflections of physiological processes* (6, p. 13).

How disastrous the influence of the P.M. stress of the psychic can be is reflected in the neurologist's attempt to integrate the psychic with the brain. Adopting the full panoply of Freudian demonology, the ego, the id, and the superego, Grinker (193) equates the id with the hypothalamus, and the ego with the cortex. Anxiety is the sign that the drives and instinct forces of the id or hypothalamus influence the ego or cortex. When the cortex or ego can not resolve the situation which has evoked the internal tension it gives up its customary activities. The result is visceral expression or organ dysfunction constituting organic neuroses.

(2) *Psychosomatic Misinterpretation of Emotion.* Besides misinterpreting emotions as psychic epiphenomena, psychosomatic and psychoanalytic writers indulge in two further misconstructions of emotional events. In the first place, in order to foster their formula of emotional influences in pathological situations they transform practically all psychological

events into emotions. Not only are authentic emotions (289, I, ch. 12; II, ch. 16) confused with affective interbehavior, but they are also not distinguished from such complex activities as thinking or reasoning.

In the second place, since emotions as psychic or non-spatiotemporal processes can not in any way be related either to behavioral or medical problems they simply misconstrue the actual events in which individuals participate, whether as adjusted or maladjusted personalities. Such writers set up words as descriptions—words which stand on the opposite bank of an uncrossable chasm from the actual human events claimed as the working materials.

According to Alexander, psychogenic organic disorders develop in two phases.

The first phase consists of a functional disturbance of a vegetative organ, caused by a chronic emotional disturbance called psychoneurosis. In the second phase the chronic functional disturbance leads in time gradually to irreversible tissue changes, to an organic disease (6, p. 16).

Certainly this construction has its starting point in events. Nevertheless, it is set into a traditional mind-body framework. As another psychosomatic writer puts it (127, p. 9), bodily changes may be brought about by mental stimuli or emotion as effectively as by bacteria and toxins. But why not investigate the individual as he develops and lives through the detailed circumstances of his life history! We may then observe how daily strains and tensions result in various sorts of maladjustments which may leave more or less permanent psychological and biological effects. Such an objective observational and constructional procedure not only obviates the psychophysical coloring but also does justice to the actual particular circumstances involved in the individual's usual and unusual situations.

But even if students of psychosomatic medicine would forego their subjective approach and study actual behavioral fields this would be only the beginning of a scientific attack.

The data elicited are only the raw materials of science. The next step is to develop technical constructions not only appropriate to the crude data but also significant for a systematic organization of principles useful for interpretation and prediction.

PSYCHOSOMATIC MEDICINE AND OBJECTIVE PSYCHOLOGY

Despite the fact that P.M. is not a new discovery (127, p. VII; 624, p. 1) and like its psychoanalytic parent is based upon common-sense psychology (157, p. 257), it still has the merit of stimulating interest in problems that are easily lost from active consideration. It is impossible to overrate the importance of the injunction to study the total organism in general medical and psychiatric practice. Such a study as Wolf and Wolff (637) make on their subject Tom eloquently attests the value of (a) treating a man rather than an organ and (b) accumulating facts concerning the interrelations of psychological and biological events in actual life circumstances.

Without an objective psychological foundation, however, such data as are recorded can not be adequately analyzed and incorporated into a scientific system. Both psychosomatic (127, 157) and psychological (541, 542) investigators have pointed out the incompatibility of the psychically or experientially constructed theories with laboratory investigations. There looms only the inevitable conclusion. As long as a mind-body dualism is implied in P.M. it can not be assimilated to a scientific psychology.

SECTION III

SUGGESTIONS FOR THE EMENDATION
OF
PHYSIOLOGICAL PSYCHOLOGY

CHAPTER 20

TOWARD AN AUTHENTIC PHYSIOLOGICAL PSYCHOLOGY

O UR survey of P.P. has amply demonstrated that so important a province of psychology merits improved treatment and that this can be achieved by removing the barriers separating events and investigative procedures from valid scientific constructions. These barriers are traditional dualism and neural dogma.

When P.P. is freed from the various forms of dualistic tradition general and physiological psychology will stand out as independent natural science unhampered by a crippling alliance with a psychic-supporting physiology. Also the development of an improved P.P. would at the same time automatically redound to the advantage of that part of physiology which intersects psychology. The close relationship between psychological and biological events suggests that to rid either science from the trammels of cultural tradition will have a beneficial effect on the other.

Granting the principle that all constructions must be derived from contacts with events by way of observation and experimentation, we suggest two steps for the emendation of P.P. The first is to summarize the faulty constructions and attitudes which have operated to compromise investigations with the traditional mind-body theory. The second is to point out alternative constructions more directly derived from contacts with original events.

COMPROMISING CONSTRUCTIONS AND ATTITUDES IN
PHYSIOLOGICAL PSYCHOLOGY

A. COMPROMISING CONSTRUCTIONS

Physiological Psychology as Psychological Theory. We must reject the construction that makes P.P. a theory of general psychology. However useful it may once have been to identify P.P. with the theory that psychological processes were at bottom natural enough to be tied up with biological factors that situation no longer exists. What was a plausible construction when workers were uninformed concerning the mechanisms of the biological organism has no place in present-day science.

Thus while the construction that P.P. is a psychological theory was made with the best of scientific intentions, today it serves only to maintain dualistic beliefs current at that time. Recall how the physiologists of Johannes Müller's day hailed his formulation of the part the brain plays in accounting for the existence of the qualities of things. They thought of psychophysical theory not only as an excellent means of finding a physical basis for what they regarded as psychic processes but also as the liquidation of the naïveté that attributed psychic qualities to things.

With the great development of chemical knowledge it is no longer naïve to look to the analysis of things for the discovery of their qualities and properties. Psychologists therefore can well content themselves with the investigation of actual interoperations of organisms and stimulus objects. Moreover, the accumulation of physiological knowledge is sufficient to counteract the bizarre theories of neural action current in the early 19th century. We need no longer fear that our psychological work will not be scientific if we begin with actual events, whether in field or laboratory, and on them as a foundation build our scientific constructions.

Physiological Psychology as Philosophy. Though it is denied by physiological psychologists they actually hold that P.P. is a philosophical viewpoint required to supply a local formula for mind-body relations. Experimental psychologists still believe it necessary to declare themselves parallelists or identists in line with traditional P.P. Actually today P.P. is in no sense a system of postulates organized to supply a biological or physiological basis of mentality. With the rejection of this general philosophical view we extrude the notion that the brain or the organism is a basis of mind or the seat of psychic processes alias the soul.

Incidentally, we may, of course, envisage philosophy as an ordering of scientifically-determined data and as a critical monitor of scientific work. In this sense philosophy is completely divorced from any entanglement with historical dualism. We have already pointed out (p. 63f.) that such a philosophy operates exclusively on the basis of constructions derived from former preoccupation with investigated events. It certainly does not perpetuate propositions derived from autistic reflection—a sort of reflection which provides ready-made moulds into which observed data are poured to fit a prefigured system.

It follows that such a scientifically-derived philosophy constitutes no universal system applicable to all investigative findings; it comprises rather a number of systems limited by particular events. A localized P.P. philosophy therefore must operate within that restricted domain, and will in no sense perpetuate the vicious circle in which P.P. derives a dualism from traditional universal philosophy which it in turn supports.

Physiological Psychology as Psychological Method. A third construction concerning P.P. which we must reject is that it is an investigative method for dealing with intangibles. The primary question here is whether we regard physiological data as causes or counterparts of psychological processes or as factors in complex interactional events. In the former case we inevitably fall back upon an acknowledged or unacknowledged traditional dualism. On the whole, the notion of P.P. as a method seriously favors that view.

When, however, P.P. is regarded as a particular field of work, a specialty concerned with certain kinds of data—namely, interbehavioral fields implicated with biological components—it is not essentially a method. It is a legitimate province of research.

B. Compromising Attitudes

The Oblivescence Attitude. Physiological psychologists persistently disregard the historical origins of the postulates and hypotheses of P.P. as well as the fact that there is an

unbroken philosophical thread running through the inaugu-
ration and continuation of P.P. investigation. In discrimination and perceptual studies, investigators continue to concern themselves with the physiological basis of sensation and
experience, whereas in the learning field they hold to the
traditional assumption that neural structures constitute a
master system. The neural basis of learning is still a predominant investigative principle, though investigators constantly pile up contrary evidences.

We have seen that the doctrine concerning the primacy
of the nervous system stems from its historical connection
with the mind or psyche. May we not then conclude that
a considerable portion of P.P. investigation basically results
in the invalidation of a traditionally-derived theory. Perhaps
this is not a serious objection. On the other hand, would it
not be an advantage to the science as a whole if investigations were pitched on a more positive level?

The oblivescence attitude implies that investigative work
is an end in itself. In other words, as long as events are observed and data accumulated nothing else matters. Despite
the objections offered to Baconian inductionism the fact that
such procedures may lead to fortuitous data and investigative
techniques does in a measure justify "work for work's sake."
Moreover, it is undeniable that the accidents of human circumstances make it possible for knowledge to accrue from
enterprises motivated by improper or even false hypotheses.

Nevertheless, while in the study of learning the oblivescence attitude may only obstruct progress, the consequences
are more serious in discrimination or perception studies.
Here the obstructional trend may be fortified by the perpetuation of undesirable theory.

The Substitutive Attitude: Physiological psychologists who
adopt a theory that mental processes or experiences are correlated with physiological or biological processes often
are misled into believing that their theory is established by
substituting biological for psychological data. For instance,
writers assume that the discovery of differences in afferent

cutaneous fibers establishes something about sensation differences.

Clearly, physiological psychologists who step over into physiology or biology not only achieve a legitimate field of activity, but may also discover important interrelations between their data, even though such work certainly constitutes the handling of borrowed assets. No one need object to a psychologist working as a neurologist, since there is always the fact that psychological investigation involves biological factors. This is no justification, however, for neglecting to distinguish between the different types of domains. And there is also the question how far the science of psychology is furthered by substitution.

It is possible, of course, that biologists and physiologists may ignore certain phases of their own domain and confine themselves to the operation of parts of organisms to the neglect of the entire animal. Psychologists are to be commended for concerning themselves with whole organisms. But can conclusions drawn from the study of biological mechanisms be directly serviceable for the solution of psychological problems? On the other hand, is it not better for psychologists who still concern themselves with psychic constructs in their own domain to move over to the biological field where they are required to work with natural events! But in this instance, to emphasize biological factors in psychological data results in a felt need to supply distinctive psychological factors, which unfortunately culminates in the addition of an undesirable mental component.

Another form of substitution is to offer references to crude data in place of descriptive constructions. Thus the physiological psychologist who is presumably describing an organism's interbehavior with colored objects in terms of light rays and physiological processes really has no color construction unless he introduces sensations. Since sensations are not spatiotemporal events the term *sensation* is merely a common-sense reference to the color of the original datum (stimulus object). The light-ray construction borrowed from the physicist may also be regarded as an illegitimate substitution for authentic psychological constructions. How fruitless is the wholesale borrowing of constructions from other sciences we have fully learned from the Herbartian analogizing of mechanics.

The Equating Attitude. Closely related to the substitutional attitude, and serving as a defense and rationalization of it, is the belief that after all there is no difference between physiological and psychological events. Unfortunately the germ of truth here may be exploited to the disadvantage of the science of psychology. Certainly psychological events so far as the organism is concerned include no factor different from organic activities. When we limit ourselves to the activities of the organism, in whatever situation it operates, its actions are all subsumed under the general biological classification.

On the other hand, even purely physiological events are not all the same. Conduction is not secretion; secretion is not contraction. Whatever conjoining facts there may be, they are partial features in a complex organismic activity. Different total physiological acts involve different kinds of chemical elements and reactions. The same point obviously must be made in every field of science. Intraphysical facts differ among themselves. Intrachemical facts show great diversity. It is true that no absolute line divides organic and inorganic events, but it is precisely the scientist's task to keep simple reactions separate from complex ones, and reactions occurring under certain conditions of temperature, pressure, etc., apart from others. To succeed in solving problems the scientist must resist equating events, a process which deprives him of the effective analysis of the factors involved. A structure-function event is different from the interbehavior of an organism with objects having not only natural but also cultural properties. There is a difference between reactions to things and the operation of the brain by electrical stimulation.

The Reduction Attitude. Beginning with the obvious prin-

ciple that scientific propositions consist of abstracting constructions, physiological psychologists proceed to misinter-
pret it by reducing the data themselves to simple factors.
Accordingly they reduce entire psychological fields to the
operation of the organism, which is, of course, only a factor
in the field. They go even further and reduce the organism to
neural mechanisms, which abstracts from properties of the
objects in motion so that simple geometric formulae may
appear. The argument is that a physicist is not concerned with
the fact that a high wind shook the apples from a tree in
September, though this event involves the laws of mechanics.
But here we ask: Do the reductionistic procedures mentioned
do justice to the events with which the psychologist is concerned?

Of course, physiological psychologists do not always reduce psychological events to neural action. They sometimes
concentrate upon muscle action. They want to make flexion
or extension either the whole psychological response or at
least the model for such responses. Obviously no psychological event is lacking in muscular action, whether a kicking
or lifting reaction or the most subtle and intricate thinking
behavior. But surely the most elaborate description of such
participating biological factors can not cover the essential
features of the psychological event.

What psychological significance lies in even the most
elaborate description of the muscle or nerve action in a
grasping act divorced from stimulus objects? Grasping acts
are performed with respect to innumerable stimulus objects.
What psychologists are interested in is precisely the form of
grasping, its intensity, suddenness, haltingness, etc., which
are all functions or correlated factors with types of things
under specific setting conditions. While it may be necessary
to analyze the hand muscles in grasping as participating
factors in interbehavioral fields, the stress of muscle elements must not lead to a construction of psychomotor correlation.

The undesirability of the reduction procedure is similarly

revealed in ablation and extirpation experiments. Mutilated animals usually display modifications in behavior. Behavior is then reduced to degrees of performance effectiveness instead of intricate interbehavior. The presence or absence of action is correlated with the presence and absence of lesions or injuries so that the reduction principle not only bypasses the actual events but also fosters the search for a seat or cause of such action inside the organism. Thus is developed the attitude of cause internalization.

The Internalization Attitude. To internalize the cause or basis of behavior paradoxically reverses the argument for abstract formulae or laws. Instead of seeking basic laws of the organism's interactions with stimuli in actual fields the internalization attitude leads to the description and explanation of behavior in terms of a limited part of the whole.

The internalization procedure is strikingly apparent when psychologists become absorbed in conditioned-reflex studies. Despite the obvious importance of many factors in the conditioning situation—the various stimulus objects and their relations as well as surrounding factors—investigators turned to the cerebral components of the total event for their explanatory constructions. Thus psychologists followed the lead of Bekhterev's reflexology and Pavlov's doctrines of cortical mechanisms.

The paradox of internalization leads to the paradox of transfer. The argument that the psychological organism is a physiological machine and that all explanatory constructions must be made in terms of what is contained within its skin boundary really amounts to transferring to the nervous system what originally were properties of a psyche. Undoubtedly this is the basis of the conception of governing brain centers. What else but a seat-of-power doctrine transforms neural-conduction mechanisms into general and special cerebral causes or controls?

The transfer principle is excellently illustrated by the integration construction (p. 317). When it is pointed out that as a widely-distributed and centrally-located structure the nervous system conducts from one point in the organism to all others, it is surely appropriate to say that it integrates the action of the individual so that it operates as a unit. The next step, however, of extrapolating integration to form some higher sort of occult power that perceives, remembers, imagines, and thinks, is to depart entirely from biological data.

An effective check on such constructive elaborations is to notice that even genuine neural integrations are not governing powers, nor are the genuine integrational processes exclusively brought about by the nervous system. Certainly the vascular system effectively operates as an integrating mechanism (80).

The Selecting Attitude. Because the selecting attitude is more closely related to problems of data than constructions it is at the same time one of the most insidious and harmful in P.P. In the end it leads to vicious constructional circles.

Physiological psychologists begin with one or both of the following presuppositions (1) that there are biological mechanisms corresponding to psychic processes or (2) that such mechanisms constitute determiners of behavior. Upon this basis they select certain behavior as essential investigative materials—for example, elementary sensory discrimination and reflex action—and finally reach the conclusion that psychological events consist of something other than interbehavior of organisms with stimulus objects, and that P.P. is concerned with radically different problems from general psychology.

Critically examined the selecting attitude operates on the inalienable right of a scientist to choose his own type of work. Now it is obvious that all psychological performances comprise organic factors and that the latter are more prominent in the simpler than in the complex ones. The greater prominence of organic factors in simpler behavior is accounted for by the fact that on the psychologico-biological continuum some of the simpler activities tend more toward the biological than the psychological pole. The question, then, arises whether there is a basis here for channelizing psychology toward certain kinds of data and investigative procedures which serve to establish the aforementioned presuppositions.

Evident it is that sensory discrimination and reflex action depend upon the biological evolution of the organism and the natural properties of stimulus objects, and thus provide occasion for attending to anatomical and physiological details. Interest in discrimination of colors or sounds naturally brings the anatomy of the eye or ear to the front, while the study of reflexes requires careful attention to the anatomical organization of the reacting organism.

From the standpoint of psychology as a whole, however, sensory discrimination and reflexes comprise only samples of a large population of behavior types, and it is not to the advantage of the science to regard them as typical. While it is to be expected that those psychologists preoccupied with such behavior make it appear extremely if not exclusively important, the operation of the selection fallacy is nevertheless apparent.

At this point, too, the fact must not be overlooked that a great divergence exists between reflexes belonging respectively to the psychological and biological domains (286a). Whereas psychological reflexes are admittedly closer than most other interbehavior to the bioecological type of events, they still constitute authentic interbehavior. In consequence their origin and operation through contact with specific sorts of stimulus objects can not be neglected. It is a grave error to allow the existence of both biological and psychological reflexes to prejudice one in favor of anatomical mechanisms.

Two consequences of the selecting attitude may be pointed out. The first is an assiduous occupation with infra-human organisms. This fact inevitably leads to a shift in the focus of one's interest, with the result that one may become more and more occupied with the organism's mechanisms to the neglect of more complex problems in which interaction with objects is the focus of interest. Even when working with human organisms one is constrained to transform the characteristics of objects interacted with into simple action-exciting properties.

The second prejudicial consequence operates on the human level. To stress the organism's action results in favoring learning and conditioning to the disadvantage of other and sometimes more complex activities, for example, intellectual behavior. Moreover, even learning is confined mostly to contacts with very simple objects—series of nonsense syllables, integers, etc. Again, the materials learned are frequently ignored though they are equally factors in learning interbehavior.

The Aspiration Attitude. This is one of two attitudes concerned primarily with explanatory neural mechanisms which not only are disturbing factors in psychological investigation but actually turn out to be strangers in the house of science. Physiological psychologists dominated by traditional ideology are naturally baffled by the absence of structures or functions to account for behavior or to serve as mediators or creators of qualities. Accordingly they bring up the heavy artillery of aspiration: If we only knew enough about physiology we could find such mechanisms and explain such actions (44, p. 12; 47, p. 189; 232, p. 336; 267, I, pp. 81-82; 369, p. 520; 501, p. 129 *et passim;* 511, p. 395; 582, p. 46)! The interesting point here is that this aspiration points toward a something which is more and more irrelevant and dispensable the more knowledge increases concerning physiological processes. The more we know about the nervous system, for example, the fewer hidden places remain for occult powers, or mechanisms which create qualities.

The Creation Attitude. Because the creation attitude in P.P. serves to traduce the scientific procedure of theory construction it is probably the most obstructive of all attitudes in the field. Faced with the evidence that increased information about the nervous system leaves no room for mechanisms underlying psychic processes and physiological causes of behavior, psychologists propose that it is legitimate to create such mechanisms. A propos of a widely-popular creative product Lashley and Wade write:

At the present time nothing whatever is known concerning the nature of the alterations in the nervous system which constitute memory traces. Knowledge of cerebral physiology is in fact so limited that it does not even lend a greater plausibility to one than to another of the many speculations concerning the organic basis of memory with which the literature is burdened (358, p. 86).

It is highly significant that the neurophysiologist (5) realizes as much as the psychologist how futile it is to explain thinking and other actions by the lesser-known neural mechanisms.

Theories are surely constructive products but they are always subject to restrictions by data and can never be set up in competition with the results of investigation. Only one merit can be accorded to the creative attitude—namely, it exposes to full view ways of thinking that otherwise are covertly practiced and therefore less available for criticism and checking.

AUTHENTIC PHYSIOLOGICAL PSYCHOLOGY

P.P. as Study of Field Factors. Basic to an authentic P.P. is the observation that the crude data of psychology consist of ways in which organisms and objects, including other organisms, interbehave. It is assumed that the stimulus-response functions as essential psychological events are inevitably set in such organism-object interbehaviors as matrices (p. 276). There is ample room, therefore, in the general psychological domain for the specialized investigation of biological factors. Accordingly, any sort of normal configuration of the organism's action as well as its hygienic and fatigue conditions, malformation or mutilation, comprise components of total psychological fields. Measurements of the biological factors, their description or other treatment, may be regarded as belonging to the subdomain of P.P.

Naturally the importance of biological factors in psychological action varies enormously. Not all psychological interbehavior requires specification of the biological components. Such is the case, for example, in speech interbehavior, in which the analysis and description of intercommunicative acts gain little from the reference to the participating biological elements. Simple reflex action, on the other hand, is closer to the borderline of biological actions. Hence, the specification of the biological configurations and their changes is highly important.

Varying Places of Organic Components in P.P. Fields. Authentic P.P. implies that biological factors are more or less closely integrated with the response and stimulus functions. The most closely localized biological components consist of malformations, lesions or more general biological conditions serving to disable the organism from interbehaving with things, because the biological components participate in the actual interbehavioral performances.

Other biological components are localized in the manner of performance or in their influence upon whether or not the essential stimulus-response-function interbehavior occurs at all. For example, a satiated or fatigued organism may be insensitive to the stimulus functions of objects. In a sense, then, such biological factors as well as some general pathologies constitute setting factors secondarily concerned with stimulus-response functions.

For an authentic P.P. any emphasis or special mention of biological factors is necessary only when we are dealing with certain types of psychological events. In other situations, humanistic factors such as kind of upbringing, cultural setting, etc., may be much more important for the description of psychological fields.

Physiological Psychology Implies Organismic Biology. Following the suggestions outlined above, authentic P.P. may be said to arise from bioecological interbehavior. Except for pathological situations P.P. is concerned with organisms and their actions as the factors in the interbehavioral field. Evidence is overwhelming that P.P. events can not be properly described in terms of cells, tissues or systems, but must be treated from the standpoint of complexly-developed organisms.

No one denies the indispensability of studying analytic segmental and even cellular elements for an understanding of the biological mechanisms of behavior. But even the biologist thoroughly appreciates that "the simplest spinal reflex 'thinks,' so to say, in movements, not in muscles," as Sherrington quotes from Hughlings Jackson (160, p. 51).

Therefore, when the foot of a spinal animal is pinched, the resulting reflex is not restricted to muscles of the dermatome stimulated, but a withdrawal of the whole limb occurs (160, p. 51).

We are reminded of Sherrington's dictum concerning the fictional character of the simple reflex (549, p. 8). A recent study of Murphy and Gellhorn (455a) confirms the multiplicity representation rather than the punctate localization construction concerning the operation of the motor cortex.

To a considerable extent the emphasis upon the total organism instead of parts marks the difference between authentic and traditional P.P. The former stresses the description of the organism, its evolution and operation while in contact with objects. By contrast, traditional P.P. makes parts of the organism perform creative and productive functions. Authentic P.P. is interested, for example, in the event of interbehaving with colors. Of course, the obvious direct point of contact with colored objects is the retina, though the retina is considered only as an anatomical feature of the individual. Traditional physiological psychologists make use of the physicist's and physiologist's constructions in order to develop a descriptive system. Because this deprives objects of their natural properties one is then forced to assume that the latter are created by biological mechanisms. Consequently biological mechanisms are not described as they occur in actual biological situations; rather a superstructure of functions is created, the net result of which is not the description of events as they happen but as endowed with properties derived from cultural traditions.

Physiological Psychology and Social Psychology. As a final attempt to characterize authentic P.P. we bring it into context with social psychology which has traditionally been regarded as its direct opposite. Recall that Wundt, for example (p. 126), differentiated between physiological and social psychology on the ground that the former is concerned with individual mentality, whereas the latter is related to more complex group facts (653, 654). Today we can not accept this differentiation. All psychological facts are specific interactivities of particular organisms with stimulus objects. This is as true of the most complex cultural as of the simplest reflex actions. A recent version of this differentiation marks off perceptual action from social attitudes on the ground that the former involves a recognizable individual biological matrix while the latter does not. The reply is surely that most adult human perceptual interbehavior also involves cultural factors (291, 295). The question is how basic we want to make organic factors as compared with cultural ones, since all psychological events constitute interbehavioral acts of organisms.

Another differentiation between physiological and social psychology prevalent since Wundt's writings is, that by contrast with P.P. events, social psychological facts are historical and developed through contacts with persons. This distinction again goes counter to the observation that all authentic psychological data constitute interactions centering in the individual's reactional biography or interbehavioral history (293, 297).

BIBLIOGRAPHY AND INDEXES

BIBLIOGRAPHY AND AUTHOR INDEX

1. ABELMANN, W., and MORGAN, C. T. The effect of cortical lesions upon light aversion behavior in the rat. *J. Comp. Psychol.*, 1943, 36, 157-168. [227]
2. ACKERLY, S. Instinctive, emotional, and mental changes following prefrontal lobe extirpation. *Amer. J. Psychiat.*, 1935, 92, 717-729. [258, 260]
3. ADRIAN, E. D. *The Basis of Sensation: The Action of the Sense Organs*. New York, Norton, 1928. [134]
4. ────── *The Mechanism of Nervous Action*. Philadelphia, Univ. Penna. Press, 1932. [159]
5. ────── The nervous system. *Science*, 1936, 84, 275-278. [162, 165 f., 342]
6. ALEXANDER, F. Psychological aspects of medicine. *Psychosom. Med.*, 1939, 1, 7-18. [323-326]
7. ALEXANDER, W., DUFF, P., HALDANE, J. B. S., IVES, G., and RENTON, D. After-effects of exposure of men to carbon dioxide. In J. B. S. Haldane, *Adventures of a Biologist*, ch. 17, New York, Harper, 1940. [287]
8. ALFORD, L. B. Defects of intelligence from focal lesions within the central parts of the left cerebral hemisphere. *Amer. J. Psychiat.*, 1937, 94, 615-633. [258, 260, 266]
9. ALLBUTT, T. C. *Greek Medicine in Rome*. London, Macmillan, 1921. [84n., 86]
10. ANASTASI, A. *Differential Psychology: Individual and Group Differences in Behavior*. New York, Macmillan, 1937. [313]
11. Annual Review of Physiology. J. M. LUCK and V. E. HALL (Eds.), Stanford, *Amer. Physiol. Soc. and Annual Revs. Inc.*, 1939 [129]
12. APPEL, K. E. Psychiatric therapy. In (242), ch. 34. [291]
13. ARISTOTLE. *De Partibus Animalium*. W. Ogle (tr.), Oxford, Oxford Univ. Press, 1911. [82]
14. ────── Physica. In W. D. Ross (Ed.). *The Students Oxford Aristotle*, vol. 2, New York, Oxford Univ. Press, 1942. [107]
15. AUGUSTINE. *De Trinitate Libri XV*. In *Patrologiae*, Serie Prima, Tomus XLII, J. P. Migne (Ed.), Paris, 1845. [89]
16. AVENARIUS, R. *Kritik Der Reinen Erfahrung*. Leipzig, Reisland, vol. 1, (3rd ed.) 1921; vol. 2, (2nd ed.) 1908. [43 f.]
17. BAILEY, P. *Intracranial Tumors*. Springfield, Thomas, 1933. [258 f.]
18. ────── The present state of American neurology. *J. Neuropath. Exper. Neurol.*, 1942, 1, 111-117. [269]
19. BAIN, A. *The Senses and the Intellect*. (3rd ed.) New York, Appleton, 1885, (4th ed., 1894). [18-21, 26]

20. —— *Mind and Body: The Theory of their Relation.* New York, Appleton, 1885. [13, 20 f.]
21. BALYEAT, R. M. The hereditary factor in allergic disease. With special reference to the general health and mental activity of allergic children. *Amer. J. Med. Sci.*, 1928, 176, 332-45. [283]
22. —— The general health and mental activity of allergic children. *Amer. J. Dis. Child.*, 1929, 37, 1193-1197. [283]
23. BARD, P. On emotional expression after decortication with some remarks on certain theoretical views. *Psychol. Rev.*, 1934, 41, 309-329. [133, 200]
24. —— The neuro-humoral basis of emotional reactions. In (454), ch. 6. [197, 199 f.]
25. BARD, P., and RIOCH, D. M. A study of four cats deprived of neocortex and additional portions of the fore-brain. *Johns Hopkins Hosp. Bull.*, 1937, 60, 73-147. [200]
26. BARTLEY, S. H. *Vision: A Study of its Basis.* New York, Van Nostrand, 1941. [146, 169 f., 181, 185]
27. BASTIAN, H. C. *The Brain as an Organ of Mind.* New York, Appleton, 1883. [254]
28. BEACH, F. A. Effects of lesions to corpus striatum upon spontaneous activity in the male rat. *J. Neurophysiol.*, 1941, 4, 191-195. [250]
29. —— Effects of brain lesions upon running activity in the male rat. *J. Comp. Psychol.*, 1941, 31, 145-178. [250]
30. BEADLE, G. W. Genes and the chemistry of the organism. *Amer. Scientist*, 1946, 34, 31-53. [296]
31. BEARE, J. I. *Greek Theories of Elementary Cognition from Alcmaeon to Aristotle.* Oxford, Clarendon Press, 1906. [83]
32. BENTLEY, M. Where does thinking come in? *Amer. J. Psychol.*, 1943, 56, 354-380. [79, 96]
33. BERKELEY, G. *A New Theory of Vision and Other Writings.* London, Dent, 1910. [168, 171]
34. BERNARD, C. Étude sur la physiologie du coeur. *Revue des deux Mondes*, 1865, 56, 236-252. [82]
35. BILLINGS, E. G. *A Handbook of Elementary Psychobiology and Psychiatry.* New York, Macmillan, 1939. [317]
36. BISHOP, G. H., and HEINBECKER, P. Fiber distribution in optic and saphenous nerves. *Proc. Soc. Exper. Biology*, New York, 1933, 1312-1314. [159]
37. BÖHLE, W. *Die Körperform als Spiegel der Seele*, Leipzig, Teubner, 1929. [305]
38. BOHR, N. Light and life. *Nature*, 1933, 131, 457-459. [186 f.]
39. BOLZANO, B. *Wissenschaftslehre: Versuch einer ausführlichen Darstellung der Logik.* (1837), Leipzig, Meiner, 1914. [68, 70]
40. BONNET, C. *Essai Analytique sur les Facultés de l'Âme.* Copenhagen, Philibert, 1760. [302]

41. —— Analyse abrégé de l'éssai analytique. In *Oeuvres d'Histoire Naturelle et de Philosophie*, Tom. 15, Neuchatel, Fauche, 1779-1783. [302]

42. BORING, E. G. The stimulus error. *Amer. J. Psychol.*, 1921, 32, 449-471. [175 f.]

43. —— A History of Experimental Psychology. New York, Appleton-Century, 1929. [4 f., 21, 50, 128, 302]

44. —— The Physical Dimensions of Consciousness. New York, Century, 1933. [47, 150, 341]

45. —— Temporal perception and operationism. *Amer. J. Psychol.*, 1936, 48, 519-522. [68n.]

46. —— Titchener on meaning. *Psychol. Rev.*, 1938, 45, 92-95. [68]

47. —— Sensation. In E. G. Boring, H. S. Langfeld, and H. P. Weld (Eds.), *Introduction to Psychology*, ch. 16, New York, Wiley, 1939. [145, 341]

48. —— *Sensation and Perception in the History of Experimental Psychology*. New York, Appleton-Century, 1942. [154, 180, 182, 280]

49. —— Mind and mechanism. *Amer. J. Psychol.*, 1946, 59, 173-192. [244n.]

50. BOROVSKI, V. M. The relation of the gull to its nest, eggs and young (Russian). *Reflexksi, Instinkti, Naviki*, 1936, 2, 139-174. [210]

51. BOURGIGNON, G. Interpretation des sensibilités thermique et douloureuse, à l'aide des chronaxies sensitives cutanées normale et de leurs variations dans la syringomyelie. *C. R. Acad. Sci.*, Paris, 1933, 197, 792-794. [156]

52. BRENTANO, F. *Psychologie vom Empirischen Standpunkte*. Leipzig, Duncker u. Humblot, 1874. [68]

53. BRETT, G. S. *A History of Psychology*. New York, Macmillan, vol. 1, 1912; vols. 2, 3, 1921. [17, 90]

54. BRICKNER, R. M. *The Intellectual Functions of the Frontal Lobes*. New York, Macmillan, 1936. [258, 260 f.]

55. —— Bilateral frontal lobectomy: follow-up report of a case. *Arch. Neurol. Psychiat.*, 1939, 41, 580-585. [258, 260 f.]

55a —— Man and his values considered neurologically. *J. Philos.*, 1944, 40, 225-243. [270]

56. BRIDGMAN, P. W. *The Logic of Modern Physics*. New York, Macmillan, 1927. [66]

57. —— Operational analysis. *Philos. Science*, 1938, 5, 114-131. [66]

58. BRILL, A. A. *Freud's Contribution to Psychiatry*. New York, Norton, 1944. [323]

59. BROWN, S., and SHÄFER, E. A. An investigation into the functions of the occipital and temporal lobes of the monkey's brain. *Philos. Trans. Roy. Soc.*, Series B, London, 1888, 179, 303-327. [229, 251]

60. BROWNING, W. The moral center in the brain. *Med. Rec.*, 1921, 99, 1043, 1089; 100, 321. [270]

61. BUCHMAN, E. F., and RICHTER, C. P. Abolition of bulbocapnine catatonia by cocaine. *Arch. Neurol. Psychiat.*, 1933, 29, 499-503. [297]

62. BUCY, P. C., and KLÜVER, H. Anatomic changes secondary to temporary lobectomy. *Arch. Neurol. Psychiat.*, 1940, 44, 1142-1146. [163n., 250]

63. BURCKHARDT, G., Uebers Rindenexcisionen als Beitrag für operativen Therapie der Psychosen. *Allg. z. f. Psychiat.*, 1890-91, 47, 463-548. [267]

64. BURCHARD, E. M. L. Physique and psychosis: an analysis of the postulated relationship between bodily construction and mental disease syndrome. *Comp. Psychol. Monog.*, 1936, no. 61. [303]

65. BURKS, B. S. The relative influence of nature and nurture upon mental development: a comparative study of foster parent-foster children resemblance and true parent-true child resemblance. 27th Yearbook, *Natl. Soc. Stud. Educ.*, 1928, Part I, 219-316. [314]

66. —— Foster-family resemblences in intelligence. In R. G. Barker, J. S. Kounin, and H. F. Wright (Eds.), *Child Behavior and Development*, New York, McGraw-Hill, 1943. [314]

67. BURTT, E. A. *The Metaphysical Foundations of Modern Physical Science: A Historical and Critical Essay.* New York, Harcourt, Brace, 1932. [28]

68. BUTLER, E. G. Old problems and new in experimental embryology. *Amer. Scientist*, 1942, 30, 218-229. [295]

69. BUYTENDIJK, F. J. Le cerveau et l'intelligence. *J. de Psychol.*, 1931, 28, 345-371. [234]

70. —— An experimental investigation into the influence of cortical lesions on the behavior of rats. *Arch. Neérl. de Physiol.*, 1932, 17, 370-434. [234]

71. CABANIS, P. J. G. *Rapports du Physique et du Moral de l'Homme.* (2nd ed.) Paris, Bechet, 1805. [77]

72. CAJORI, F. *A History of Physics in its Elementary Branches including the Evolution of Physical Laboratories.* New York, Macmillan, 1935. [37]

73. CAMERON, D. E. *Objective and Experimental Psychiatry.* (2nd ed.) New York, Macmillan, 1941. [291n., 298]

74. CAMERON, N. Cerebral destruction in its relation to maze learning. *Psychol. Monog.*, 1928, no. 177. [234]

75. —— Physiological Psychology. In J. M. Luck (Ed.), *Annual Review of Physiology*, vol. 5, Stanford, California, 1943. [125, 212]

76. —— The functional psychoses. In (242), ch. 19. [320]

76a. CAMPBELL, R. J., and HARLOW, H. F. Problem solution by

monkeys following bilateral removal of the frontal areas. V. Spatial delayed reactions. *J. Exper. Psychol.*, 1945, 35, 110-126. [243]

77. CAMPION, G. G., and SMITH, G. E. *The Neural Basis of Thought.* New York, Harcourt, Brace, 1934. [270]

78. CANNON, W. B. The James-Lange theory of emotions: a critical examination and an alternative theory. *Amer. J. Psychol.*, 1927, 39, 106-124. [199 f.]

79. —— *Bodily Changes in Pain, Hunger, Fear and Rage: An Account of Recent Researches into the Function of Emotional Excitement.* (2nd ed.), New York, Appleton, 1929. [198 f.]

80. —— The integrative action of the vascular system. In E. V. Cowdry (Ed.), *Human Biology and Racial Welfare*, pp. 219-245. New York, Hoeber, 1930. [99, 339]

81. CANTRIL, H., and HUNT, W. A. Emotional effects produced by the injection of adrenalin. *Amer. J. Psychol.*, 1932, 44, 300-307. [202]

82. CARNAP, R. Ueberwindung der Metaphysik durch logische Analyse der Sprache. *Erkenntnis*, 1931, 2, 219-241. [67]

83. —— Psychologie in physikalischer Sprache. *Erkenntnis*, 1932, 3, 107-142. [67]

84. —— Testability and meaning. *Philos. Science*, 1936, 3, 419-471; 1937, 4, 1-40. [67 f.]

85. —— Encyclopedia and unified science. In *Foundations of the Unity of Science*, pp. 42-62, Chicago, Univ. Chicago Press, 1938. [67 f.]

86. CARR, H. A. The relation between emotion and its expression. *Psychol. Rev.*, 1917, 24, 369-375. [201]

87. CASSENS, A. Ueber die Beeinflussung des Winterschlafes durch vitamin D 3. *Z. f. die gesamte exp. Med.*, 1939, 106, 521-530. [297]

88. CATTELL, R. B. The effects of alcohol and caffeine on intelligence and associative performance. *Brit. J. Med. Psychol.*, 1930, 10, 20-33. [289]

89. CHANG, H. C., and HARRAP, G. A. JR. The determination of the circulatory blood volume with carbon monoxide. *J. Clin. Invest.*, 1928, 5, 393-405. [286]

90. CHEVALIER, J. *Henri Bergson.* New York, Macmillan, 1928. [255]

91. COBB, S. Personality as affected by lesions of the brain. In (242), ch. 18. [213-215, 262, 266]

92. DE CONDILLAC, E. B. *Traité des Sensations.* Paris, Hachette, 1902. [302]

93. COWDRY, E. V. The vital units called cells. In E. V. Cowdry (Ed.), *Human Biology and Racial Welfare*, New York, Hoeber, 1930. [97]

94. CREED, R. S. The physiological integration of the sensory proc-

esses within the gray matter of the nervous system: a critical review. *Brain*, 1931, 54, 29-54. [161]

95. CRILE, G. W. *Man: An Adaptive Mechanism*. New York, Macmillan, 1916. [276]

96. —— *The Phenomena of Life: A Radio-Electric Interpretation*. New York, Norton, 1936. [276]

97. —— A neuro-endocrine formula for civilized man. *Educ. Rec.*, 1941, 22, no. 14, 57-76. [276]

98. CROZIER, W. J. Chemoreception. In (454), ch. 19. [279]

99. CULLER, E. A. Observations on the spinal dog. *Psychol. Bull.*, 1937, 34, 742-743. [244]

100. CULLER, E. A., and METTLER, F. A. Conditioned behavior in a decorticate dog. *J. Comp. Psychol.*, 1934, 18, 291-303. [133, 244]

101. DALE, H. H. Chemical ideas in medicine and biology. *Science*, 1934, 80, 343-351. [277]

102. —— Physiology of the nervous system. *Science*, 1939, 90, 393-394. [277]

103. DALLENBACH, K. M. The temperature spots and end organs. *Amer. J. Psychol.*, 1927, 39, 402-427. [154]

104. —— Somethesis. In E. G. Boring, H. S. Langfeld, and H. P. Weld (Eds.), ch. 7, *Psychology: A Factual Textbook*, New York, Wiley, 1935. [156]

105. DANA, C. L. The anatomic seat of the emotions: a discussion of the James-Lange theory. *Arch. Neurol. Psychiat.*, 1921, 6, 634-639. [200]

106. DANDY, W. E. Changes in our conception of localization of certain functions of the brain. *Amer. J. Physiol.*, 1930, 93, 643. [257]

107. —— Physiological studies following extirpation of the right cerebral hemisphere in man. *Bull. Johns Hopkins Hosp.*, 1933, 53, 31-51. [258, 260]

107a. —— The location of the conscious center in the brain —the corpus striatum. *Bull. Johns Hopkins Hosp.*, 1946, 69, 34-58. [258]

108. DANIEL, R. S. The distribution of muscular action potentials during maze learning. *J. Exper. Psychol.*, 1939, 24, 621-629. [196]

108a. DARROW, C. Relation of electroencephalogram to photometrically observed vasomotor changes in the brain. *J. Neurophysiol.*, 1945, 8, 440-462. [205n.]

108b. —— The electroencephalogram and psychophysiological regulation in the brain. *Amer. J. Psychiat.*, 1946, 102, 791-798. [205n.]

109. DARWIN, C. *The Expression of the Emotions in Man and Animals*. New York, Appleton, 1873. [23]

110. DAVIDOFF, E., and REIFENSTEIN, E. C., JR. The stimulating action of benzedrine sulfate: a comparative study of the re-

sponses of normal persons and of depressed patients. *J. Amer. Med. Assn.*, 1937, 108, 1770-1776. [290]

111. DAVIS, R. C. The relation of certain muscle action potentials to "mental work." *Indiana Univ. Publs., Science Series*, no. 5, 1937. [194]

112. —— Patterns of muscular activity during "mental work" and their constancy. *J. Exper. Psychol.*, 1939, 24, 451-465. [196]

113. —— Set and muscular tension. *Indiana Univ. Publs., Science Series*, no. 10, 1940. [195]

114. —— The pattern of muscle action in simple voluntary movement. *J. Exper. Psychol.*, 1942, 31, 347-366. [196]

115. —— The psychophysiology of set. In P. L. Harriman (Ed.), *20th Century Psychology*, New York, Philosophical Library, 1946. [196]

116. DESCARTES, R. Correspondence. In C. Adam and P. Tannery (Eds.), *Oeuvres de Descartes*, vol. III, Paris, Cerf, 1899. [77 n.]

117. —— Les passions de l'âme, In C. Adam and P. Tannery (Eds.), *Oeuvres de Descartes*, vol. XI, Paris, Cerf, 1909. [12, 77n.]

118. —— Principia Philosophiae. In C. Adams and P. Tannery (Eds.), *Oeuvres de Descartes*, vol. VIII, Paris, Cerf, 1905. [12]

119. DIELS, H. *Die Fragmente der Vorsokratiker.* (4th ed.) Berlin, Weidmannsche Buchhandlung, 1922. [86]

120. DISPENSA, J. Relationship of the thyroid with intelligence and personality. *Amer. J. Psychol.*, 1938, 48, 471-474. [284]

121. DOBZHANSKY, T. What is heredity? *Science*, 1944, 100, 406. [308 f., 311]

122. DONALDSON, H. H. On the temperature sense. *Mind*, 1885, 10, 399-416. [154]

123. DRAPER, G. *Human Constitution: A Consideration of its Relationship to Disease.* Philadelphia, Sanders, 1924. [303]

124. —— *Disease and the Man.* London, Kegan Paul, 1930. [303]

125. DuBOIS-REYMOND, E. *Über die Grenzen des Naturekennens.* Leipzig, Veit, 1882. [40, 59, 77]

126. DUNBAR, H. F. *Emotions and Bodily Changes: A Survey of Literature on Psychosomatic Interrelationships: 1910-1933.* (2nd ed.) New York, Columbia Univ. Press, 1938. [322]

127. —— *Psychosomatic Diagnosis.* New York, Hoeber, 1943. [326 f.]

128. DUNLAP, K. *The Elements of Scientific Psychology.* St. Louis, Mosby, 1922. [145]

129. —— Alleged binocular color mixing. *Amer. J. Psychol.*, 1944, 57, 559-563. [177, 179]

130. DUSSER DE BARENNE, J. G. Recherches expérimentales sur les fonctions du système nerveux central, faites en particulier sur deux chats dont le néopallium avait été enlevé. *Arch.*

Neérl. Physiol., 1919, 4, 31, 123. [133]

131. Duus, P. Ueber psychische Störungen bei Tumoren des Orbitalhirns. *Arch. Psychiat. Nervenkr.*, 1939, 109, 596-648. [256]

131a. Ebbinghaus, H. *Ueber das Gedächtniss: Untersuchungen zur experimentellen Psychologie.* Leipzig, Duncker u. Humblot, 1885. [48]

132. Ellis, W. *The Idea of the Soul in Western Philosophy and Science.* London, Allen and Unwin, 1940. [87n.]

133. Erickson, S. C. The relative effect of a cerebral lesion upon learning, retention, and transfer. *J. Comp. Psychol.*, 1939, 27, 373-391. [234]

134. Erlanger, J. The interpretation of the action potential in cutaneous and muscle nerves. *Amer. J. Physiol.*, 1927, 82, 644-655. [158]

134a. Erlanger, J., and Gasser, H. S. The action potential in fibers of slow conduction in spinal roots and somatic nerves. *Amer. J. Physiol.*, 1930, 92, 43-82. [158]

135. ——— *Electrical Signs of Nervous Activity.* Philadelphia, Univ. Penna. Press, 1937. [158-160]

136. Ewert, P. H. A study of the effect of inverted retinal stimulation upon spatially coordinated behavior. *Genet. Psychol. Monog.*, 1930, 7, 177-363. [180]

137. Feigl, H. Logical analysis of the psycho-physical problem. *Philos. Science*, 1934, 1, 420-455. [67]

137a. Feldberg, W. Present views on the mode of action of acetylcholine in the central nervous system. *Physiol. Rev.*, 1945, 25, 596-642. [277]

138. Féré, C. Note sur les modifications de la résistance électrique sous l'influence des excitations sensorielles et des emotions. *C. R. de la Soc. de Biol.*, 1888, 40, 217-219. [202]

139. Ferrier, D. Experiments on the brain of monkeys. (2nd series) *Philos. Trans.*, 1875, 165, 433-488. [226, 229]

140. ——— *The Functions of the Brain.* (2nd ed.) London, Smith-Elder, 1886. [215, 229]

141. Finan, J. L. Effects of frontal lobe lesions on temporally organized behavior in monkeys. *J. Neurophysiol.*, 1939, 2, 208-226. [237 f.]

142. ——— An analysis of frontal lobe function in monkeys by means of two "delayed response" methods. *Psychol. Bull.*, 1940, 37, 496-497. [237, 239]

143. ——— Delayed response with predelay reinforcement in monkeys after the removal of the frontal lobes. *Amer. J. Psychol.*, 1942, 55, 202-214. [237, 239]

144. Finley, C. B. Equivalent losses in accuracy of response after central and after peripheral sense deprivation. *J. Comp. Neurol.*, 1941, 74, 203-237. [242 f.]

145. Flechsig, P. *Die Leitungsbahnen im Gehirn und Rückenmark*

des Menschen auf grund Entwicklungsgeschichtlicher Untersuchungen. Leipzig, Engelmann, 1876. [229]

146. FLOURENS, P. *Recherches Expérimentales sur les Propriétés et les Fonctions du Système Nerveux dans les Animaux Vertébres.* Paris, Crevot, 1824. [219, 224]

147. FÖLLING, A. Ueber auscheidung von Phenylbrenztraubensaüre in den Harn als Stoffwechselanomalie in Verbindung mit Imbezilität. *Z. f. Physiol. Chem.,* 1934, 227, 169-176. [298]

148. FOX, J. C., and GERMAN, W. J. Observations following left (dominant) temporal lobectomy. *Arch. Neurol. Psychiat.,* 1935, 33, 791-806. [260]

149. FREEMAN, F. N., HOLZINGER, K. J., and MITCHELL, B. C. The influence of environment on the intelligence, school achievement, and conduct of foster children. *27th Yearbook, Natl. Soc. Stud. Educ.,* 1928, Part I, 103-217. [314]

150. FREEMAN, G. L. Muscular activity and the mental processes. *Psychol. Rev.,* 1931, 38, 428-429. [196]

151. —— *Introduction to Physiological Psychology.* New York, Ronald, 1934. [127, 129, 196]

152. —— The spread of neuromuscular activity during mental work. *J. Genl. Psychol.,* 1935, 5, 479-494. [196]

153. —— The optimal locus of "anticipatory tensions" in muscular work. *J. Exper. Psychol.,* 1937, 21, 554-564. [196]

154. FREEMAN, W., and WATTS, J. W. *Psychosurgery, Intelligence, Emotion and Social Behavior following Prefrontal Lobotomy for Mental Disorders.* Springfield, Thomas, 1942. [237, 254, 258, 260, 266-270]

155. FREGE, F. L. G. *Die Grundlagen der Arithmetik: Eine logisch-mathematische Untersuchung über den Begriff der Zahl.* Breslau, Koebner, 1884. [68, 70]

156. —— *Grundgesetze der Arithmetik, begriffsschriftlich abgeleitet.* vol. I, Jena, Phole, 1893; vol. II, Jena, Phole, 1903. [68, 70]

157. FRENCH, T. M. Clinical approach to the dynamics of behavior. In (242), ch. 7. [327]

158. FRIEDLANDER, H. Die Wahrnehmung der Schwere. *Z. f. Psychologie,* 1920, 83, 1929-210. [176]

159. FRITSCH, G., and HITZIG, E. Ueber die elektrische Erregbarkeit des Grosshirns. *Arch. f. Anat. Physiol. u. Wissen. Med.,* 1870, 37, 300. [256]

160. FULTON, J. F. *Physiology of the Nervous System.* (2nd ed.) New York, Oxford Univ. Press, 1943. [82 f., 106, 156, 229-231, 237 f., 250, 267, 277]

161. —— *Howell's Textbook of Physiology.* Philadelphia and London, Saunders, 1946. [80, 286]

162. FULTON, J. F., and NACHMANSOHN, D. Acetylcholine and the physiology of the nervous system. *Science,* 1943, 97, 569-571. [277]

163. FULTON, J. F., and SHERRINGTON, C. S. Nervous integrations in man. In E. V. Cowdry (Ed.), *Human Biology and Racial Welfare*, New York, Hoeber, 1930. [93, 106]

164. GALL, F. J., and SPURZHEIM, J. C. *Anatomie et Physiologie du Système Nerveux en général, et du Cerveau en particulier, avec observations sur la possibilité de reconnaître plusieurs dispositions intellectuelles et morales de l'homme et des animaux par la configuration de leurs têtes*. Paris, Schoell, 1810-1819. [302]

165. GALT, W. The male-female dichotomy in human behavior: a phylobiological evaluation. *Psychiat.*, 1943, 6, 1-14. [306]

166. GALTON, F. *Inquiries into Human Faculty and its Development*. London, Dent, 1883. [303, 313]

167. GARDINER, W. J. Removal of right cerebral hemisphere for infiltrating glioma. *J. Amer. Med. Assn.*, 1933, 101, 823-826. [258 f.]

168. GASKILL, H. V., and FRITZ, M. F. Basal metabolism and the college freshman psychological test. *J. Genl. Psychol.*, 1946, 34, 29-45. [284]

169. GASSER, H. S. The control of excitation in the nervous system. In *The Harvey Lecture Series 32*, Baltimore, Williams and Wilkins, 1937. [160 f.]

170. ——— The classification of nerve fibers. *Ohio J. Science*, 1941, 41, 145-159. [158]

171. GELLHORN, E. Value of carbon dioxide in counteracting oxygen lack. *Nature*, 1936, 137, 700-701. [287]

172. GERMAN, W. J., and FOX, J. C. Observations following unilateral lobectomies. In *Localization of Function in the Cerebral Cortex: An Investigation of the Most Recent Advances*. Ch. 13, Baltimore, Williams and Wilkins, 1934. [260]

173. GHISELLI, E. E. The superior colliculus in vision, *J. Comp. Neurol.*, 1937, 67, 451-467. [228]

174. GHISELLI, E. E., and BROWN, C. W. Subcortical mechanisms in learning. III. Brightness discrimination. *J. Comp. Psychol.*, 1938, 26, 93-107. [228]

175. GIBSON, J. J. Adaptation, after-effect and contrast in the perception of curved lines. *J. Exper. Psychol.*, 1933, 16, 1-31. [180]

176. GIOVANNI, A., DE. *Clinical Commentaries deduced from the Morphology of the Human Body*. London, Rebman, 1909. [303]

177. GIRDEN, E., METTLER, F. A., FINCH, G., and CULLER, E. Conditioned responses in a decorticate dog to acoustic, thermal, and tactile stimulation .*J. Comp. Psychol.*, 1936, 21, 367-385. [133]

178. GOLDENWEISER, A., *History, Psychology, and Culture*. New York, Knopf, 1933. [306]

179. GOLDSCHEIDER, A. Histologische Untersuchungen ueber die

Endigungsweise der Hautsinnesnerven beim Menschen. *Arch. Anat. Physiol. Physiolog. Abt.*, 1886, Supp. Bd. 5, 191-227. [154]

180. GOLDSCHEIDER, A., and BRÜCKNER, A. Zur Physiologie des Schmertzes: die Sensibilität der Haut des Auges. *Klin. Wchnschr.*, 1919, 16, 1126. [154 f.]

181. GOLDSTEIN, K. *The Organism: A Holistic Approach to Biology Derived from Pathological Data in Man.* New York, Amer. Book Co., 1939. [223, 315, 318 f.]

182. —— *After-effects of Brain Injuries in War: Their Evaluation and Treatment.* New York, Grune-Stratton, 1942. [219, 223, 318 f.]

183. —— The mental changes due to frontal lobe damage. *J. Psychol.*, 1944, 17, 187-208. [223, 260, 262 f., 318]

184. GOLTZ, F. L. *Beiträge zur Lehr von den Functionen der Nervencentren des Frosches.* Berlin, Hirschwald, 1869. [224]

185. —— Der Hunt Ohne Grosshirn. *Arch. f. d. ges. Physiol.*, 1892, 51, 570-614. [224]

186. GOTTLOBER, A. B. The relationship between brain potentials and personality. *J. Exper. Psychol.*, 1938, 22, 67-74. [204]

187. GRAHAM, C. H. Vision. III. Some neural correlations. In (454), ch. 15. [162]

188. GRAHAM, C. H., and HARTLINE, H. E. The response of single visual sense cells to lights of different wave length. *J. Genl. Physiol.*, 1935, 18, 917-931. [149]

189. GRAHAM, C. H., KEMP, E. H., and RIGGS, L. A. An analysis of the electrical responses of a color-discriminating eye to lights of different wave lengths. *J. Genl. Psychol.*, 1935, 13, 275-296. [149]

190. GRAHAM, C. H., and RIGGS, L. A. The visibility curve of the white rat as determined by the electrical retinal response to lights of different wave lengths. *J. Genl. Psychol.*, 1935, 12, 279-295. [149]

191. GRIFFITH, C. R. *Principles of Systematic Psychology.* Urbana, Univ. of Illinois Press, 1943. [184]

192. GRIMSLEY, G. A study of individual differences in binocular coloi fusion. *J. Exper. Psychol.*, 1943, 32, 82-86. [177 f.]

193. GRINKER, R. R. Hypothalamic functions in psychosomatic interrelations. *Psychosom. Med.*, 1939, 1, 19-47. [325]

194. GROLLMAN, A. *Essentials of Endocrinology.* Philadelphia, Lippincott, 1941. [281]

194a. GUETZKOW, H., and BROZEK, J. Intellectual functions with restricted intakes of B-complex vitamins. *Amer. J. Psychol.*, 1946, 59, 358-381. [285]

195. GUTTMAN, E. Artificial psychoses produced by mescalin. *J. Ment. Science*, 1936, 82, 203-221. [290]

196. GUTTMAN, E., and MACLAY, W. S. Mescalin and depersonalization. *J. Neurol. Psychopath.*, 1936, 16, 193-212. [290]

197. GWYNN, H. B., and YATER, W. M. A study of the temporary use of therapeutic doses of benzedrine sulphate in 147 supposedly normal young men (medical students). *Med. Ann. Dist. Columbia*, 1937, 6, 356-359. [290]

198. HÄGGQVIST, G. Histophysiologische Studien ueber die Temperatursinne der Haut des Menschen. *Ant. Anz.* 1914, 45, 46-63. [154]

199. HALDANE, J. B. S. *New Paths in Genetics*. New York, Harper, 1942. [296, 308, 310]

200. HALSTEAD, W. C. Preliminary analysis of grouping behavior in patients with cerebral injury by the method of equivalent and non-equivalent stimuli. *Amer. J. Psychiat.*, 1940, 96, 1263-1294. [260, 262 f.]

201. HARTLEY, D. *Observations on Man, his Frame, his Duty, and his Expectations*. Bath, Leake and Fredericks, 1749. [16]

202. HATHAWAY, S. R. An action potential study of neuromuscular relations. *J. Exper. Psychol.*, 1935, 18, 285-298. [195]

203. ——— *Physiological Psychology*. New York, Appleton-Century, 1942. [127, 129, 281 f., 293]

204. HEAD, H. *Studies in Neurology*. 2 vols., London, Hodder and Stoughton, 1920. [157]

205. ——— *Aphasia and Kindred Disorders of Speech*. 2 vols., New York, Macmillan, 1926. [220]

206. HEBB, D. O. Review of (533). *Psychol. Bull.*, 1939, 36, 796-797. [262, 265]

207. ——— Intelligence in man after large removals of cerebral tissue: defects following right temporal lobectomy. *J. Genl. Psychol.*, 1939, 21, 437-446. [258, 260]

208. ——— Intelligence in man after large removals of cerebral tissue: report of 4 left frontal cases. *J. Genl. Psychol.*, 1939, 21, 73-87. [258, 260]

208a. ——— Man's frontal lobes. *Arch. Neurol. Psychiat.*, 1945, 54, 10-24. [260, 264]

209. HEBB, D. O., and PENFIELD, W. Human behavior after extensive bilateral removal from the frontal lobes. *Arch. Neurol. Psychiat.*, 1940, 44, 421-438. [258, 260]

210. HECHT, S. On the binocular fusion of colors and its relation to the theories of color vision. *Proc. Nat. Acad. Science*, 1928, 14, 237-241. [177 f.]

211. ——— Vision: II. The nature of the photoreceptor process. In (454), ch. 14. [149, 153, 160, 178]

212. VON HEISENBERG, W. Wandlungen der Grundlagen der Exacten Naturwissenschaften in jüngster Zeit. *Die Naturwissenschaften*, 1934, 22, 669-675. [186]

213. HELMHOLTZ, H. *Popular Lectures on Scientific Subjects*. E. Atkinson (trs.), New York, Appleton, 1885. [32 f., 55]

214. ——— *Treatise on Physiological Optics*. 3 vols., J. P. C. Southall (Ed.), Rochester, Optical Soc. Amer., 1924-25. [33]

215. ——— *Vorträge und Reden.* 2 vols., Braunschweig, Vieweg, 1884. [32n.]

216. HENNING, H. Physiologie und Psychologie des Geschmacks. *Ergeb. d. Physiol.,* 1921, 19, 1-78. [279]

217. ——— *Der Geruch.* (2nd ed.) Leipzig, Barth, 1924. [279]

218. HENRY, C. E., and KNOTT, J. R. A note on the relationship between "personality" and the alpha rhythm of the electroencephalogram. *J. Exper. Psychol.,* 1941, 28, 362-366. [204]

219. HENSCHEN, S. E. *Klinische und anatomische Beiträge zur Pathologie des Gehirns.* vols. 1-2, Uppsala, Almquist u. Wiksell, 1890-1894; vols. 5-7, Stockholm, Nordiska Bokhandeln, 1920-1922. [226, 230, 270]

220. ——— Ueber Sinnes und Vorstellungszentren in der Rinde des Grosshirns. *Z. f. d. ges. Neurol. u. Psychiat.,* 1919, 47, 55-111. [226, 270]

221. ——— On the function of the right hemisphere of the brain in relation to the left in speech, music and calculation. *Brain,* 1926, 49, 110-123. [270]

222. HERRICK, C. J. *Brains of Rats and Men.* Chicago, Univ. Chicago Press, 1926. [228]

223. ——— *Introduction to Neurology.* Philadelphia, Saunders, 1931. [94-96]

224. ——— *The Thinking Machine.* (2nd ed.) Chicago, Univ. Chicago Press, 1932. [94 f., 100, 102]

225. ——— The functions of the olfactory parts of the cerebral cortex. *Prac. Natl. Acad. Science,* 1933, 19, 7-14. [230]

226. ——— The evolution of cerebral localization patterns. *Science,* 1933, 78, 439-444. [230]

227. ——— Neurological foundations of animal behavior. In J. Jastrow (Ed.), *The Story of Human Error,* New York, Appleton-Century, 1936, 251-267. [94]

228. HESCHL, R. L. *Ueber die Vorderquere Schläfenwindungen des Menschlichen Grosshirns.* Vienna, Braumüller, 1878. [229]

229. HEYER, G. R. Psychische Faktoren bei organischen Krankheiten. *München. med. Wochenschrift,* 1922, 69, 1241. [323]

230. ——— *Das korperliche-seelische Zusammenwirken in den Lebensvorgangen, an Hand klinischer und experimenteller Tatsachen dargestellt.* München, Bergmann, 1925. [315, 323]

231. ——— *The Organism of the Mind: An Introduction to Analytical Psychotherapy.* E. and C. Paul (trs.), New York, Harcourt, Brace, 1934. [315, 323]

232. HILGARD, E. R., and MARQUIS, D. G. *Conditioning and Learning.* New York, Appleton-Century, 1940. [52, 104, 133, 227, 229, 236, 341]

233. HINES, M. On cerebral localization. *Physiol. Rev.,* 1929, 9, 462-574. [270]

234. HINTON, R. T. JR. The role of the basal metabolic rate in the

intelligence of ninety grade-school students. *J. Educ. Psychol.*, 1936, 27, 546, 550. [284]

235. —— A further study on the role of the basal metabolic rate in the intelligence of children. *J. Educ. Psychol.*, 1939, 30, 309-314. [284]

236. HITZIG, G. *Untersuchungen ueber das Gehirn.* Berlin, Hirschwald, 1874. [226]

237. HOBBES, T. *Human Nature, or the Fundamental Elements of Policy.* London, Bohn, 1840. [16]

238. HONZIK, C. H. The sensory basis of maze learning in rats. *Comp. Psychol. Monog.*, 1936, no. 64. [234, 243]

239. HOSKINS, R. G. *Endocrinology: The Glands and their Functions.* New York, Norton, 1941. [281 f.]

240. HOWELL, W. H. *A Textbook of Physiology.* (11th ed.) Philadelphia and London, Saunders, 1931. [79, 153, 164]

241. HUME, D. *A Treatise of Human Nature. Being an Attempt to Introduce the Experimental Method of Reasoning into Moral Subjects.* L. A. Selby-Bigge (Ed.), Oxford, Clarendon Press, 1896. [69]

242. HUNT, J. McV. (Ed.) *Personality and the Behavior Disorders.* 2 vols., New York, Ronald, 1944. [See Bib. nos., 12, 76, 91, 157, 372, 542, 548, 554]

243. HUNTER, W. S. A consideration of Lashley's theory of the equipotentiality of cerebral action. *J. Genl. Psychol.*, 1930, 3, 455-468. [247]

244. —— Lashley on "Cerebral Control vs. Reflexology." *J. Genl. Psychol.*, 1931, 5, 230-234. [247]

245. HURST, A. F. *The Croonian Lectures on the Psychology of the Special Senses and their Functional Disorders.* London, Hodder and Stoughton, 1920. [184]

246. HUSSERL, E. *Logische Untersuchungen.* (3rd ed.) Halle, Niemeyer, 1922. [68, 70 f.]

247. —— *Formale und Transcendentale Logik.* Halle, Niemeyer, 1929. [68, 70 f.]

248. HUXLEY, T. H. Animal Automatism. In *Humboldt Library of Popular Science Literature,* vol. V. New York, Humboldt Publishing Company, n.d. [11 f.]

249. —— *Hume with Helps to the Study of Berkeley.* New York, Appleton, 1902. [27 f.]

250. ISENSCHMID, R., and SCHNITZLER, W. Beitrag zur Lokalization der Wärmeregulation vorstehenden Zentralapparates im Zwischenhirn. *Arch. Exper. Path. Pharmak.*, 1914, 76, 202-223. [82]

251. JACKSON, J. H. On affections of speech from disease of the brain. *Brain,* 1878-1879, 1, 304-330. [265]

252. —— *Selected Writings of John Hughlings Jackson.* (J, Taylor Ed.) 2 vols., London, Hodder and Stoughton, vol. I, 1931, vol. II, 1932. [24n., 219-221, 266]

253. JACOBSEN, C. F. Functions of the frontal association areas in primates. *Arch. Neurol. Psychiat.*, 1935, 33, 558-569. [237]

254. —— Studies of cerebral function in primates. I. The functions of the frontal association areas in monkeys. *Comp. Psychol. Monog.*, 1936, no. 63. [237]

255. —— The effects of extirpations on higher brain processes. *Physiol. Revs.*, 1939, 303-322. [250]

256. JACOBSEN, C. F., and ELDER, J. H. Studies of cerebral functions in primates. II. The effect of temporal lobe lesions on delayed response in monkeys. *Comp. Psychol. Monog.*, 1936, no. 63. [230]

257. JACOBSEN, C. F., and HASELRUD, G. M. Studies of cerebral function in primates. III. A note on the effect of motor and premotor area lesions on delayed response in monkeys. *Comp. Psychol. Monog.*, 1936, no. 63. [237]

258. JACOBSEN, C. F., and NISSEN, H. W. Studies of cerebral function in primates. IV. The effects of frontal lobe lesions on the delayed alternative habit in monkeys. *J. Comp. Psychol.* 1937, 23, 101-112. [237]

259. JACOBSEN, C. F., WOLFE, J. B., and JACKSON, T. A. An experimental analysis of the functions of the frontal association areas in primates. *J. Nerv. Ment. Dis.* 1935, 82, 1-14. [237]

260. JACOBSON, E. Electrical measurements of neuromuscular states during mental activities. *Amer. J. Physiol.*, 1930, 91, 567-606. [193]

261. —— Electrical measurements of neuromuscular states during mental activities: II. Imagination and recollection of various muscular acts. *Amer. J. Physiol.*, 1930, 94, 27-34. [193]

262. —— Electrical measurements of neuromuscular states during mental activities: III. Visual imagination and recollection. *Amer. J. Physiol.*, 1930, 95, 694-702. [193]

263. —— Electrical measurements of neuromuscular states during mental activities: IV. Evidence of contraction of specific muscles during imagination. V. Variation of specific muscles contracting during imagination. *Amer. J. Physiol.*, 1931, 96, 115-121. [193]

264. —— Electrical measurements of neuromuscular states during mental activities: VI. A note on the mental activities concerning the amputated limb. *Amer. J. Physiol.*, 1931, 96, 122-125. [193]

265. —— Electrical measurements of neuromuscular states during mental activities: VII. Imagination, recollection and abstract thinking involving the speed musculature. *Amer. J. Physiol.*, 1931, 97, 200-209. [193]

266. —— The electrophysiology of mental activities. *Amer. J. Psychol.*, 1932, 44, 677-694. [196]

267. JAMES, W. *Principles of Psychology.* 2 vols., New York, Holt, 1890. [25, 198 f., 207 f., 273, 341]

268. JASPER, H. H. Electrical signs of cortical activity. *Psychol. Bull.,* 1937, 34, 411-481. [204]
269. —— Electroencephalography. In W. Penfield and T. C. Erickson, *Epilepsy and Cerebral Localization,* Springfield, Thomas, 1941. [204]
270. JASTROWITZ, M. Beiträge zur localisation im Grosshirn und über deren praktische Verwerthung. *Dtsch. med. Wchnschr.,* 1888, 14, 108. [256]
271. JEANS, J. *The Mysterious Universe.* (2nd ed.) New York, Macmillan, 1934. [54]
272. —— *The New Background of Science.* Cambridge, Cambridge Univ. Press, 1932. [54]
273. —— *The Universe Around Us.* (3rd ed.) New York, Macmillan, 1934. [54]
274. —— *Physics and Philosophy.* New York, Macmillan, 1943. [54]
275. JEFFERSON, G. Removal of right or left frontal lobes in man. *Brit. Med. J.,* 1937, 2, 199-206. [260]
276. JENNINGS, H. S. *Prometheus.* New York, Dutton, 1925. [308]
277. JERVIS, G. A. Phenylpyruvic oligophrenia: Introductory study of 50 cases of mental deficiency associated with excretion of phenylpyruvic acid. *Arch. Neurol. Psychiat.,* 1937, 38, 944-936. [298]
278. —— The genetics of phenylpyruvic oligophrenia. *J. Mental Science,* 1939, 85, 719-762. [298]
279. JOHNSON, H. M. Did Fechner measure introspectional sensations? *Psychol. Rev.,* 1929, 36, 257-284. [184]
280. —— Pre-experimental assumptions as determiners of experimental results. *Psychol. Rev.,* 1940, 47, 338-346. [290]
281. JOHNSTON, J. Chemistry. In L. L. Woodruff (Ed.), *The Development of the Sciences.* ch. 3, New Haven, Yale Univ. Press, 1923. [56]
282. JONES, H. E. The retention of conditioned emotional responses in infancy. *J. Genet. Psychol.,* 1930, 37, 485-498. [203]
283. KALISCHER, O. Ueber die Bedeutung des Stirnteils des Grosshirns für die Fresstondressur. *Zbl. Physiol.,* 1910, 24, 716-719. [230]
284. KANT, F. Katatone Motilitätspsychose nach CO-Vergiftung; ein Beitrag zur Pathogenese der Katatonen Symptome. *Arch. Psychiat.,* 1926, 78, 365-374. [286]
285. KANT, I. *Critique of Pure Reason.* (Max Müller, tr.) (2nd ed.) New York, Macmillan, 1911. [58]
286. KANTOR, J. R. Can the psychophysical experiment reconcile introspectionists and objectivists? *Amer. J. Psychol.,* 1922, 33, 481-510. [63, 136, 142, 150, 175 f., 184]
286a. —— The psychology of reflex action. *Amer. J. Psychol.,* 1922, 33, 19-42. [340]

287. ——— The nervous system: psychological fact or fiction. *J. Philos.*, 1922, 19, 38-49. [79, 101]

288. ——— The organismic vs. the mentalistic attitude toward the nervous system. *Psychol. Bull.*, 1923, 12, 684-692. [79]

289. ——— *Principles of Psychology.* New York, Knopf, vol. 1, 1924; vol. II, 1926. [101, 122n., 136, 150, 189, 201, 276, 279, 326]

290. ——— Philosophical implications of organismic psychology. In T. V. Smith and W. K. Wright (Eds.), *Essays in Philosophy*, Chicago, Open Court, 1929. [54]

291. ——— *An Outline of Social Psychology.* Chicago, Follett, 1929. [136, 276n., 345]

292. ——— *A Survey of the Science of Psychology.* Bloomington, Principia Press, 1933. [122n., 136, 150, 201, 276, 279]

293. ——— The evolution of mind. *Psychol. Rev.*, 1935, 42, 455-465. [133, 295, 345]

294. ——— The operational principle in the physical and psychological sciences. *Psychol. Rec.*, 1938, 2, 1-32. [67]

295. ——— The current situation in social psychology. *Psychol. Bull.*, 1939, 36, 307-360. [345]

296. ——— Current trends in psychological theory. *Psychol. Bull.*, 1941, 38, 29-65. [52, 109n., 135]

297. ——— Preface to interbehavioral psychology. *Psychol. Rec.*, 1942, 5, 173-193. [122n., 150, 278, 345]

298. ——— Toward a scientific analysis of motivation. *Psychol. Rec.*, 1942, 5, 225-275. [116n.]

299. ——— *Psychology and Logic.* vol. 1, Bloomington, Principia Press, 1945. [68n.]

300. KELLER, A. D. Observations on the localization in the brain stem of mechanisms controlling body temperature. *Amer. J. Med. Sci.*, 1933, 185, 746-748. [83]

301. KELLER, A. D., and HARE, W. K. The hypothalamus and heat regulation. *Proc. Soc. Exper. Biol.*, 1932, 29, 1069-1070. [83]

302. KELLOGG, W. N., DEESE, J., PRONKO, N. H., and FEINBERG, M. An attempt to condition the chronic spinal dog. *J. Exper. Psychol.*, 1947, 37, 99-117. [245 f.]

303. KELLOGG, W. N., PRONKO, N. H., and DEESE, J. Spinal conditioning in dogs. *Science*, 1946, 103, 49-50. [245 f.]

304. KENNARD, M. A. Vasomotor representation in the cerebral cortex. *Science*, 1934, 348-349. [82]

305. ——— Vasomotor disturbances resulting from cortical lesions. *Arch. Neurol. Psychiat.*, Chicago, 1935, 33, 537-545. [82]

306. KENNARD, M. A., and ECTORS, L. Forced circling movements in monkeys following lesions of the frontal lobes. *J. Neurophysiol.*, 1938, 1, 45-54. [250]

307. KENNARD, M. A., SPENCER, A. S., and FOUNTAIN, G., JR. Hyperactivity in monkeys following lesions of the frontal lobes. *J. Neurophysiol.*, 1941, 4, 512-524. [250]

307a. KENNEDY, J. L. The effects of complete and partial occipital lobectomy upon the thresholds of visual real movement in the cat. *J. Genet. Psychol.*, 1939, 54, 119-149. [229]

308. KIRK, S. A. Extra-striate functions in the discrimination of complex visual patterns. *J. Comp. Psychol.*, 1936, 21, 146-159. [229]

309. KLEBANOFF, S. G. Psychological changes in organic brain lesions and ablations. *Psychol. Bull.*, 1945, 42, 585-623. [254, 256, 260]

310. KLEIST, K. Gehirnpathologic Vornehmlich auf Grund der Kriegserfahrungen. In *Handbuch der ärztlichen Erfahrungen im Weltkriege.* Bd. 4, Leipzig, Barth, 1934. [270]

311. —— Störungen des Denkens und ihre hirnpathologischen Grundlagen (paralogische und alogische Denkstörungen). In C. H. Roggenbau (Ed.), *Gegenwartsprobleme der psychologische-neurologische Forschung.* Stuttgart, Enke, 1939. [270]

312. KLINEBERG, O., ASCH, S. E., and BLOCK, H. An experimental study of constitutional types. *Genet. Psychol. Monog.*, 1934, 16, 145-221. [304]

313. KLÜVER, H. *Mescal: The "divine" plant and its psychological effects.* London, Kegan Paul, 1928. [290]

314. —— The equivalence of stimuli in the behavior of monkeys. *J. Genet. Psychol.*, 1931, 39, 3-27. [263]

315. —— *Behavior Mechanisms in Monkeys.* Chicago, Univ. Chicago Press, 1933. [263]

316. —— The study of personality and the method of equivalent and non-equivalent stimuli. *Character and Personality*, 1936, 5, 91-112. [263]

317. —— An analysis of the effects of the removal of the occipital lobes in monkeys. *J. Psychol.*, 1936, 2, 49-61. [228]

318. —— Certain effects of lesions of the occipital lobes in macaques. *J. Psychol.*, 1937, 4, 383-401. [228, 251]

319. —— Porphyrins, the nervous system, and behavior. *J. Psychol.*, 1944, 17, 209-227. [298]

320. KLÜVER, H., and BUCY, P. C. An analysis of certain effects of bilateral temporal lobectomy in the rhesus monkey, with special reference to "psychic blindness." *J. Psychol.*, 1938, 5, 33-54. [230, 250 f.]

321. —— Preliminary analysis of functions of the temporal lobes in monkeys. *Arch. Neurol. and Psychiat.*, 1939, 42, 979-1000. [230, 250]

322. KNOTT, J. R. Electroencephalography and physiological psychology: evaluation and statement of problem. *Psychol. Bull.*, 1941, 38, 944-975. [204]

323. KOHLRAUSCH, A. Elektrische Erscheinungen am Auge. In A. Bethe, G. V. Bergmann, G. Enden, and A. Ellinger (Eds.), *Handbuch der Normalen und Pathologischen Physiologie,* vol. XII, part 2, Berlin, Springer, 1931. [149]

324. KOLB, L., and VOGEL, V. H. Use of shock therapy in 305 mental hospitals. *Amer. J. Psychiat.*, 1942, 99, 90-100. [291]

325. KOPELOFF, N. *Bacteriology in Neuropsychiatry.* Springfield, Thomas, 1941. [212]

326. KRECHEVSKY, I. Brain mechanisms and brightness discrimination learning. *J. Comp. Psychol.*, 1936, 21, 405-441. [227, 243]

327. —— Brain mechanisms and Umweg behavior. *J. Comp. Psychol.*, 1938, 25, 147-170. [235]

328. KRETSCHMER, E. *Physique and Character: An Investigation of the Nature of Constitution and the Theory of Temperament.* New York, Harcourt, Brace, 1925. [303]

329. KÜLPE, O. *Erkenntnistheorie und Naturwissenschaft.* Leipzig, Hirzel, 1910. [68]

330. —— *Die Philosophie der Gegenwart in Deutschland.* (7th ed.). Leipzig, Teubner, 1920. [68]

331. —— *Die Realisierung: Ein Beitrag zur Grundlegung der Realwissenschaften.* Leipzig, Hirzel, vol. 1, 1912; vol. 2, 1920; vol. 3, 1923. [68]

332. LADD, G. T., and WOODWORTH, R. S. *Elements of Physiological Psychology: A Treatise of the Activities and Nature of the Mind from the Physical and Experimental Points of View.* New York, Scribners, (rev.ed.) 1911. [127]

333. LADD-FRANKLIN, C. *Colour and Colour Theories.* New York, Harcourt, Brace, 1929. [170-172]

334. LANDIS, C. An attempt to measure emotional traits in juvenile delinquency. In K. S. Lashley (Ed.), *Studies in Dynamics of Behavior*, pp. 265-323, Chicago, Univ. Chicago Press, 1932. [203]

335. —— Emotion: II. The expressions of emotion. In (454), ch. 7. [202]

336. LANGE, F. A. *The History of Materialism and Criticism of its Present Importance.* 3 vols. (2rd ed.) New York, Harcourt, Brace, 1925. [33, 77]

337. LANGFELD, H. S. A response interpretation of consciousness. *Psychol. Rev.*, 1931, 38, 87-108. [52]

338. LANGLEY, G. N. On the union of cranial autonomic (visceral) fibers with the nerve cells of the superior cervical ganglion. *J. Physiol.*, 1898, 23, 240-270. [160]

339. LANIER, L. H., and LEEDY, J. L. Speed of reaction in relation to basal metabolism and blood pressure. *Psychol. Bull.*, 1933, 30, 609-610. [284]

340. LANIER, L. H., CARNEY, H. M., and WILSON, W. D. Cutaneous innervation and experimental study. *Arch. Neurol. Psychiat.*, 1935, 34, 1-60. [154]

341. LARIONOW, W. Ueber die Musikalischen Centern des Gehirns. *Pflüg. Arch. ges. Physiol.*, 1899, 76, 608-625. [230]

342. Lashley, K. S. The behavioristic interpretation of consciousness. *Psychol. Rev.*, 1923, 30, 237-272, 329-352. [51]

343. —— *Brain Mechanisms and Intelligence: A Quantitative Study of Injuries to the Brain.* Chicago, Univ. Chicago Press, 1929. [225 f., 228, 233, 235, 241 f., 246-249]

344. —— Mass action in cerebral function. *Science*, 1931, 73, 245-254. [230n.]

345. —— Cerebral control vs. reflexology: A reply to Professor Hunter. *J. Genl. Psychol.*, 1931, 5, 3-20. [247]

346. —— Integrative functions of the cerebral cortex. *Psychol. Rev.*, 1933, 13, 1-42. [229]

347. —— Nervous mechanisms in learning. In (454), ch. 10. [104, 225]

348. —— Studies of cerebral function in learning. XI. The behavior of rats in latch box situations. *Comp. Psychol. Monog.*, 1935, 11, 5-42. [228, 235, 243]

349. —— The Mechanism of Vision. XII. Nervous Structures concerned in the acquisition and retention of habits based on reactions to light. *Comp. Psychol. Monog.*, 1935, 11, 43-79. [246]

350. —— The thalamus and emotion. *Psychol. Rev.*, 1938, 45, 42-61. [200]

351. —— Experimental analysis of instinctive behavior. *Psychol. Rev.*, 1938, 45, 445-471. [210 f.]

352. —— The mechanism of vision. XV. Preliminary studies of the rat's capacity of detail vision. *J. Genl. Psychol.*, 1938, 18, 123-193. [229]

353. —— Coalescense of neurology and psychology. *Proc. Amer. Philos. Soc.*, 1941, 84, 461-469. [49, 130 f., 138, 209, 242]

354. —— The problem of cerebral organization in vision. In H. Klüver (Ed.), *Visual Mechanisms,* Lancaster, Cattell, 1942. [209]

355. —— An examination of the "continuity theory" as applied to discrimination learning. *J. Genl. Psychol.*, 1942, 26, 241-265. [211n.]

356. Lashley, K. S., and Frank, M. The mechanism of vision: X. Post-operative disturbances of habits based on detail vision in the rat after lesions in the cerebral visual areas. *J. Comp. Psychol.*, 1934, 17, 355-391. [227]

357. Lashley, K. S., and McCarthy, D. A. The survival of the maze habit after cerebellar injuries. *J. Comp. Psychol.*, 1926, 6, 423-432. [210]

358. Lashley, K. S., and Wade, M. The Pavlovian theory of generalization. *Psychol. Rev.*, 1946, 53, 72-87 [342]

359. Lavater, J. K. *Essays on Physiognomy: For the promotion of the Knowledge and the Love of Mankind.* (2nd ed.) 4 vols., London, Whittingham, 1804. [302]

360. Leahy, A. M. Nature-nurture and intelligence. *Genet. Psychol. Monog.*, 1935, 17, 236-308. [314]

361. Lebedinskaia, S. I., and Rosenthal, J. S. Reactions of a dog after removal of the cerebral hemispheres. *Brain*, 58, 412-419. [132]

362. Leibnitz, G. W. von. *The Philosophical Works of Leibnitz.* G. M. Duncan (Ed.), New Haven, Tuttle, Morehouse and Taylor, 1908. [13]

363. Lemere, F. The significance of individual differences in the Berger rhythm. *Brain*, 1936, 59, 366-375. [204]

364. Lennox, W. G., Gibbs, F. A., and Gibbs, E. L. Relationship of unconsciousness to cerebral blood flow and to anoxemia, *Arch. Neurol. Psychiat.*, 1935, 34, 1001-1013. [286]

365. Lenzen, V. F. Mind in Observation. In G. P. Adams, J. Loewenberg, and C. Pepper (Eds.), *University of California Publications in Philosophy*, vol. 19, Berkeley, Univ. Calif. Press, 1936. [186]

366. Levy, J. A. A quantitative study of the relationship between basal metabolic rate and children's behavior problems. *Amer. J. Orthopsychiat.*, 1931, 1, 298-310. [284]

367. Lewes, G. H. *The Physical Basis of Mind.* London, Kegan Paul, 1893. [208, 224]

368. Liddell, H. S. Physiological psychology. *Ann. Rev. Physiol.*, 1941, 3, 487-508. [127]

369. ———— The nervous system as a whole: the conditioned reflex. In (160), ch. 26. [130, 209, 341]

370. Lidz, T. A study of the effect of right frontal lobectomy on intelligence and temperament. *J. Neurol. Psychiat.*, 1939, 2, 211-222. [260]

371. Lindsley, D. B. Electrical potentials in children and adults. *J. Genl. Psychol.*, 1938, 19, 285-306. [204]

372. ———— Electroencephalography. In (242), ch. 33. [204]

373. Livingston, W. K. *Pain Mechanisms: A Physiologic Interpretation of Causalgia and Its Related States.* New York, Macmillan, 1943. [155, 159, 183]

374. Loewi, O. Chemical transmission of nerve impulses. *Amer. Scientist*, 1945, 33, 159-174. [277]

375. Lombroso, C. *L'Uomo Deliquente.* Turin, Bocca, 1889. [303]

376. ———— *The Man of Genius.* New York, Scribners, 1895. [303]

377. ———— *Crime, Its Causes and Remedies.* Boston, Little, Brown, 1911, [303]

378. Lombroso, C., and Ferrero, W. *The Female Offender.* New York, Scribners, 1898. [303]

379. Lorente de No, R. Analysis of the activity of the chains of internuncial neurons. *J. Neurophysiol.*, 1938, 64, 207-244. [138]

380. Lotze, R. H. *Outline of Psychology.* Minneapolis, Williams, n.d. [31]

381. LOUCKS, R. B. Efficacy of the rat's motor cortex in delayed alternation. *J. Comp. Neurol.*, 1931, 53, 511-567. [234]

382. —— An appraisal of Pavlov's systematization of behavior from the experimental standpoint. *J. Comp. Psychol.*, 1933, 15, 1-47. [132n.]

383. —— Reflexology and the psychobiological approach. *Psychol. Rev.*, 1937, 44, 320-338. [132]

384. —— The contribution of physiological psychology. *Psychol. Rev.*, 1941, 48, 105-126. [79, 136]

385. LUCIANI, L., and SEPPILI, G. *Die Functions-Localization auf der Grosshirnrinde.* Leipzig, Deuticke, 1886. [226]

386. LYERLY, J. Neurosurgical treatment of certain abnormal mental states. *J. Amer. Med. Assn.*, 1941, 117, 517-520. [268]

387. MACALISTER, A. Phrenology. *Encyclopedia Britannica*, (13th ed.) London, New York, 1926. [269, 302]

388. MACH, E. *The Science of Mechanics.* Chicago, Open Court, 1907. [61]

389. MAGNUS, R. *Körperstellung.* Berlin, Springer, 1924. [207]

390. —— Some results of studies in the physiology of posture. *Lancet*, 1926, 2, 531-536, 585-588. [207]

391. MAIER, N. R. F. The effect of cerebral destruction on reasoning and learning in rats. *J. Comp. Neurol.*, 1932, 54, 45-75. [239]

392. —— Cortical destruction of the posterior part of the brain and its effect on reasoning in rats. *J. Comp. Neurol.*, 1932, 56, 179-214. [239]

393. —— The pattern of cortical injury and its relation to mass action. *J. Comp. Neurol.*, 1934, 60, 409-436. [234, 239]

394. MAIER, N. R. F., and SCHNEIRLA, T. C. *Principles of Animal Psychology.* New York, McGraw-Hill, 1934. [228, 334]

395. MALMO, R. B. Interference factors in delayed response in monkeys after removal of frontal lobes. *J. Neurophysiol.*, 1942, 5, 295-308. [237]

396. MALZBERG, B. Outcome of insulin treatment of one thousand patients with dementia praecox. *Psychiat. Quart.*, 1938, 12, 528-533. [291]

397. MARAÑON, G. Contribution à l'étude de l'action émotive de l'adrenaline. *Rev. fr. d'ednocrinal.*, 1924, 2, 301-325. [202]

398. MARQUIS, D. G. Effects of the removal of the visual cortex in mammals, with observations on the retention of light discrimination in dogs. *Res. Publ. Assn. Nerv. Ment. Dis.*, 1934, 13, 558-592. [228]

399. —— The neurology of learning. In F. A. Moss (Ed.), *Comparative Psychology*, ch. 7, New York, Prentice-Hall, 1942. [103]

400. MARQUIS, D. G., and HILGARD, E. R. Conditioned lid responses to light in dogs after removal of the visual cortex. *J. Comp. Psychol.*, 1936, 22, 157-178. [228]

401. —— Conditioned responses to light in monkeys after removal of the occipital lobes. *Brain*, 1937, 60, 1-12. [228]

402. MARRACK, J. The social implications of biochemistry. In G. Needham, and D. E. Green (Eds.), *Perspective in Biochemistry*, Cambridge, Univ. Press, 1939. [310]

403. MARSHALL, H. Alcohol: a critical review of the literature 1929-1940. *Psychol. Bull.*, 1941, 38, 193-217. [289]

404. MASSERMAN, J. H. Is the hypothalamus a center of emotion? *Psychosom. Med.*, 1941, 3, 3-25. [200]

405. —— *Behavior and Neurosis: An Experimental Psychoanalytic Approach to Psychological Principles.* Chicago, Univ. Chicago Press, 1943. [53n.]

406. —— *Principles of Dynamic Psychiatry including an Integrative Approach to Abnormal and Clinical Psychology.* Philadelphia, Saunders, 1946. [324 f.]

407. MATHEWS, A. P. *Physiological Chemistry.* Baltimore, Williams and Wilkins, 1939. [283]

408. MAX, L. W. An experimental study of the motor theory of consciousness. III. Action current responses in deaf-mutes during sleep. Sensory stimulation and dreams. *J. Comp. Psychol.*, 1935, 19, 469-486. [194]

409. —— Experimental study of the motor theory of consciousness. IV. Action current responses during awakening kinaesthetic imagery and abstract thinking. *J. Comp Psychol.*, 1937, 24, 301-344, [194]

410. MAYER, F. *The Chemistry of Natural Coloring Matters.* A. H. Cook (tr.), New York, Reinhold, 1943. [173]

411. McFARLAND, R. A. The psychological effects of oxygen deprivation (anoxemia) on human behavior. *Arch. Psychol.*, 1932, 22, no. 145. [285]

412. —— Psychophysiological studies at high altitudes in the Andes. *J. Comp. Psychol.*, 1937, 23, 191-258; 1938, 24, 147-220. [285]

413. —— The psycho-physiological effects of reduced oxygen pressure. *Res. Publ. Assn. Nerv. Ment. Dis.*, 1939, 19, 112-143. [285]

414. —— The internal environment and behavior. I. Introduction and the role of oxygen. *Amer. J. Psychiat.*, 1941, 97, 858-877. [285]

415. McFARLAND, R. A., and BARACH, A. L. The relationship between alcoholic intoxication and anoxemia. *Amer. J. Med Scien.*, 1936, 192, 186-198. [289]

416. McGEOCH, J. A. The acquisition of skill. *Psychol. Bull.*, 1929, 26, 457-498. [79]

417. —— Forgetting and the law of disuse. *Psychol. Rev.*, 1932, 39, 352-370. [79]

418. McNAMARA, W. J., and MILLER, R. E. Effect of benzedrine sulphate on mental work. *Psychol. Rec.*, 1937, 1, 78-84. [290]

419. McNemar, Q. C. A critical examination of the University of Iowa studies of environmental influences upon the IQ. *Psychol. Bull.*, 1940, 37, 63-92. [314]

420. Meduna, L. V. Versuche ueber die biologische Beeinflussung des Ablaufes der Schizophrenia: Kampfer und Kardizolkrämpfe. *Z. ges Neurol. Psychiat.*, 1935, 235-262. [291]

421. Meduna, L. V., and Friedman, E. Convulsive irritative therapy of the psychoses. *J. Amer Med. Assn.*, 1939, 112, 501-509. [291]

422. Meinong, A., von. *Ueber die Stellung der Gegenstandstheorie im System der Wissenschaften*. Leipzig, Eckardt, 1907. [68, 70]

423. ——— *Gesammelte Abhandlungen*. 3 vols., Leipzig, Barth, 1914. [68, 70]

424. ——— *Ueber Möglichkeit und Warscheinlichkeit*. Leipzig, Barth, 1915. [68, 70]

425. ——— *Ueber Annahmen*. (3rd ed.) Leipzig, Barth, 1928. [68, 70]

426. Merriman, C. The intellectual resemblance of twins. *Psychol. Monog.*, 1924, no. 5. [313]

427. Merz, J. T. *A History of European Thought in the 19th Century*. 4 vols., Edinburgh and London, 1902-1923. [19]

428. Mettrie, J. O., de la. *L'Homme Machine*. Leyden, Luzac. 1748. [302]

429. Meyer, A. The problems of mental reaction-types, mental causes and diseases. *Psychol. Bull.*, 1908, 5, 245. [315 f.]

430. ——— Objective psychology or psychobiology with subordination of the medically useless contrast of mental and physical. *J. Amer. Med. Assn.*, 1915, 65, 860-863. [315 f.]

431. ——— Leading concepts of Psychobiology (Ergasiology) and of Psychiatry (Ergasiatry), *Proc. 4th Confer. on Psychiat. and Educ.*, Baltimore, Apr. 8-10, 1936. [315 f.]

432. Miles, W. R. Psychological effects of alcohol in man. In H. Emerson (Ed.), *The Effects of Alcohol on Man in Health and Disease*. New York, Macmillan, 1932. [289]

433. Mill, J. *Analysis of the Phenomena of the Human Mind*. London, Baldwin, 1829; J. S. Mill edition, London, Longmans-Green, 1869. [38n.]

434. Miller, E. *Types of Mind and Body*. New York, Norton, 1927. [304]

435. Molitch, M., and Eccles, A. K. The relations between mental level and basal metabolism in juvenile delinquents. *J. Juv. Res.*, 1934, 18, 135-139. [284]

436. Monakow, C., von. *Die Lokalization im Grosshirn*. Wiesbaden, Bergman, 1914. [249]

436a. Moncrieff, R. W. *The Chemical Senses*. London, Leonard Hill, 1944; New York, John Wiley, 1946. [280]

437. Moniz, E. *Tentatives Operatoires dans le Traitment de certaines Psychoses*. Paris, Masson, 1936. [267]

438. —— Prefrontal leucotomy in treatment of mental disorder. *Amer. J. Psychiat.*, 1937, 93, 1379-1385. [267]
439. MOREL, F. The surgical treatment of dementia praecox. *Amer. J. Psychiat.*, 1938, 94, 309-314. [267]
440. MORGAN, C. L. *Animal Life and Intelligence.* Boston, Ginn, 1891. [23n., 238]
441. —— *Habit and Instinct.* London, Arnold, 1896. [23n.]
442. —— *Animal Behavior.* London, Arnold, 1900. [23n.]
443. —— *Instinct and Experience.* New York, Macmillan, 1913. [23n.]
444. MORGAN, C. T. *Physiological Psychology.* New York, McGraw-Hill, 1943. [158, 227-229, 234, 239, 248, 250]
445. MORGAN, T. H. The mechanism and laws of heredity. In (454), ch. 2. [310]
446. MOWRER, O. H. Preparatory set (expectancy): some methods of measurement. *Psychol. Monog.*, 1940, no. 52. [195]
447. —— Preparatory set (expectancy): Further evidence of its "central" locus. *J. Exper. Psychol.*, 1941, 28, 116-133. [195]
448. MOWRER, O. H., RAYMAN, N. N., and BLISS, E. L. Preparatory set (expectancy): An experimental demonstration of its "central" locus. *J. Exper. Psychol.*, 1940, 26, 357-372. [195]
449. MUENZINGER, K. F. *Psychology: The Science of Behavior.* New York, Harper, 1942. [137]
450. MULLER, H. S. Mental traits and heredity. *J. Hered.*, 1925, 16, 433-438. [313]
451. MUNCIE, W. *Psychobiology and Psychiatry: A Textbook of Normal and Abnormal Human Behavior.* St. Louis, Mosby, 1939. [317]
452. MUNK, H. *Ueber die Funktionen der Grosshirnrinde: gesammelte Mittheilungen aus den Jahren 1877-1880.* Berlin, Hirschwald, 1881. [226, 229]
453. —— Ueber die Sehsphären der Grosshirnrinde. *Monatsber. Preuss. Akad. Wiss.*, 1880, 485-507. [226, 229]
454. MURCHISON, C. (Ed.), *A Handbook of General Experimental Psychology*, Worcester, Clark Univ. Press, 1934. [See Bib. nos., 24, 98, 187, 211, 335, 347, 445, 458, 602]
455. MURPHY, G. *A Historical Introduction to Modern Psychology.* New York, Harcourt, Brace, 1929. [21]
455a. MURPHY, J. P., and GELLHORN, E. Multiplicity of representation versus punctate localization in the motor cortex; an experimental investigation. *Arch. Neurol. Psychiat.*, 1945, 54, 256-273. [344]
456. NACCARATI, S. The morphologic aspect of intelligence. *Arch. Psychol.*, 1921, no. 45. [303]
457. NAFE, J. P. A quantitative theory of feeling. *J. Genl. Psychol.*, 1929, 2, 199-211. [157]
458. —— The Pressure, Pain, and Temperature Senses. In (454), ch. 20. [157]

459. NAFE, J. P., and WAGONER, K. S. The sensitivity of the cornea of the eye. *J. Psychol.*, 1936, 2, 433-439. [155]

460. ———— The insensitivity of the cornea to heat and pain derived from high temperatures. *Amer. J. Psychol.*, 1938, 49, 631-649. [155]

461. VON NEUMANN, J. *Mathematische Grundlagen der Quantenmechanik.* Berlin, Springer, 1932. [186]

462. NEURATH, O. Physicalism: The philosophy of the Vienese Circle. *Monist.*, 1931, 41, 618-623. [67]

463. NEWMAN, H. H., FREEMAN, F. N., and HOLZINGER, K. S. *Twins: A Study of Heredity and Environment.* Chicago, Univ. Chicago Press, 1937. [313]

464. NEWTON, I. Optics. In S. Horsley (Ed.). *Isaaci Newtoni Quae Exstant Omnia*, Tome 4. London, Nichols, 1782. [60]

465. NICHOLS, I. C., and HUNT, J. McV. A case of partial frontal bilateral lobectomy. *Amer. J. Psychiat.*, 1940, 96, 1063-1087. [260]

466. NIELSEN, J. M., and RANEY, R. B. Recovery from aphasia studied in cases of lobectomy. *Arch. Neurol. Psychiat.*, 1939, 42, 189-200. [260, 270]

467. NORDENSKIOLD, E. *The History of Biology: A Survey.* L. B. Eyre, (tr.), New York, Knopf, 1932. [34]

468. O'BRIEN, J. D. Removal of the right cerebral hemisphere: Case report. *Ohio State Med. J.*, 1932, 28, 645-649. [258 f.]

469. ———— Further report on case removal of right cerebral hemisphere. *J. Amer. Med. Assn.*, 1936, 107, 657. [258]

470. ODY, F. Le traitment de la démence précoce par récection du lobe préfrontal. *Arch. Ital. di Chir.*, 1938, 53, 321-330. [267]

471. OGLE, W. *Aristotle on the Parts of Animals.* London, Kegan Paul, 1882. [81]

472. OMWAKE, K. T., DEXTER, E. S., and LEWIS, L. W. The interrelations of certain physiological measurements and aspects of personality. *Character & Personality*, 1934, 3, 64-71. [284]

473. PALMER, W. L. Review of (557). *Science*, 1943, 98, 450-452. [320]

474. PANIZZA, B. Osservazioni sul nervo ottico, *G.I.R. Ist. Lomb.*, 1855, 7, 237-252. [226]

475. PARKER, G. H. The evolution of the brain. In E. V. Cowdry, *Human Biology and Racial Welfare*, New York, Hoeber, 1930. [94]

476. PATERSON, D. G. *Physique and Intellect.* New York, Century, 1930. [304, 308]

477. PATRICK, G. T. W. *What is the Mind?* New York, Macmillan, 1929. [95]

478. PATRICK, J. R., and ROWLES, E. Intercorrelations among metabolic rate, vital capacity, blood pressure, intelligence, scholarship, personality, and other measures on university women. *J. Appl. Psychol.*, 1933, 17, 507-521. [284]

479. PAVLOV, I. P. *Conditioned Reflexes: An Investigation of the Physiological Activity of the Cerebral Cortex.* G. V. Anrep (Ed.), London, Oxford Univ. Press, 1927. [214]

480. PEARL, R. *Constitution and Health.* London, Kegan Paul, 1933. [303]

481. PENDE, N. *Constitutional Inadequacies.* Philadelphia, Lea and Febiger, 1928. [303]

482. PENDELTON, C. R. The cold receptor. *Amer. J. Psychol.*, 1928, 40, 353-371. [154]

483. PENFIELD, W., and EVANS, J. Functional defects produced by cerebral lobectomies. *Res. Publ. Assn. Nerv. Ment. Dis.*, 1934, 13, 352-377. [258 f., 264]

484. ——— The frontal lobe in man: A clinical study of maximum removals. *Brain*, 1935, 58, 115-133. [258]

485. PENFIELD, W., and ERICKSON, T. C. *Epilepsy and Cerebral Localization: A Study of the Mechanism, Treatment and Prevention of Epileptic Seizures.* Springfield, Thomas, 1941. [217, 221]

486. PENNINGTON, L. A. The auditory localizing of the white rat in relation to cerebral function. *J. Genet. Psychol.*, 1935, 46, 264-283. [230]

487. ——— The function of the brain in auditory localization. II. The effect of cortical operation upon original learning. *J. Comp. Neurol.*, 1937, 66, 415-442. [230]

488. ——— The function of the brain in auditory localization. III. Postoperative solution of an auditory spatial problem. *J. Comp. Neurol.*, 1937, 67, 33-48. [230]

489. PENROSE, L. S. Inheritance of phenylpyruvic amentia. *Lancet*, 1935, 129, 192-194. [298]

490. PEPPER, S. C. A criticism of a positivistic theory of mind. In *The Nature of Mind*, Univ. California Publications in Philosophy, vol. 19, Berkeley, Univ. California Press, 1936. [67]

491. PETERSON, W. F. Constitution and disease. *Physiol. Rev.*, 1932, 12, 283-308. [303]

492. PFLÜGER, E. *Die Sensorischen Funktionen des Rückenmarks der Wirbelthiere nebst einer neuen Lehre ueber die Leitungsgesetze der Reflexionen.* Berlin, Hirschwald, 1853. [224]

493. Physiological Reviews. D. R. Hooker (Ed.). Baltimore, *Amer. Physiol. Soc.*, 1921- [129]

494. PINKSTON, J. O., BARD, P., and RIOCH, D. McK. The responses to changes in environmental temperature after removal of portions of the fore-brain. *Amer. J. Physiol.*, 1934, 109, 515-531. [82]

495. PINKSTON, J. O., and RIOCH, D. McK. The influence of the cerebral cortex on peripheral circulation. *Amer. J. Physiol.*, 1938, 121, 49-54. [82]

496. PLATO, *Phaedo.* Oxford, Clarendon Press, 1911. [85 f.]

497. POINCARÉ, H. *Foundations of Science*. Lancaster, Science Press, 1921. [55, 111]

498. POLTYREV, S. S. Die Rolle der Rinde und Subrindeknoten in der Bildung der bedingte Reflexe. *Z. Biol.*, 1936, 97, 180-186. [133]

499. POLTYREV, S. S., and ZELIONY, G. P. Grosshirnrinde und Assozia-tions-funktion. *Z. Biol.*, 1930, 90, 157-160. [132, 137]

500. PORTEUS, S. D., and KEPNER, R. D. Mental changes after bi-lateral prefrontal lobotomy. *Genetic Psychol. Monog.*, 1944, 29, 3-115. [258, 260]

501. PRATT, C. C. *The Logic of Modern Psychology*. New York, Mac-millan, 1939. [61, 79, 145, 208, 341]

502. PRIDEAUX, E. The psychogalvanic reflex: A review. *Brain*, 1920, 43, 50-73. [202 f.]

503. ———. Expression of emotion in cases of mental disorder as shown by the psychogalvanic reflex. *Brit. J. Psychol.*, (Med. Sec.) 1921, 2, 23-46. [202]

504. PROSSER, C. L., and HUNTER, W. S. The extinction of startle re-sponses and spinal reflexes in the white rat. *Amer. J. Physiol.*, 1936, 117, 609-618. [243, 246]

505. *Psychosomatic Medicine, Experimental and Clinical Studies*. F. Dunbar (Ed.), Washington, Nat. Res. Council, 1939- [320, 323]

506. PURDY, D. M. Vision. In E. G. Boring, H. S. Langfeld and H. P. Weld (Eds.), *Introduction to Psychology*, ch. 17, New York, Wiley, 1939. [146]

507. PUTNAM, T. J. The significance of the alterations of mental and emotional processes produced by diseases of the brain. *Res. Publ. Assn. Nerv. Ment. Dis.*, 1939, 19, 81-107. [212]

508. PUUSEPP, L. Alcune considerazioni sugli interventi chirurgici nelle malattie mentali. *Gior. della r. Accad. di Med. di Torino*, 1937, 100, pte. 2, 3-16. [267]

509. RAND, B. *The Classical Psychologists: Selections Illustrating Psy-chology from Anaxogoras to Wundt*. Boston, Houghton-Mifflin, 1912. [87 f., 163, 302]

510. RANSON, S. W. Non-medullated nerve fibers in the spinal nerves. *Amer. J. Anat.*, 1911, 12, 67-87. [158]

511. ——— Cutaneous sensation. *Science*, 1933, 78, 395-399. [159, 163, 341]

512. ——— Regulation of body temperature. *Res. Publ. Assn. Nerv. Ment. Dis.*, 1940, 20, 342-399. [83]

513. RANSON, S. W. and DAVENPORT, H. K. Sensory unmyelinated fibers in the spinal nerves. *Amer. J. Anat.*, 1931, 48, 331-353. [158]

514. RANSON, S. W., and INGRAM, W. R. Hypothalamus and regula-tion of body temperature. *Proc. Soc. Exper. Biol. Med.*, 1935, 32, 1439. [83]

515. REIFENSTEIN, E. C., JR., and DAVIDOFF, E. The psychological

effects of benzedrine sulphate. *Amer. J. Psychol.*, 1939, 52, 56-64. [290]

516. RIBBELING, C. H. A catatonic condition in poisoning by carbon monoxide. *Psychiat. Neurol. Bull.*, 1929, 33, 94-99. [286]

517. RICHTER, C. P. Total Self Regulatory Functions in Animals and Human Beings. *The Harvey Lectures*, Series 38, Lancaster, Science Press, 1943. [280]

518. RICHTER, C. P., and HAWKES, C. D. Increased spontaneous activity and food intake produced in rats by removal of the frontal poles of the brain. *J. Neurol. Psychiat.*, 1939, 2, 231-242. [250]

519. RICHTER, C. P., and HINES, M. Increased spontaneous activity produced in monkeys by brain lesions. *Brain*, 1938, 61, 1-16. [250]

520. RICHTER, C. P., and SCHMIDT, C. H., JR. Increased fat and decreased carbohydrate appetite of pancreatomized rats. *Endocrinology*, 1941, 28, 179-192. [280]

521. RIVERS, W. H. R. On binocular color mixture. *Proc. Cambridge Philos. Soc.*, 1895, 8, 273-277. [178]

522. ROBINSON, E. S. *Association Theory Today.* New York, Century, 1932. [150]

523. ROMANES, G. J. *Animal Intelligence.* New York, Appleton, 1881. [23n.]

524. ———— *Mental Evolution in Animals.* New York, Appleton, 1885. [23n.]

525. ———— *Mental Evolution in Man.* New York, Appleton, 1902. [23n.]

526. ROSETT, J. *The Mechanism of Thought, Imagery, and Hallucination.* New York, Columbia Univ. Press, 1939. [270]

527. ROTHBART, H. B. Basal metabolism in children of normal and of subnormal intelligence, with blood cholesterol and creatinine values. *Amer. J. Dis. Child.*, 1935, 49, 672-688. [284]

528. ROWE, S. N. Mental changes following the removal of the right cerebral hemisphere for brain tumor. *Amer. J. Psychiat.*, 1937, 94, 605-614. [258, 260]

529. RUCH, T. C. Cortical localization of somatic sensibility: The effect of precentral, postcentral and posterior parietal lesions upon the performance of monkeys trained to discriminate weights. *Res. Publ. Assn. Nerv. Ment. Dis.*, 1935, 15, 289-330. [231]

530. RUCH, T. C., FULTON, J. F., and GERMAN, W. J. Sensory discrimination in monkey, chimpanzee, and man after lesions of the parietal lobe. *Arch. Neurol. Psychiat.*, 1938, 39, 919-937. [231 f.]

531. RUCKMICK, C. A. *The Psychology of Feeling and Emotion.* New York, McGraw-Hill, 1936. [200]

532. RUFFIN, H. Stirnhirnsymptomatologie und Stirnhirnsyndrome. *Fortschr. Neurol. Psychiat.*, 1939, 11, 34-52. [256]

533. RYLANDER, G. *Personality Changes after Operation on the Frontal Lobes: A Clinical Study of 32 Cases.* Copenhagen, Munksgaard, 1939. [258, 260-263]
534. SAKEL, M. *Neue Behandlungsmethode der Schizophrenie.* Vienna, Perles, 1935. [291]
535. —— The methodical use of hypoglycemia in the treatment of psychoses. *Amer. J. Psychiat.*, 1937, 94, 111-129. [291]
536. —— The pharmocological shock treatment of schizophrenia. J. Wortis (tr.) *Nerv. Ment. Dis. Monog.*, no. 62, 1938. [291]
537. SARGANT, W., and BLACKBURN, J. N. The effect of benzedrine on intelligence scores. *Lancet*, 1936, 231, 1385-1387. [290]
538. SAUL, L. J., DAVIS, H., and DAVIS, P. A. Correlations between electroencephalograms and the psychological organization of the individual. *Trans. Amer. Neurol. Assn.*, 1937, 63, 167-169. [204]
539. SCHÄFER, E. A. Experiments on the electrical excitation of the visual area of the cerebral cortex in the monkey. *Brain*, 1888, 11, 1-6. [226]
540. SEARS, R. R. Psychogalvanic responses in arithmetical work: effects of experimental change in addition. *Arch. Psychol.*, 1933-4, 24, no. 155. [203]
541. —— Survey of objective studies of psychoanalytic concepts. *Soc. Sci. Res. Coun. Bull.*, no. 51, 1943. [327]
542. —— Experimental analysis of psychoanalytic phenomena. In (242), ch. 9. [327]
543. SEWARD, J. P., and SEWARD, G. H. Galvanic skin reactions. *J. Exper. Psychol.*, 1935, 18, 64-79. [203]
544. SHAW, W. A. The distribution of muscle action potentials during imaging. *Psychol. Rec.*, 1938, 2, 195-215. [196]
545. SHEEHAN, D. The clinical significance of the nerve endings in the mesentery. *Lancet*, 1933, 224, 409-413. [155]
546. SHELDON, W. H. *The Varieties of Human Physique: An Introduction to Constitutional Psychology.* New York, Harpers, 1940. [304 f.]
547. —— *The Varieties of Temperament: A Psychology of Constitutional Differences.* New York, Harpers, 1942. [304 f.]
548. —— Constitutional factors in personality. In (242), ch. 17. [304 f.]
549. SHERRINGTON, C. S. *The Integrative Action of the Nervous System.* New Haven, Yale Univ. Press, 1906. [199, 207, 344]
550. —— *The Brain and Its Mechanisms.* Cambridge, Cambridge Univ. Press, 1933. [93, 97, 165]
551. SHILLITO, F. H., DRINKER, C. K., and SHAUGHNESSY, T. J. The problem of nervous and mental sequelae in carbon monoxide poisoning. *J. Amer. Med. Assn.*, 1936, 106, 669-674. [286]
552. SHIPLEY, W., and KANT, F. The insulin-shock and metrazol treatments of schizophrenia with emphasis on psychological aspects. *Psychol. Bull.*, 1940, 37, 259-284. [291]

553. SHOCK, N. W. Some psychophysiological relations. *Psychol. Bull.*, 1939, 36, 447-476. [288]

554. —— Physiological factors in behavior. In (242), ch. 19. [282, 285-287]

555. SHOCK, N. W., and JONES, H. E. The relationship between basal physiological functions and intelligence in adolescents. *J. Educ. Psychol.*, 1940, 31, 369-375. [284]

556. SHOCK, N. W., and SCOW, R. C. The effect of learning of repeated exposures to lowered oxygen tension of the inspired air. *J. Comp. Psychol.*, 1942, 34, 55-63. [286]

557. SHURRAGER, P. S., and CULLER, E. Conditioning in the spinal dog. *J. Exper. Psychol.*, 1940, 26, 133-159. [244]

558. SIGERIST, H. E. *Civilization and Disease.* Ithaca, Cornell Univ. Press, 1943. [301]

559. SKEELS, H. M. Mental development of children in foster homes. *J. Genet. Psychol.*, 1938, 2, 33-43. [314]

560. —— Some Iowa studies of the mental growth of children in relation to differentials of the environment: a summary. *39th Yearbook Natl. Soc. Stud. Educ.*, 1940, II, 281-308. [314]

561. SKINNER, B. F. The concept of the reflex in the description of behavior. *J. Genl. Psychol.*, 1931, 427-458. [79, 104n., 136]

562. —— *The Behavior of Organisms: An Experimental Analysis.* New York, Appleton-Century, 1938. [79, 136]

563. SKODAK, M. Children in foster homes: A study of mental development. *Univ. Iowa Stud. Child Welf.*, 1939, 16, no. 1. [314]

564. Von Skramlik, E. *Handbuch der Physiologie der niederen Sinne.* Vol. I, *Die Physiologie des Geruchs und Geschmasksinnes.* Leipzig, Thieme, 1926. [279]

565. SMITH, K. U. The postoperative effects of removal of the striate cortex upon certain unlearned visually controlled reactions in the cat. *J. Genet. Psychol.*, 1937, 50, 137-156. [228 f.]

566. —— Visual discrimination in the cat. V. The postoperative effects of the removal of the striate cortex upon intensity discrimination. *J. Genet. Psychol.*, 1937, 51, 329-369. [228 f.]

567 —— Visual discrimination in the cat. VI. The relation between pattern and visual acuity and the optic projection centers of the nervous system. *J. Genet. Psychol.*, 1938, 53, 251-272. [229]

568. SNYGG, D. The relation between intelligence of mothers and their children living in foster homes. *J. Genet. Psychol.*, 1938, 52, 401-406. [314]

569. SOUTHARD, E. E. On the somatic sources of somatic delusions. *J. Abnor. Psychol.*, 1912, 7, 326-339. [316]

570. —— Psychopathology and neurology. *Amer. J. Psychiat.*, 1912, 23, 230-235. [316]

571. —— The mind twist and brain spot hypotheses in psycho-

pathology and neurology. *Psychol. Bull.*, 1914, 11, 117-130. [316]

572. —— Data concerning delusions 'of personality with note on the association of Bright's disease and unpleasant delusions. *J. Abnor. Psychol.*, 1915-16, 10, 241-262. [316]

573. SPEER, G. S. The intelligence of foster children. *J. Genet. Psychol.*, 1940, 57, 49-55. [314]

574. SPENCER, H. *The Principles of Psychology.* 2 vols., New York, Appleton, 1883. [25 f.]

574a. SPIEGELMAN, S., and KAMEN, M. D. Genes and nucleoproteins in the synthesis of enzymes. *Science,* 1946, 104, 581-584. [296, 308 f.]

575. DE SPINOZA, B. *Ethics.* London, Dent, 1910. [13]

576. STEINBERG, J. The relation between basal metabolism and mental speed. *Arch. Psychol.*, 1934, 26, no. 172. [284]

577. STEVENS, S. S. The operational definition of concepts. *Psychol. Rev.*, 1935, 42, 517-527. [67]

578. —— Psychology: the propaedeutic science. *Philos. of Science,* 1936, 3, 90-103. [67, 69]

579. —— Psychology and the science of science. *Psychol. Bull,* 1939, 36, 221-263. [69]

580. STOCKARD, C. R. *The Physical Basis of Personality.* New York, Norton, 1931. [304]

581. STOCKINGS, G. T. A clinical study of the mescalin psychosis, with special reference to the mechanism of the genesis of schizophrenia and other psychotic states. *J. Ment. Science,* 1940, 86, 29-47. [290]

582. STODDARD, G. D. *The Meaning of Intelligence.* New York, Macmillan, 1943. [314, 341]

583. STONE, C. P. The congenital sexual behavior of the young male albino rat. *J. Comp. Psychol.*, 1922, 2, 95-153. [211]

584. STONE, L. G., and JENKINS, W. L. Recent research in cutaneous sensitvity. I. Pain and temperature. *Psychol. Bull.*, 1940, 37, 285-311. [156]

585. STOOKEY, B., SCARFF, J. E., and TEITELBAUM, M. H. Frontal lobectomy in treatment of brain tumors. *Annals Surgery,* 1941, 113, 161-169. [270]

586. STRATTON, G. M. Vision without inversion of the retinal image. *Psychol. Rev.*, 1897, 341-360, 463-481. [180]

587. —— *Theophrastus and the Greek Physiological Psychology Before Aristotle.* New York, Macmillan, 1917. [80]

588. STRECKER, E. A., PALMER, H. D., and GRANT, F. C. A study of frontal lobotomy: Neurosurgical and psychiatric features and results in 22 cases with detailed report on 5 chronic schizophrenics. *Amer. J. Psychiat.*, 1942, 98, 524-532. [268]

589. STRONG, E. W. *Procedures and Metaphysics: A Study in the Philosophy of Mathematical Physical Science in the 16th and 17th Centuries.* Berkeley, Univ. Calif. Press, 1936. [11n.]

590. TALLMAN, G. G. A comparative study of identical and non-identical twins with respect to intelligence resemblances. *27th Yearbook, Natl. Soc. Stud. Educ.*, 1928, Part I, 83-96. [313]

591. TARCHANOFF, J. Ueber die galvanischen Ersheinungen in der Haut des Menschen bei Reizingen der Sinnesorgane und bei verschiedenen Formen der menschlichen Tätigkeiten. *Pflüg., Arch. f. d. ges. Physiol.*, 1890, 46, 46-55. [202]

592. TEN CATE, J. Können die Bedingten Reaktionen sich auch ausserhalf der grosshirnrinde bilden? *Arch. neérl. Physiol.*, 1934, 19, 469-481. [133]

593. THORNDIKE, E. L. Measurement of twins. *Arch. Psychol.*, 1905, no. 1. [313]

594. THORNDIKE, R. L. "Constancy" of the I.Q. *Psychol. Bull.*, 1940, 37, 167-186. [314]

595. THOULESS, R. E. Phenomenal regression to the real object. *Brit. J. Psychol.*, 1930, 21, 23-59. [152]

596. TILNEY, F. *The Brain from Ape to Man: A Contribution to the Study of the Evolution and Development of the Human Brain.* New York, Hoeber, 1928. [98]

597. TITCHENER, E. B. *A Textbook of Psychology.* New York, Macmillan, 1912. [42, 45, 62 f., 192 f., 197]

598. ——— Sensation and system. *Amer. J. Psychol.*, 1915, 26, 258-267. [63n.]

599. ——— Experimental psychology: a retrospect. *Amer. J. Psychol.*, 1925, 36, 313-323. [137]

600. ——— *Systematic Psychology: Prolegomena.* New York, Macmillan, 1929. [42-45]

601. TREDGOLD, A. F. *Mental Deficiency.* (6th ed.) Baltimore, Wood, 1937. [216]

602. TROLAND, L. T. Vision. I. Visual phenomena and their stimulus correlations. In (454), ch. 4. [153, 164]

603. ——— *The Principles of Psychophysiology.* New York, Van Nostrand, vol. 1, 1929; vol. 2, 1930; vol. 3, 1932. [127, 153]

604. TSANG, Y. C. The functions of the visual areas of the cerebral cortex of the rat in the learning and retention of the maze. I. *Comp. Psychol. Monog.*, 1934, 10, 1-56; 1936, 12, 1-41. [242, 247]

605. VAN LIERE, E. J. *Anoxia: Its Effect on the Body.* Chicago, Univ. Chicago Press, 1942. [286]

606. VERAGUTH, O. *Das Psychogalvanische Reflexphänomen.* Berlin, Karger, 1909. [202]

607. VIOLA, G. *La Constituzione Individuale.* Bologna, Cappelli, 1933. [303]

608. VOGT, C. *Physiologische Briefe für Gebildete aller Stände.* (2nd ed.) Giessen, Ricker, 1854. [77]

609. ——— *Köhlerglaube und Wissenschaft.* (3rd ed.) Giessen, Ricker, 1855. [77]

610. VOLLMER, E. P., KING, B. G., BIRREN, J. E., and FISHER, M. B. The effects of carbon monoxide on three types of performance, at simulated altitudes of 10,000 and 15,000 feet. *J. Exper. Psychol.*, 1946, 36, 244-251. [286 f.]

611. WALLS, G. L. *The Vertebrate Eye and its Adaptive Radiation.* Bloomfield Hills, Mich., Cranbrook Institute of Science, 1942. [172 f.]

612. WALTER, H. E. *Biology of the Vertebrates.* New York, Macmillan, 1929. [97]

613. WARREN, H. C. *Human Psychology.* Boston, Houghton-Mifflin, 1919. [208]

614. ———— Neurology: mystical and magical. *Psychol. Bull.*, 1923, 20, 438-443. [79, 101]

615. ———— Reply to Dr. Kantor. *Psychol. Bull.*, 1923, 20, 693-694. [79, 101]

616. WATERSTON, D. Observations on sensation: The sensory function of the skin for touch and pain. *J. Physiol.*, 1933, 77, 251-257. [156, 260]

617. WATSON, J. B. Kinaesthetic and organic sensations, their role in the reactions of the white rat in the maze. *Psychol. Monog.*, 1907, no. 33. [232, 242]

618. ———— *Psychology from the Standpoint of a Behaviorist.* Philadelphia, Lippincott, 1919. [101]

619. WEDDELL, G. The pattern of cutaneous innervation in relation to cutaneous sensibility. *J. Anat.*, London, 1941, 75, 346-367. [155]

620. WEISENBURG, T. H., and McBRIDE, K. E. *Aphasia, A Clinical and Psychological Study.* New York, Commonwealth Fund, 1935. [220 f.]

621. WEISS, A. P. The relation between physiological psychology and behavior psychology. *J. Philos. Psychol.*, 1919, 16, 626-634. [137]

622. ———— Mind and the man within. *Psychol. Rev.*, 1919, 26, 327-334. [137]

623. ———— Behavior and the central nervous system. *Psychol. Rev.*, 1922, 29, 329-343. [137]

624. WEISS, E., and ENGLISH, O. S. *Psychosomatic Medicine: The Clinical Application of Psychopathology to General Medicinal Problems.* Philadelphia, Saunders, 1943. [322, 327]

625. WELD, H. P. *Psychology as Science: Its Problems and Points of View.* New York, Holt, 1928. [44]

626. WELLMAN, B. L. Growth in intelligence under differing school environments. *J. Exper. Educ.*, 1934-35, 3, 59-83. [314]

627. ———— Iowa studies on the effects of schooling. *39th Yearbook Nat. Soc. Stud. Educ.*, 1940, Part II, 377-399. [314]

628. WELLMAN, B. L., SKEELS, H. M., and SKODAK, M. Review of McNemar's Critical examination of Iowa studies. *Psychol. Bull.*, 1940, 37, 93-111. [314]

629. WERTHAM, F., and WERTHAM, F. *The Brain as an Organ: Its Postmortem Study and Interpretation.* New York, Macmillan, 1934. [217, 222]

630. WHITEHEAD, A. N. *Introduction to Mathematics.* New York, Holt, 1911. [Preface]

631. WILBRAND, H. *Die hemianoptischen Gesichtsfeld Formen und das optische Wahrnehmungscentrum.* Wiesbaden, Bergman, 1890. [226]

632. WILEY, L. E. The function of the brain in audition. *J. Comp. Neurol.,* 1932, 54, 109-141. [230]

633. WILHELMI, A. E. Energy transformations in muscle. In (160), ch. 13. [278]

634. WILLENS, S. L., and WALLER, R. K. Voluntary intake of calcium and phosphorous in partially nephrectomized and parathyroidectomized rats. *Endocrinology,* 1941, 28, 828-834. [280]

634a. WILLIAMS, R. J. Vitamins in the future. *Science,* 1942, 95, 340-344. [285]

635. WINDELBAND, W. *History of Philosophy.* New York, Macmillan, 1910. [33, 88 f.]

636. WITTY, P. A., and SCHACTER, H. S. Hypothyroidism as a factor in maladjustment. *J. Psychol.,* 1934, 26, no. 172. [284]

637. WOLF, S., and WOLFF, H. G. *Human Gastric Function: An Experimental Study of Man and His Stomach.* New York, Oxford Univ. Press, 1943. [327]

638. WOOD, R. W. *Physical Optics.* (3rd ed.) New York, Macmillan, 1934. [148]

639. WOODWORTH, R. S. Dynamic psychology. In C. Murchison (Ed.), *Psychologies of 1930,* ch. 17, Worcester, Clark Univ. Press, 1930. [142]

640. —— *Experimental Psychology.* New York, Holt, 1938. [102 f., 174 f., 177 f., 185, 280]

641. —— Heredity and environment: a critical survey of recently published material on twins and foster children. *Soc. Sci. Res. Counc. Bull.,* 1941, no. 47. [313]

642. WOOLARD, H. H. Anatomy of peripheral sensation. *Brit. Med. J.,* 1936, 2, 861-862. [156]

643. WOOLARD, H. H., WEDDELL, G., and HARPMAN, J. A. Observations on the neurohistological basis of cutaneous pain. *J. Anat. Lond.,* 1940, 74, 413-440. [156]

644. WOOSTER, M. Certain factors in the development of new spatial coordination. *Psychol. Monog.,* 1923, 32, no. 4. [180]

645. WORCHEL, P., and LYERLY, J. G. Effects of prefrontal lobotomy on depressed patients. *J. Neurophysiol.,* 1941, 4, 62-67. [258]

646. WRIGHT, S. Physiology of the gene. *Physiol. Rev.,* 1941, 21, 487-527. [308 f.]

647. WUNDT, W. M. *Beiträge Zur Theorie des Sinneswahrnehmung.* Leipzig, Winter, 1862. [36]

648. —— *Gustav Theodor Fechner: Rede zur Feier seines hundert-jährigen Geburtstages.* Leipzig, Engelmann, 1901. [31]
649. —— *System der Philosophie.* 2 vols., (3rd ed.) Leipzig, Engelmann, 1907. [35 f., 38]
650. —— *Outlines of Psychology.* C. H. Judd (tr.), Leipzig, Engelmann, 1907. [4, 38, 46, 207]
651. —— *Grundzüge der physiologischen Psychologie.* 3 vols., (6th ed.) Leipzig, Engelmann, 1908-11. [37 f.]
652. —— *Grundriss der Psychologie.* (10th ed.) Leipzig, Engelmann, 1911. [38]
653. —— *Elements of Folk Psychology.* E. L. Shaub (trs.), New York, Macmillan, 1916. [345]
654. —— *Völkerpsychologie: Eine Untersuchung der Entwicklungs-geschichte von Sprache, Mythus und Sitte.* 10 vols., Leipzig, Engelmann, 1911-1920. [345]
654a. —— *Erlebtes und Erkanntes.* Stuttgart, Kröner, 1920. [31]
655. —— Metaphysik. In Systematische Philosophie: Die Kulture der Gegenwart, Teil I, Abteilung VI, Berlin-Leipzig, Teubner, 1921. [35]
656. YOUNG, H. H. *Genital Abnormalities: Hermaphroditism and Related Adrenal Diseases.* Baltimore, Williams and Wilkins, 1937. [306]
657. ZELIONY, G. P. Effets de l'ablation des hemispheres cerebraux. *Rev. Med.*, 1929, 46, 191-214. [132]
658. ZELIONY, G. P., and KADYKOV, B. I. Contribution to the study of condiitoned reflexes in the dog after cortical extirpation. *Med. Exper.*, Kharkov, 1938, 3, 31-34; (*Psychol. Abstr.*, 1938, 12, 5829). [133]
659. ZOLLINGER, R. Removal of the left cerebral hemisphere. *Arch. Neurol. Psychiat.*, 1935, 34, 1055-1064. [259]
660. ZOLLINGER, R., and SCHNITKER, M. T. Skin temperature reactions following removal of the left cerebral hemisphere. *Science,* 1934, 79, 540. [82]

SUBJECT AND NAME INDEX[1]

[1] This index includes names when referred to without bibliographical number. P.P. = Physiological Psychology.